HANDBOOK OF HEATING
VENTILATING AND AIR CONDITIONING

HANDBOOK OF HEATING
VENTILATING AND AIR CONDITIONING

USEFUL TABLES AND DATA ARRANGED IN A
MANNER CONVENIENT FOR READY REFERENCE

By

JOHN PORGES, M.I.Mech.E., M. Inst. F.

WITH 8 FOLDING CHARTS

Edited by
F. PORGES, L.L.B., B.Sc. (Eng.)

LONDON
GEORGE NEWNES LIMITED
TOWER HOUSE, SOUTHAMPTON STREET
LONDON, W.C.2

First Edition 1942
Second Edition 1946
Third Edition 1952
Fourth Edition 1960
Fifth Edition 1964

Made and printed in Great Britain
By Jarrold & Sons Limited, Norwich

PREFACE TO THE FIFTH EDITION

The preface to the fourth edition is reprinted in full overleaf because it was the last written by my father.

His sudden death occurred when he had already prepared the material for this edition. I have confined myself to completing the work from the notes he left, and have tried to make this new edition exactly as it would have been had he finished it himself. In doing this I have been greatly helped by the advice of my brother.

In view of the greater interest now being taken in the metric system, the section on conversion factors has been completely revised and expanded. Other new matter includes more detailed data on heat emissions on high buildings, and a section on high velocity air conditioning.

I am grateful to the Institution of Heating and Ventilating Engineers for permission to reproduce several tables from the *Guide to Current Practice.* My thanks are due to Sulzer Bros. (London) Ltd., to Ozonair Engineering Ltd., and to Mr. A. J. Roberts of Air Control Installations Ltd., for much of the data on high velocity air conditioning. I also wish to thank the many readers who have made suggestions for improvements and additions. These have been incorporated as far as possible.

To avoid undue resetting of type we have retained abbreviations used in the earlier editions although they do not conform entirely to current British Standards.

Finally, I must express my special thanks to the staff of the publishers, without whose courtesy and help I would not have been able to complete the work my father left unfinished.

FRED PORGES

PREFACE TO THE FOURTH EDITION

Although there are several good books on Heating, Ventilating and Air Conditioning, nevertheless, the need has long been apparent for a concise manual containing data, charts and tables which may be required by the heating engineer many times a day.

This book is intended to fulfil the need in a concise manner in order to facilitate the work of the heating and ventilating engineer.

The Handbook is designed for daily use, and a comprehensive bibliography has been included for the benefit of those who wish to pursue the theoretical side of any particular branch.

This book has been accepted as a day-to-day reference work by heating and ventilating engineers. In the second and third editions revisions and additions were made, but they were kept to the minimum.

In this edition the opportunity has been taken to revise the book completely, and to add further information on aspects of design and installation which have become of increasing importance to the practising engineer.

I should like to express my gratitude for permission to reproduce in Section VI some data and tables on heat transmittance from *A Guide to Current Practice* published by the Institution of Heating and Ventilating Engineers, and accepted throughout the profession as the basis for design of heating and ventilating plants.

Sections which have been revised and extended include Section III, which now contains data on oil firing, and Section X, where schemes for the control of air conditioning will be found, with explanatory notes.

I should like again to thank readers of previous editions for their helpful suggestions. These have been incorporated as far as possible.

JOHN PORGES

CONTENTS

Section I

SIGNS AND SYMBOLS

ABBREVIATIONS

in.	...	inch	gcal, cal	...	gram-calorie	F.P.M.	...	ft. per min.
ft.	...	foot	°F.	...	°Fahrenheit	C.F.M.	...	cu. ft. per min.
yd.	...	yard	°C.	...	°Centigrade	G.P.M.	...	gal. per min.
sq. in.	...	square inch	ft.-lb.	...	foot-pound	mm. ...	...	millimetre
sq. ft.	...	square foot	lb.p.s.i.	...	pounds per sq. in.	cm. ...	...	centimetre
cu. in.	...	cubic inch	hr.	...	hour	m. ...	...	metre
cu. ft.	...	cubic foot	min. ...	...	minute	mm.² ...	...	square millimetre
gal.	...	gallon	sec. ...	...	second	cm.² ...	...	square centimetre
gr.	...	grain	atm.	...	atmosphere	m.² ...	...	square metre
lb.	...	pound	W.	...	watt	cm.³ ...	...	cubic centimetre
cwt.	...	hundredweight	kW ...	...	kilowatt	m.³ ...	...	cubic metre
t	...	ton	V	...	volt	l. ...	...	litre
B.t.u.	...	Brit. thermal unit	A	...	ampere	g. ...	...	gramme
CHU.	...	Centigrade heat U	h.p. ...	...	horse power	kg. ...	...	kilogramme
kcal	...	kilo-calorie	b.h.p. ...	...	brake horse power	met.t ...	...	metric ton

ABBREVIATIONS USED IN DRAWINGS

BBOE...	...	bottom bottom opposite ends (radiator connections)	FB	...	from below	PRIM ...	...	primary (hot water flow)
			FS	...	fire service	R	...	return
BV	...	Butterfly valve	FTA	...	from and to above	SEC ...	...	secondary (hot water flow)
CF	...	cold feed	FTB	...	from and to below			
CW	...	cold water	FW	...	fresh water	TA	...	to above
CWM...	...	cold water main	GV	...	gate valve	TB	...	to below
CWS	...	cold water service	HTG ...	...	heating	TBOE...	...	top bottom opposite ends (radiator connections)
DC	...	draw-off cock	HWS ...	...	hot water service			
EC	...	emptying cock	LSV	...	lockshield valve	TBSE ...	...	top bottom same end (radiator connections)
EXP	...	expansion (tank or pipe)	MF	...	mixed flow			
			MV	...	mixing valve	TW ...	...	tank water
F		flow	NB	...	nominal bore	TWDS	...	tank water down service
FA	...	from above	NTS ...	...	not to scale			

SYMBOLS

l	length	...	ft.	t	temperature	°F.	U	coeff. of heat trans.	B.t.u./sq. ft./h./°F.
r, R	radius	...	ft.						
D,Dia.	diameter	...	ft.	t_1	initial temperature ...	°F.	a	surface coeff. of heat	B.t.u./sq. ft./h.
t	thickness	...	in.	t_2	final temperature ...	°F.	k	thermal conductance	B.t.u./sq. ft./h./°F.
A	area	...	sq. ft.						
V	volume	...	gal., cu. ft.	T	absolute temp.	°F.			
h, H	height	...	ft.	t_o	outside temp.	°F.	C	thermal conductivity	B.t.u./sq. ft./h./°F./in.
A	heating surface		sq. ft.	t_r	room temp.	°F.			
W	weight	...	lb.						
H	heat loss	...	B.t.u./h.	H	heat content	B.t.u./lb.	R	thermal resistance ...	°F./B.t.u./h.
D	density	...	lb /cu. ft.	DB	dry bulb temp.	°F.	x	quality of steam	per cent
sp.gr.	spec. gravity		—	WB	wet bulb temp.	°F.			
Q	quantity of water or air		cu. ft./min. gall./min.	RH	relative humidity ...	per cent	g=accelerating effect of gravity		ft./sec.²
							=32·2 ft. per sec.²		
p	pressure	...	lb./sq. in.				=981 cm./sec.²		—
Cp	spec. heat at const. pr.		B.t.u./lb.°F.	hp	horse power input ...	h.p.	1 as a subscript initial conditions		—
				E	efficiency ...	per cent			
Cv	ditto at const. volume ...		B.t.u./lb.°F.	C	constant ...	—	2 ditto, final cond.		—

CONVERSIONS

Length
1 in.	=25·3995 mm.
1 cm.	=0·3937 in.
1 m.	=3·2809 ft.
	=1·0936 yd.
1 ft.=12 in.	=0·3048 m.
1 yd.=3 ft.	=0·9144 m.
1 m.=100cm.=1,000 mm.	

Area
1 sq. in.	=6·452 cm.²
1 cm.²	=0·155 sq. in.
1 sq. ft.	=0·093 m.²
1 m.²	=10·764 sq. ft.
	=1·196 sq. yd.
1 sq. yd.	=0·836 m.²

Volume
1 cu. in.	=16·39 cm.³	
1 cm.³	=0·061 cu. in.	
1 cu. ft.	=0·0283 m.³	
1 m.³	=35·31 cu. ft.	
	=1·308 cu. yd.	
1 cu. yd.	=0·7646 m.³	
1 gal.	=4·546 l.	=0·16 cu. ft.
1 cu. ft.	=6·23 gal.	
1 l.	=0·22 gal.	=1·66 pints
	=0·88 qt.	=0·035 cu. ft.
1 pint	=0·568 l.	
1 qt.	=1·136 l.	
1 U.S. gal.	=0·83 Imp. gal.	

Weight:
1 grain	=0·0143 lb.	=0·0648 g.
1 g.	=0·001 kg.	=15·43 grains
1 lb.	=7,000 gr.	=0·4536 kg.
1 kg.	=1,000 g.	=2·205 lb.
1 t.	=20 cwt.	=80 qtr.
	=160 stones	=2,240 lb.
	=35,840 oz.	=1·017 metric t.
1 metric ton	=1,000 kg.	=0·984 t.
1 gr. per lb.	=0·143 g. per kg.	
1 gr. per cu. ft.=2·29 g. per m.³		
1 g. per kg.	=7·0 gr. per lb.	
1 g. per m.³	=0·437 gr. per cu. ft.	
1 lb. per cu. ft.=0·016 g. per cm.³		
1 g. per cm.³	=62·425 lb. per cu. ft.	
1 gr. per gal.	=0·01426 g. per l.	

Pressure:
1 lb. per sq. in.	=0·0703 kg. per cm.²
	=0·0680 atm.
	=2·0416 in. MERCURY at 62° F.
	=2·309 ft. WATER at 62° F.
	=27·71 in. WATER at 62° F.
1 atm.	=14·7 lb. per sq. in.
	=2116·3 lb. per sq. ft.
	=33·974 ft. WATER at 62° F.
	=30 in. MERCURY at 62° F.
	=29·921 in. MERCURY at 32° F.

1 atm.	=1·033 kg. per cm.²
	=760 mm. MERCURY at 62° F.
	=10·33 m. WATER at 62° F.
1 kg. per cm.²=14·22 lb. per sq. in.	
	=32·80 ft. WATER at 62° F.
	=28·95 in. MERCURY at 62° F.
1 ft. WATER=0·433 lb. per sq. in. at 62° F.	

One Millibar, abbreviated mb., equals a force of 1,000 Dynes per sq. in.
The Dyne is the Unit of Force in the C.G.S. system.
The average pressure of the atmosphere is 1013·2 mb.
1000 mb.=750·1 mm. Hg=29·531 ins. Hg.

1 in. of MERCURY	=70·59 lb. per sq. ft.
	=0·49 lb. per sq. in.
1 kg. per cm.²	=735·5 mm. MERCURY
	=10·0 m. WATER
	=0·9677 atm.
1 lb. per sq. ft.	=4·88 kg. per m.²
1 kg. per m.²	=0·205 lb. per sq. ft.
1 ft. WATER	=0·433 lb. per sq. in.
	=0·935 in. MERCURY

ENERGY—Heat
1 B.t.u.	=0·252 kcal
	=777·5 ft.-lb.=1055 joules
	=0·293 watt hours
1Kcal=3·9683 B.t.u.	=427 kg. m.
	=1,000 cal=4183 joules
1 B.t.u. per sq. ft.	=2·713 kcal per m.²
1 B.t.u. p. sq. ft. p. °F.=4·88 kcal per m.² per °C.	
1 B.t.u. p. cu. ft.	=8·9 kcal per m.³
1 B.t.u. per lb.	=0·556 kcal per kg.
1 kcal per m.²	=0·369 B.t.u. per sq. ft.
1 kcal p. m.: p. °C.	=0·205 B.t.u. p. sq. ft. per °F.
1 kcal p. m.	=0·1125 B.t.u. per cu. ft.
1 kcal per kg.	=1·800 B.t.u. per lb.
1 h.p.	=550 ft.-lb. per sec.
	=33,000 ft.-lb. per min.
	=1·0139 metric horse power
	=746 W.=2545 B.t.u./h.
1 metric h.p.	=75 kg. m. per sec.
	=0·986 engl. h.p.
	=735·56 W.
1 kW=1000 W	=1·3045 h.p.=1000 Joules
	per sec.
	=1·358 metric h.p.
	=737·0 ft.-lb. per sec.
1 kW hour	=3412 B.t.u.=860 kcal.
1 ft.-lb.=0·1383 kg.m.=0·001 1286 B.t.u.	
1 kg.m.=7·233 ft.-lb.=0·009301 B.t.u.	
1 TON REFRIGERATION=12 000 B.t.u. per hr.	
	=1·36 Joules
	=200 B.t.u. per min.

°F.=9/5° C.+32.   °C.=5/9° F.—32.
1° F.=0·555° C.   1° C.=1·8° F.

1 GALLON OF FRESH WATER AT 62° F.=10·00 lb.
1 cu. ft.	DITTO	=62·28 lb.
1 cu. ft. OF SEA WATER at 62° F.		=64·00 lb.
1 Joule	=1 Watt second	
	=0·74 ft.-lb.	
	=0·00095 B.t.u.	

B.S. 308: 1953. ENGINEERING DRAWING PRACTICE

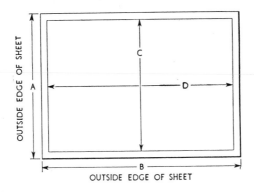

OUTSIDE EDGE OF SHEET

STANDARD SIZES OF DRAWINGS

Nominal sizes of drawings and tracings. Overall dimensions in inches across edges of sheet (see diagram above)		Maximum frame size. Dimensions in inches between border lines (see diagram above)	
A	B	C	D
*40 ×	72	*38 ×	70
*40 ×	60	*38 ×	58
*30 ×	53	*29 ×	52
*30 ×	40	*29 ×	39
27 ×	40	26 ×	39
15 ×	40	14 ×	39
22 ×	30	21 ×	29
*20 ×	30	*19 ×	29
20 ×	27	19 ×	26
*15 ×	20	*14 ×	19
*10 ×	15	* $9\frac{1}{4}$ ×	$14\frac{1}{4}$
†13 ×	8	$12\frac{1}{4}$ ×	$7\frac{1}{4}$
†10 ×	8	$9\frac{1}{4}$ ×	$7\frac{1}{4}$

* Preferred sizes.

† Additional sizes to be in conformity with commercial stationery. Drawings which are to be filed in binders and which have heights of 13 in. or 10 in. may have widths greater than 8 in.

COLOURING TO REPRESENT MATERIALS

Where it is desired to indicate materials in section by colours, the following are recommended:

Material	Colour
Cast iron	Payne's grey
Wrought iron	Prussian blue
Steel	Purple
Brass, phosphor bronze and gunmetal ...	Light yellow
Copper	Crimson lake
Aluminium, tin, white metals and light alloys	Light green
Brickwork	Vermilion
Concrete	Light green
Earth, rock	Sepia
Timber	Burnt sienna
Glass	Pale blue wash
Insulation (electrical)	Black

ALTERNATIVE METHODS FOR SHOWING SCREW THREADS

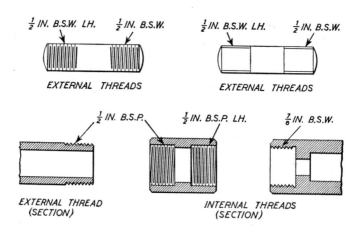

EXTERNAL THREADS

EXTERNAL THREADS

EXTERNAL THREAD
(SECTION)

INTERNAL THREADS
(SECTION)

FOR REPRESENTING PIPE JUNCTIONS, VALVES AND FITTINGS

————	*PIPING IN GENERAL*	
——	*NON-INTERSECTING PIPES*	
————	*STEAM PIPES*	
- - - - -	*CONDENSATE PIPES*	
————	*COLD WATER PIPES*	
— · —	*HOT WATER PIPES*	
++++++	*AIR PIPES*	
●●●●●●	*VACUUM PIPES*	
- - - -	*GAS PIPES*	
—·—·	*REFRIGERANT PIPES*	
— — -	*OIL PIPES*	
	LOCK & SHIELD VALVE	
	REDUCING VALVE	
	DIAPHRAGM VALVE	
Ⓣ	*THERMOSTAT*	
+⊗	*RADIATOR TRAP, PLAN*	
	RADIATOR TRAP, ELEVATION	
	GATE VALVE	
	GLOBE VALVE	
	ANGLE GLOBE VALVE	
	CHECK VALVE	
	STOP COCK	
	SAFETY VALVE	
	QUICK OPENING VALVE	
	FLOAT OPERATING VALVE	
	MOTOR OPERATED VALVE	
	EXPANSION JOINT	
	REDUCING FLANGE	

▭	*WALL RADIATOR, PLAN*
▢	*WALL RADIATOR, ELEVATION*
⊏⊐	*INDIRECT RADIATOR, PLAN*
⊠	*INDIRECT RADIATOR, ELEVATION*
⊠	*SUPPLY DUCT, SECTION*
▢	*EXHAUST DUCT, SECTION*
	BUTTERFLY DAMPER
	VANES
	AIR SUPPLY OUTLET
	EXHAUST INLET
—‖—	*JOINT, FLANGES*
—+—	*JOINT, SCREWED*
—✕—	*JOINT, WELDED*
	ELBOW 90°, FLANGED
⊙—	*ELBOW, TURNED UP*
⊙—	*ELBOW, TURNED DOWN*
	ELBOW, LONG RADIUS
	BASE ELBOW
	DOUBLE BRANCH ELBOW
	SINGLE SWEEP TEE
	TEE
	REDUCING ELBOW
	CROSS
	REDUCER
	ECCENTRIC REDUCER

CONVERSION TABLES

TEMPERATURE CONVERSION TABLE

Degrees Fahrenheit to Degrees Centigrade

(Figures in italics represent negative values on the Centigrade Scale)

Degrees F.	0	1	2	3	4	5	6	7	8	9
	°C.	°C.	°C.	°C.	°C.	°C.	°C.	°C.	°C.	°C.
0	*17·8*	*17·2*	*16·7*	*16·1*	*15·6*	*15·0*	*14·4*	*13·9*	*13·3*	*12·8*
10	*12·2*	*11·7*	*11·1*	*10·6*	*10·0*	*9·4*	*8·9*	*8·3*	*7·8*	*7·2*
20	*6·7*	*6·1*	*5·6*	*5·0*	*4·4*	*3·9*	*3·3*	*2·8*	*2·2*	*1·7*
30	*1·1*	*0·6*	—	—	—	—	—	—	—	—
	0	1	2	3	4	5	6	7	8	9
30	—	0	0	0·6	1·1	1·7	2·2	2·8	3·3	3·9
40	4·4	5·0	5·6	6·1	6·7	7·2	7·8	8·3	8·9	9·4
50	10·0	10·6	11·1	11·7	12·2	12·8	13·3	13·9	14·4	15·0
60	15·6	16·1	16·7	17·2	17·8	18·3	18·9	19·4	20·0	20·6
70	21·1	21·7	22·2	22·8	23·3	23·9	24·4	25·0	25·6	26·1
80	26·7	27·2	27·8	28·3	28·9	29·4	30·0	30·6	31·1	31·7
90	32·2	32·8	33·3	33·9	34·4	35·0	35·6	36·1	36·7	37·2
100	37·8	38·3	38·9	39·4	40·0	40·6	41·1	42·7	42·2	42·8
110	43·3	43·9	44·4	45·0	45·6	46·1	46·7	47·2	47·8	48·3
120	48·9	49·4	50·0	50·6	51·1	51·7	52·2	52·8	53·3	53·9
130	54·4	55·0	55·6	56·1	56·7	57·2	57·8	58·3	58·9	59·4
140	60·0	60·6	61·1	61·7	62·2	62·8	63·3	63·9	64·4	65·0
150	65·6	66·1	66·7	67·2	67·8	68·3	68·9	69·4	70·0	70·6
160	71·1	71·7	72·2	72·8	73·3	73·9	74·4	75·0	75·6	76·1
170	76·7	77·2	77·8	78·3	78·9	79·4	80·0	80·6	81·1	81·7
180	82·2	82·8	83·3	83·9	84·4	85·0	85·6	86·1	86·7	87·2
190	87·8	88·3	88·9	89·4	90·0	90·6	91·1	91·7	92·2	92·8
200	93·3	93·9	94·4	95·0	95·6	96·1	96·7	97·2	97·8	98·3
210	98·9	99·4	100·0	100·6	101·1	101·7	102·2	102·8	103·3	103·9
220	104·4	105·0	105·6	106·1	106·7	107·2	107·8	108·3	108·9	109·4
230	110·0	110·6	111·1	111·7	112·2	112·8	113·3	113·9	114·4	115·0
240	115·6	116·1	116·7	117·2	117·8	118·3	118·9	119·4	120·0	120·6
250	121·1	121·7	122·2	122·8	123·3	123·9	124·4	125·0	125·6	126·1

$$F = (C \times 1·8) + 32$$

TEMPERATURE CONVERSION TABLE

Degrees Fahrenheit to Degrees Centigrade—*continued*

Degrees F.	0	1	2	3	4	5	6	7	8	9
	°C.	°C.	°C.	°C.	°C.	°C.	°C.	°C.	°C.	°C.
260	126·7	127·2	127·8	128·3	128·9	129·4	130·0	130·6	131·1	131·7
270	132·2	132·8	133·3	133·9	134·4	135·0	135·6	136·1	136·7	137·2
280	137·8	138·3	138·9	139·4	140·0	140·6	141·1	141·7	142·2	142·8
290	143·3	143·9	144·5	145·0	145·6	146·1	146·7	147·2	147·8	148·3
300	148·9	149·4	150·0	150·6	151·1	151·7	152·2	152·8	153·3	153·9
310	154·4	155·0	155·6	156·1	156·7	157·2	157·8	158·3	158·9	159·4
320	160·0	160·6	161·1	161·7	162·2	162·8	163·3	163·9	164·4	165·0
330	165·6	166·1	166·7	167·2	167·8	168·3	168·9	169·4	170·0	170·6
340	171·1	171·7	172·2	172·8	173·2	173·9	174·4	175·0	175·6	176·1
350	176·7	177·2	177·8	178·3	178·9	179·4	180·0	180·6	181·1	181·7
360	182·2	182·8	183·3	183·9	184·4	185·0	185·6	186·1	186·7	187·2
370	187·8	188·3	188·9	189·4	190·0	190·6	191·1	191·7	192·2	192·8
380	193·3	193·9	194·4	195·0	195·6	196·1	196·7	197·2	197·8	198·3
390	198·9	199·4	200·0	200·6	201·1	201·7	202·2	202·8	203·3	203·9
400	204·4	205·0	205·6	206·1	206·7	207·2	207·8	208·3	208·9	209·4
410	210·0	210·6	211·1	211·7	212·2	212·8	213·3	213·9	214·4	215·0
420	215·6	216·1	216·7	217·2	217·8	218·3	218·9	219·4	220·0	220·6
430	221·1	221·7	222·2	222·8	223·3	223·9	224·4	225·0	225·6	226·1
440	226·7	227·2	227·8	228·3	228·9	229·4	230·0	230·6	231·1	231·7
450	232·2	232·8	233·3	233·9	234·4	235·0	235·6	236·1	236·7	237·2
460	237·8	238·3	238·9	239·4	240·0	240·6	241·1	241·7	242·2	242·8
470	243·3	243·9	244·4	245·0	245·6	246·1	246·7	247·2	247·8	248·3
480	248·9	249·4	250·0	250·6	251·1	251·7	252·2	252·8	253·3	253·9
490	254·4	255·0	255·6	256·1	256·7	257·2	257·8	258·3	258·9	259·4
500	260·0	—	—	—	—	—	—	—	—	—

$$F = (C \times 1·8) + 32$$

Degrees Centigrade to Degrees Fahrenheit

Degrees C.	0	1	2	3	4	5	6	7	8	9
	°F.	°F.	°F.	°F.	°F.	°F.	°F.	°F.	°F.	°F.
0	32·0	33·8	35·6	37·4	39·2	41·0	42·8	44·6	46·4	48·2
10	50·0	51·8	53·6	55·4	57·2	59·0	60·8	62·6	64·4	66·2
20	68·0	69·8	71·6	73·4	75·2	77·0	78·8	80·6	82·4	84·2
30	86·0	87·8	89·6	91·4	93·2	95·0	96·8	98·6	110·4	102·2
40	104·0	105·8	107·6	109·4	111·2	113·0	114·8	116·6	118·4	120·2
50	122·0	123·8	125·6	127·4	129·2	131·0	132·8	134·6	136·4	138·2
60	140·0	141·8	143·6	145·4	147·2	149·0	150·8	152·6	154·4	156·2
70	158·0	159·8	161·6	163·4	165·2	167·0	168·8	170·6	172·4	174·2
80	176·0	177·8	179·6	181·4	183·2	185·0	186·8	188·6	190·4	192·2
90	194·0	195·8	197·6	199·4	201·2	203·0	204·8	206·6	208·4	210·2
100	212·0	213·8	215·6	217·4	219·2	221·0	222·8	224·6	226·4	228·2
110	230·0	231·8	233·6	235·4	237·2	239·0	240·8	242·6	244·4	246·2
120	248·0	249·8	251·6	253·4	255·2	257·0	258·8	260·6	262·4	264·2
130	266·0	267·8	269·6	271·4	273·2	275·0	276·8	278·6	280·4	282·2
140	284·0	285·8	287·6	289·4	291·2	293·0	294·8	296·6	298·4	300·2
150	302·0	303·8	305·6	307·4	309·2	311·0	312·8	314·6	316·4	318·2
160	320·0	321·8	323·6	325·4	327·2	329·0	330·8	332·6	334·4	336·2
170	338·0	339·8	341·6	343·4	345·2	347·0	348·8	350·6	352·4	354·2
180	356·0	357·8	359·6	361·4	363·2	365·0	366·8	368·6	370·4	372·2
190	374·0	375·8	377·6	379·4	381·2	383·0	384·8	386·6	388·4	390·2
200	392·0	393·8	395·6	397·4	399·2	401·0	402·8	404·6	406·4	408·2
210	410·0	411·8	413·6	415·4	417·2	419·0	420·8	422·6	424·4	426·2
220	428·0	429·8	431·6	433·4	435·2	437·0	438·8	440·6	442·4	444·2
230	446·0	447·8	449·6	451·4	453·2	455·0	456·8	458·6	460·4	462·2
240	464·0	465·8	467·6	469·4	471·2	473·0	474·8	476·6	478·4	480·2
250	482·0	483·8	485·6	487·4	489·2	491·0	492·8	494·6	496·4	498·2
260	500·0	501·8	503·6	505·4	507·2	509·0	510·8	512·6	514·4	516·2
270	518·0	519·8	521·6	523·4	525·2	527·0	528·8	530·6	532·4	534·2
280	536·0	537·8	539·6	541·4	543·2	545·0	546·8	548·6	550·4	552·2
290	554·0	555·8	557·6	559·4	561·2	563·0	563·8	566·6	568·4	570·2
300	572·0	573·8	575·6	577·4	579·2	581·0	582·8	584·6	586·4	588·2

$$C = (F-32) \div 1·8$$

Fractions of an Inch.

With decimal and metric equivalents.

Fraction		Decimal	Millimetres	Fraction		Decimal	Millimetres
	1/64	0·015625	0·397		33/64	0·515625	13·097
1/32		0·03125	0·794	17/32		0·53125	13·494
	3/64	0·046875	1·191		35/64	0·546875	13·891
1/16		0·0625	1·587	9/16		0·5625	14·287
	5/64	0·078125	1·984		37/64	0·578125	14·684
3/32		0·09375	2·381	19/32		0·59375	15·081
	7/64	0·109375	2·778		39/64	0·609375	15·478
1/8		0·125	3·175	5/8		0·625	15·874
	9/64	0·140625	3·572		41/64	0·640625	16·272
5/32		0·15625	3·969	21/32		0·65625	16·669
	11/64	0·171875	4·366		43/64	0·671875	17·066
3/16		0·1875	4·762	11/16		0·6875	17·462
	13/64	0·203125	5·160		45/64	0·703125	17·859
7/32		0·21875	5·556	23/32		0·71875	18·256
	15/64	0·234375	5·953		47/64	0·734375	18·653
1/4		0·25	6·349	3/4		0·75	19·049
	17/64	0·265625	6·747		49/64	0·765625	19·477
9/32		0·28125	7·144	25/32		0·78125	19·844
	19/64	0·296875	7·541		51/64	0·796875	20·241
5/16		0·3125	7·937	13/16		0·8125	20·637
	21/64	0·328125	8·333		53/64	0·828125	21·034
11/32		0·34375	8·731	27/32		0·84375	21·431
	23/64	0·359375	9·128		55/64	0·859375	21·828
3/8		0·375	9·524	7/8		0·875	22·224
	25/64	0·390625	9·922		57/64	0·890625	22·622
13/32		0·40625	10·319	29/32		0·90625	23·019
	27/64	0·421875	10·716		59/64	0·921875	23·416
7/16		0·4375	11·112	15/16		0·9375	23·812
	29/64	0·453125	11·509		61/64	0·953125	24·209
15/32		0·46875	11·906	31/32		0·96875	24·606
	31/64	0·484375	12·303		63/64	0·984375	25·003
1/2		0·50	12·699	1		1·00	25·400

Feet and Inches to Metres

Feet	0	1	2	3	4	5	Inches 6	7	8	9	10	11
	m —	m 0·0254	m 0·0508	m 0·0762	m 0·1016	m 0·1270	m 0·1524	m 0·1778	m 0·2032	m 0·2286	m 0·2540	m 0·2794
1	0·3048	0·3302	0·3556	0·3810	0·4064	0·4318	0·4572	0·4826	0·5080	0·5334	0·5588	0·5842
2	0·6096	0·6350	0·6604	0·6858	0·7112	0·7366	0·7620	0·7874	0·8128	0·8382	0·8636	0·8890
3	0·9144	0·9398	0·9652	0·9906	1·0160	1·0414	1·0668	1·0922	1·1176	1·1430	1·1684	1·1938
4	1·2192	1·2446	1·2700	1·2954	1·3208	1·3462	1·3716	1·3970	1·4224	1·4478	1·4732	1·4986
5	1·5240	1·5494	1·5748	1·6002	1·6256	1·6510	1·6764	1·7018	1·7272	1·7526	1·7780	1·8034
6	1·8288	1·8542	1·8796	1·9050	1·9304	1·9558	1·9812	2·0066	2·0320	2·0574	2·0828	2·1082
7	2·1336	2·1590	2·1844	2·2098	2·2352	2·2606	2·2860	2·3114	2·3368	2·3622	2·3876	2·4130
8	2·4384	2·4638	2·4892	2·5146	2·5400	2·5654	2·5908	2·6162	2·6416	2·6670	2·6924	2·7178
9	2·7432	2·7686	2·7940	2·8194	2·8448	2·8702	2·8956	2·9210	2·9464	2·9718	2·9972	3·0226
10	3·0480	3·0734	3·0988	3·1242	3·1496	3·1750	3·2004	3·2258	3·2512	3·2766	3·3020	3·3274
11	3·3528	3·3782	3·4036	3·4290	3·4544	3·4798	3·5052	3·5306	3·5560	3·5814	3·6068	3·6322
12	3·6576	3·6830	3·7084	3·7338	3·7592	3·7846	3·8100	3·8354	3·8608	3·8862	3·9116	3·9370
13	3·9624	3·9878	4·0132	4·0386	4·0640	4·0894	4·1148	4·1402	4·1656	4·1910	4·2164	4·2418
14	4·2672	4·2926	4·3180	4·3434	4·3688	4·3942	4·4196	4·4450	4·4704	4·4958	4·5212	4·5466
15	4·5720	4·5974	4·6228	4·6482	4·6736	4·6990	4·7244	4·7498	4·7752	4·8006	4·8260	4·8514
16	4·8768	4·9022	4·9276	4·9530	4·9784	5·0038	5·0292	5·0546	5·0800	5·1054	5·1308	5·1562
17	5·1816	5·2070	5·2324	5·2578	5·2832	5·3086	5·3340	5·3594	5·3848	5·4102	5·4356	5·4610
18	5·4864	5·5118	5·5372	5·5626	5·5880	5·6134	5·6388	5·6642	5·6896	5·7150	5·7404	5·7658
19	5·7912	5·8166	5·8420	5·8674	5·8928	5·9182	5·9436	5·9690	5·9944	6·0198	6·0452	6·0706
20	6·0960	6·1214	6·1468	6·1722	6·1976	6·2230	6·2484	6·2738	6·2992	6·3246	6·3500	6·3754

Feet	0	1	2	3	4	5	6	7	8	9	10	11
30	9.1440	9.1694	9.1948	9.2202	9.2456	9.2710	9.2964	9.3218	9.3472	9.3726	9.3980	9.4234
40	12.1920	12.2174	12.2428	12.2682	12.2936	12.3190	12.3444	12.3698	12.3952	12.4206	12.4460	12.4714
50	15.2400	15.2654	15.2908	15.3162	15.3416	15.3670	15.3924	15.4178	15.4432	15.4686	15.4940	15.5194
60	18.2880	18.3134	18.3388	18.3642	18.3896	18.4150	18.4404	18.4658	18.4912	18.5166	18.5420	18.5674
70	21.3360	21.3614	21.3868	21.4122	21.4376	21.4630	21.4884	21.5138	21.5392	21.5646	21.5900	21.6154
80	24.3840	24.4094	24.4348	24.4602	24.4856	24.5110	24.5364	24.5618	24.5872	24.6126	24.6380	24.6634
90	27.4320	27.4574	27.4828	27.5082	27.5336	27.5590	27.5844	27.6098	27.6352	27.6606	27.6860	27.7114
100	30.4800											

Metres to Feet

Metres	0	1	2	3	4	5	6	7	8	9
0	—	3.281	6.562	9.843	13.123	16.404	19.685	22.966	26.247	29.528
10	32.808	36.089	39.370	42.651	45.932	49.213	52.493	55.774	59.055	62.336
20	65.617	68.898	72.179	75.459	78.740	82.021	85.302	88.583	91.864	95.144
30	98.425	101.706	104.987	108.268	111.549	114.829	118.110	121.391	124.672	127.953
40	131.234	134.515	137.795	141.076	144.357	147.638	150.919	154.200	157.480	160.761
50	164.042	167.323	170.604	173.885	177.166	180.446	183.727	187.008	190.289	193.570
60	196.851	200.131	203.412	206.693	209.974	213.255	216.536	219.816	223.097	226.378
70	229.659	232.940	236.221	239.502	242.782	246.063	249.344	252.625	255.906	259.187
80	262.467	265.748	269.029	272.310	275.591	278.872	282.152	285.433	288.714	291.995
90	295.276	298.557	301.838	305.118	308.399	311.680	314.961	318.242	321.523	324.803
100	328.08									

Cubic Feet to Cubic Metres

cu. ft.	0 cu. m	1 cu. m	2 cu. m	3 cu. m	4 cu. m	5 cu. m	6 cu. m	7 cu. m	8 cu. m	9 cu. m
0	—	0·0283	0·0566	0·0850	0·1133	0·1416	0·1699	0·1982	0·2265	0·2549
10	0·2832	0·3115	0·3398	0·3681	0·3564	0·4248	0·4531	0·4814	0·5097	0·5380
20	0·5663	0·5947	0·6230	0·6583	0·6796	0·7079	0·7362	0·7646	0·7929	0·8212
30	0·8495	0·8778	0·9061	0·9345	0·9628	0·9911	1·0194	1·0477	1·0760	1·1044
40	1·1327	1·1610	1·1893	1·2176	1·2459	1·2743	1·3026	1·3369	1·3592	1·3875
50	1·4158	1·4442	1·4725	1·5008	1·5291	1·5574	1·5857	1·6141	1·6424	1·6707
60	1·6990	1·7273	1·7556	1·7840	1·8123	1·8406	1·8689	1·8972	1·9255	1·9539
70	1·9822	2·0105	2·0388	2·0671	2·0954	2·1238	2·1521	2·1804	2·2087	2·2370
80	2·2653	2·2937	2·3220	2·3503	2·3786	2·4069	2·4352	2·4636	2·4919	2·5202
90	2·5485	2·5768	2·6051	2·6335	2·6618	2·6901	2·7184	2·7467	2·7750	2·8034
100	2·8317	—	—	—	—	—	—	—	—	—

Cubic Metres to Cubic Feet

cu. m	0	1	2	3	4	5	6	7	8	9
	cu. ft.	cu. ft.	cu. ft.	cu. ft.	cu. ft.	cu. ft.	cu. ft.	cu. ft.	cu. ft.	cu. ft.
0	—	35·3148	70·6295	105·9443	141·2590	176·5738	211·8885	247·2033	282·5181	317·8328
10	353·1476	388·4623	423·7771	459·0918	494·4066	529·7214	565·0361	600·3509	635·6656	670·9804
20	706·2951	741·6099	776·9247	812·2394	847·5542	882·8689	918·1837	953·4984	988·8132	1024·1280
30	1059·4427	1094·7575	1130·0722	1165·3870	1200·7017	1236·0165	1271·3313	1306·6460	1341·9608	1377·2755
40	1412·5903	1447·9050	1483·2198	1518·5346	1553·8493	1589·1641	1624·4788	1659·7936	1695·1083	1730·4231
50	1765·7379	1801·0526	1836·3674	1871·6821	1906·9969	1942·3116	1977·6264	2012·9411	2048·2559	2083·5707
60	2118·8854	2154·2002	2189·5149	2224·8297	2260·1444	2295·4592	2330·7740	2366·0887	2401·4035	2436·7182
70	2472·0330	2507·3477	2542·6625	2577·9773	2613·2920	2648·6068	2683·9215	2719·2363	2754·5510	2789·8658
80	2825·1806	2860·4953	2895·8101	2931·1248	2966·4396	3001·7543	3037·0691	3072·3839	3107·6986	3143·0134
90	3178·3281	3213·6429	3248·9576	3284·2724	3319·5872	3354·9019	3390·2167	3425·5314	3460·8462	3496·1609
100	3531·47	—	—	—	—	—	—	—	—	—

Gallons to Litres

gal.	0	1	2	3	4	5	6	7	8	9
	l.	l.	l.	l.	l.	l.	l.	l.	l.	l.
0	—	4·546	9·092	13·638	18·184	22·730	27·276	31·822	36·368	40·914
10	45·460	50·006	54·552	59·098	63·643	68·189	72·735	77·281	81·827	86·373
20	90·919	95·465	100·011	104·557	109·103	113·649	118·195	122·741	127·287	131·833
30	136·379	140·925	145·471	150·017	154·563	159·109	163·655	168·201	172·747	177·293
40	181·839	186·384	190·930	195·476	200·022	204·568	209·114	213·660	218·206	222·752
50	227·298	231·844	236·390	240·936	245·482	250·028	254·574	259·120	263·666	268·212
60	272·758	277·304	281·850	286·396	290·942	295·488	300·034	304·580	309·125	313·671
70	318·217	322·763	327·309	331·855	336·401	340·947	345·493	350·039	354·585	359·131
80	363·677	368·223	372·769	377·315	381·861	386·407	390·953	395·499	400·045	404·591
90	409·137	413·683	418·229	422·775	427·321	431·866	436·412	440·958	445·504	450·050
100	454·596	—	—	—	—	—	—	—	—	—

Litres to Gallons

litres	0	1	2	3	4	5	6	7	8	9
	gal.	gal.	gal.	gal.	gal.	gal.	gal.	gal.	gal.	gal.
0	—	0·2200	0·4400	0·6600	0·8800	1·1000	1·3199	1·5398	1·7598	1·9798
10	2·1998	2·4197	2·6397	2·8597	3·0797	3·2996	3·5196	3·7396	3·9596	4·1795
20	4·3995	4·6195	4·8395	5·0594	5·2794	5·4994	5·7194	5·9393	6·1593	6·3793
30	6·5993	6·8192	7·0392	7·2592	7·4792	7·6991	7·9191	8·1391	8·3591	8·5790
40	8·7990	9·0190	9·2390	9·4589	9·6789	9·8989	10·1189	10·3388	10·5588	10·7788
50	10·9988	11·2187	11·4387	11·6587	11·8787	12·0986	12·3186	12·5386	12·7586	12·9785
60	13·1985	13·4185	13·6385	13·8584	14·0784	14·2984	14·5184	14·7384	14·9583	15·1783
70	15·3983	15·6183	15·8382	16·0582	16·2782	16·4982	16·7181	16·9381	17·1581	17·3781
80	17·5980	17·8180	18·0380	18·2580	18·4779	18·6979	18·9179	19·1379	19·3578	19·5578
90	19·7978	20·0178	20·2377	20·4577	20·6777	20·8977	21·1176	21·3376	21·5576	21·7776
100	21·9975	—	—	—	—	—	—	—	—	—

Pounds to Kilogrammes

lb.	0	1	2	3	4	5	6	7	8	9
	kg.	kg.	kg.	kg.	kg.	kg.	kg.	kg.	kg.	kg.
0	—	0.4535	0.9071	1.3607	1.8143	2.2679	2.7215	3.1751	3.6287	4.0823
10	4.5359	4.9895	5.4431	5.8967	6.3503	6.8039	7.2575	7.7111	8.1647	8.6183
20	9.0718	9.5254	9.9790	10.4326	10.8862	11.3398	11.7934	12.2470	12.7006	13.1542
30	13.6078	14.0614	14.5150	14.9686	15.4221	15.8757	16.3293	16.7829	17.2365	17.6901
40	18.1437	18.5973	19.0509	19.5045	19.9581	20.4117	20.8653	21.3188	21.7724	22.2260
50	22.6796	23.1332	23.5868	24.0404	24.4940	24.9476	25.4012	25.8548	26.3084	26.7620
60	27.2155	27.6691	28.1227	28.5763	29.0299	29.4835	29.9371	30.3907	30.8443	31.2979
70	31.7515	32.2051	32.6587	33.1122	33.5658	34.0194	34.4730	34.9266	35.3802	35.8338
80	36.2874	36.7410	37.1946	37.6482	38.1018	38.5554	39.0089	39.4625	39.9161	40.3697
90	40.8233	41.2769	41.7305	42.1841	42.6377	43.0913	43.5449	43.9985	44.4521	44.9057
100	45.3592	—	—	—	—	—	—	—	—	—

Kilogrammes to Pounds

kg.	0	1	2	3	4	5	6	7	8	9
	lb.	lb.	lb.	lb.	lb.	lb.	lb.	lb.	lb.	lb.
0	—	2.204	4.409	6.613	8.818	11.023	13.227	15.432	17.637	19.841
10	22.0462	24.250	26.455	28.660	30.864	33.069	35.273	37.478	39.683	41.887
20	44.0924	46.297	48.502	50.706	52.911	55.116	57.320	59.525	61.729	63.934
30	66.139	68.343	70.548	72.753	74.957	77.162	79.366	81.571	83.776	85.980
40	88.185	90.389	92.594	94.799	97.003	99.208	101.413	103.617	105.822	108.026
50	110.231	112.436	114.640	116.845	119.050	121.254	123.459	125.663	127.868	130.073
60	132.277	134.482	136.686	138.891	141.096	143.300	145.505	147.710	149.914	152.119
70	154.324	156.528	158.733	160.937	163.142	165.347	167.551	169.756	171.960	174.165
80	176.370	178.574	180.779	182.984	185.188	187.393	189.597	191.802	194.007	196.211
90	198.416	200.620	202.825	205.030	207.234	209.439	211.644	213.848	216.053	218.258
100	220.462	—	—	—	—	—	—	—	—	—

Pounds Per Square Inch to Kilogrammes Per Square Centimetre

lb./sq. in.	0	1	2	3	4	5	6	7	8	9
	kg./sq. cm.	kg./sq. cm.	kg./sq. cm.	kg./sq. cm.	kg./sq. cm.	kg./sq. cm.	kg./sq. cm.	kg./sq. cm.	kg./sq. cm.	kg./sq. cm.
0	—	0·07031	0·14061	0·21092	0·28123	0·35154	0·42184	0·49215	0·56246	0·63276
10	0·70307	0·77338	0·84369	0·91399	0·98430	1·05461	1·12491	1·19522	1·26553	1·33583
20	1·40614	1·47645	1·54676	1·61706	1·68737	1·75768	1·82798	1·89829	1·96860	2·03891
30	2·10921	2·17952	2·24983	2·32013	2·39044	2·46075	2·53106	2·60136	2·67167	2·74198
40	2·81228	2·88259	2·95290	3·02320	3·09351	3·16382	3·23413	3·30443	3·37474	3·44505
50	3·51535	3·58566	3·65597	3·72628	3·79658	3·86689	3·93720	4·00750	4·07781	4·14812
60	4·21483	4·28873	4·35904	4·42935	4·49965	4·56996	4·64027	4·71058	4·78088	4·85119
70	4·92150	4·99180	5·06211	5·13242	5·20272	5·27303	5·34334	5·41365	5·48395	5·55426
80	5·62457	5·69487	5·76518	5·83549	5·90580	5·97610	6·04641	6·11365	6·18702	6·25733
90	6·32764	6·39795	6·46825	6·53856	6·60887	6·67917	6·74948	6·81979	6·89010	6·96040
100	7·0307	—	—	—	—	—	—	—	—	—

Kilogrammes Per Square Centimetre to Pounds Per Square Inch

kg./sq. cm.	0	1	2	3	4	5	6	7	8	9
	lb./sq. in.	lb./sq. in.	lb./sq. in.	lb./sq. in.	lb./sq. in.	lb./sq. in.	lb./sq. in.	lb./sq. in.	lb./sq. in.	lb./sq. in.
0	—	14·223	28·447	42·670	56·893	71·117	85·340	99·563	113·787	128·010
10	142·233	156·456	170·680	184·903	199·126	213·350	227·573	241·796	256·020	270·243
20	284·466	298·690	312·913	327·136	341·360	355·583	369·806	384·030	398·253	412·476
30	426·699	440·923	455·146	469·369	483·593	497·816	512·039	526·263	540·486	554·709
40	568·933	583·156	597·379	611·603	625·826	640·049	654·273	668·496	682·719	696·942
50	711·166	725·389	739·612	753·836	768·059	782·282	796·506	810·729	824·952	839·176
60	853·399	867·622	881·846	896·069	910·292	924·516	938·739	952·262	967·185	981·409
70	995·632	1009·855	1024·079	1038·302	1052·525	1066·749	1080·972	1095·195	1109·419	1123·642
80	1137·865	1152·089	1166·312	1180·535	1194·759	1208·982	1223·205	1237·428	1251·652	1265·875
90	1280·098	1294·322	1308·545	1322·768	1336·992	1351·215	1365·438	1379·662	1393·885	1408·108
100	1422·33	—	—	—	—	—	—	—	—	—

British Thermal Units to Kilocalories

B.t.u.	0	100	200	300	400	500	600	700	800	900
	kcal.	kcal.	kcal.	kcal.	kcal.	kcal.	kcal.	kcal.	kcal.	kcal.
0	—	25.2	50.4	75.6	100.8	126.0	151.2	176.4	201.6	226.8
1000	252	277.2	302.4	327.6	352.8	378.0	403.2	428.4	453.6	478.8
2000	504	529.2	554.4	579.6	604.8	630.0	655.2	680.4	705.6	730.8
3000	756	781.2	806.4	831.6	856.8	882.0	907.2	932.4	957.6	982.8
4000	1008	1033.2	1058.4	1083.6	1108.8	1134.0	1159.2	1184.4	1209.6	1234.8
5000	1260	1285.2	1301.4	1335.6	1360.8	1386.0	1411.2	1436.4	1461.6	1486.8
6000	1512	1537.2	1562.4	1587.6	1612.8	1638.0	1663.2	1688.4	1713.6	1738.8
7000	1764	1789.2	1814.4	1839.6	1864.8	1890.0	1915.2	1940.4	1965.6	1990.8
8000	2016	2041.2	2066.4	2091.6	2116.8	2142.0	2167.2	2192.4	2217.6	2242.8
9000	2268	2293.2	2318.4	2343.6	2368.8	2394.0	2419.2	2444.4	2469.6	2494.8
10000	2520	—	—	—	—	—	—	—	—	—

Kilocalories to British Thermal Units

kcal.	0	100	200	300	400	500	600	700	800	900
	B.t.u.	B.t.u.	B.t.u.	B.t.u.	B.t.u.	B.t.u.	B.t.u.	B.t.u.	B.t.u.	B.t.u.
0	—	396.8	793.7	1190.5	1587.3	1984.2	2381.0	2777.8	3174.7	3571.5
1000	3968.3	4365.1	4762.0	5158.8	5555.6	5952.5	6349.3	6746.1	7143.0	7539.8
2000	7936.6	8333.5	8730.3	9127.1	9524.0	9920.8	10317.6	10714.5	11111.3	11508.1
3000	11905.0	12301.8	12698.6	13095.5	13492.3	13889.1	14286.0	14682.8	15079.6	15476.5
4000	15873.3	16270.1	16666.9	17063.8	17460.6	17857.4	18254.3	18651.1	19047.9	19444.8
5000	19841.6	20238.4	20635.3	21032.1	21428.9	21825.8	22222.6	22619.4	23016.3	23413.1
6000	23809.9	24206.8	24603.5	25000.4	25397.3	25794.1	26190.9	26587.7	26984.6	27381.4
7000	27778.2	28175.1	28571.9	28968.7	29365.6	29762.4	30159.2	30556.1	30952.9	31349.7
8000	31746.6	32143.4	32540.2	32937.1	33333.9	33730.7	34127.6	34524.4	34921.2	35318.1
9000	35714.9	36111.7	36508.6	36905.4	37302.2	37699.0	38095.9	38492.7	38889.5	39286.4
10000	39683.2	—	—	—	—	—	—	—	—	—

B.t.u. per Sq. Ft. to Cal. per Sq. M.

B.t.u./sq.ft.	0	1	2	3	4	5	6	7	8	9
	cal./sq.m.	cal./sq.m.	cal./sq.m.	cal./sq.m.	cal./sq.m.	cal./sq.m.	cal./sq.m.	cal./sq.m.	cal./sq.m.	cal./sq.m.
0	—	2·712	5·424	8·136	10·848	13·560	16·272	18·984	21·696	24·408
10	27·120	29·832	32·544	35·256	37·968	40·680	43·392	46·104	48·816	51·528
20	54·240	56·952	59·664	62·376	65·088	67·800	70·512	73·224	75·936	78·648
30	81·360	84·072	86·784	89·496	92·208	94·920	97·632	100·344	103·056	105·768
40	108·480	111·192	113·904	116·616	119·328	122·040	124·752	127·464	130·176	132·888
50	135·600	138·312	141·024	143·736	146·448	149·160	151·872	154·584	157·296	160·008
60	162·720	165·432	168·144	170·856	173·568	176·280	178·992	181·704	184·416	187·128
70	189·840	192·552	195·264	197·976	200·688	203·400	206·112	208·824	211·536	214·248
80	216·960	219·672	222·384	225·096	227·808	230·520	233·232	235·944	238·656	241·368
90	244·080	246·792	249·504	252·216	254·928	257·640	260·352	263·064	265·776	268·488
100	271·200	—	—	—	—	—	—	—	—	—

Cal. per Sq. M. to B.t.u. per Sq. Ft.

cal./sq.m.	0	1	2	3	4	5	6	7	8	9
	B.t.u./sq.ft.	B.t.u./sq.ft.	B.t.u./sq.ft.	B.t.u./sq.ft.	B.t.u./sq.ft.	B.t.u./sq.ft.	B.t.u./sq.ft.	B.t.u./sq.ft.	B.t.u./sq.ft.	B.t.u./sq.ft.
0	—	0·3687	0·7374	1·1061	1·4748	1·8435	2·2122	2·5809	2·9496	3·3183
10	3·687	4·056	4·424	4·793	5·162	5·531	5·899	6·268	6·637	7·005
20	7·374	7·743	8·111	8·480	8·849	9·218	9·586	9·955	10·324	10·692
30	11·061	11·430	11·798	12·167	12·536	12·905	13·273	13·632	14·011	14·379
40	14·748	15·117	15·485	15·854	16·223	16·592	16·960	17·329	17·698	18·066
50	18·435	18·804	19·172	19·541	19·910	20·279	20·647	21·016	21·385	21·753
60	22·122	22·491	22·860	23·228	23·597	23·966	24·334	24·703	25·072	25·440
70	25·809	26·178	26·546	26·915	27·234	27·656	28·021	28·390	28·759	29·127
80	29·496	29·865	30·233	30·602	30·971	31·340	31·708	32·077	32·446	32·814
90	33·183	33·552	33·920	34·289	34·658	35·027	35·395	35·764	36·133	36·501
100	36·870	—	—	—	—	—	—	—	—	—

B.t.u. per Sq. Ft. per Deg. F. to Cal. per Sq. M. per Deg. C.

B.t.u./sq.ft.°F.	0	1	2	3	4	5	6	7	8	9
	cal./sq. m.°C.	cal./sq. m.°C.	cal./sq. m.°C.	cal./sq. m.°C.	cal./sq. m.°C.	cal./sq. m.°C.	cal./sq. m.°C.	cal./sq. m.°C.	cal./sq. m.°C.	cal./sq. m.°C.
0	—	4·882	9·764	14·646	19·528	24·410	29·292	34·174	39·056	43·938
10	48·820	53·702	58·504	63·466	68·348	73·230	78·112	82·994	87·876	92·758
20	97·640	102·522	107·404	112·286	117·168	122·050	126·932	131·814	136·696	141·578
30	146·460	151·342	156·224	161·106	165·988	170·870	175·752	180·634	185·516	190·398
40	195·280	200·162	205·044	209·926	214·808	219·690	224·572	229·454	234·336	239·218
50	244·100	248·982	253·864	258·746	263·628	265·510	273·392	278·274	283·156	288·038
60	292·920	297·802	302·684	307·566	312·448	317·330	322·212	327·094	331·976	336·858
70	341·740	346·622	351·504	356·386	361·268	366·150	371·032	375·914	380·796	385·678
80	390·560	395·442	400·324	405·206	410·088	414·970	419·852	424·734	429·616	434·498
90	439·380	444·262	449·144	454·026	458·908	463·790	468·672	473·554	478·436	483·318
100	488·200	—	—	—	—	—	—	—	—	—

Cal. per Sq. M. per Deg. C. to B.t.u. per Sq. Ft. per Deg. F.

cal./sq. m.°C.	0	1	2	3	4	5	6	7	8	9
	B.t.u./ sq.ft.°F.	B.t.u./ sq.ft.°F.	B.t.u./ sq.ft.°F.	B.t.u./ sq.ft.°F.	B.t.u./ sq.ft.°F.	B.t.u./ sq.ft.°F.	B.t.u./ sq.ft.°F.	B.t.u./ sq.ft.°F.	B.t.u./ sq.ft.°F.	B.t.u./ sq.ft.°F.
0	—	0·205	0·410	0·614	0·819	1·024	1·229	1·434	1·638	1·843
10	2·048	2·253	2·458	2·662	2·867	3·072	3·277	3·482	3·686	3·891
20	4·096	4·301	4·506	4·710	4·915	5·120	5·325	5·530	5·734	5·940
30	6·144	6·349	6·554	6·758	6·963	7·168	7·373	7·579	7·783	7·988
40	8·192	8·397	8·602	8·806	9·011	9·216	9·421	9·623	9·830	10·035
50	10·240	10·445	10·650	10·854	11·059	11·264	11·469	11·674	11·878	12·083
60	12·288	12·493	12·698	12·902	13·107	13·312	13·517	13·722	13·926	14·131
70	14·336	14·541	14·746	14·950	15·155	15·360	15·565	15·770	15·974	16·179
80	16·384	16·589	16·794	16·998	17·203	17·408	17·613	17·818	18·022	18·227
90	18·432	18·637	18·842	19·046	19·251	19·456	19·661	19·866	20·070	20·275
100	20·480	—	—	—	—	—	—	—	—	—

AREAS AND CIRCUMFERENCES OF CIRCLES

(DIAMETERS ADVANCING BY $\frac{1}{8}$ IN.)

Dia.	Circum.	Area.	Dia.	Circum.	Area.	Dia.	Circum.	Area.
$\frac{1}{16}$	0·1963	0·00307	$2\frac{5}{16}$	7·2649	4·2	$6\frac{1}{4}$	19·63	30·67
$\frac{1}{8}$	0·3927	0·01227	$2\frac{3}{8}$	7·4613	4·4302	$6\frac{1}{2}$	20·42	33·18
$\frac{3}{16}$	0·589	0·02761	$2\frac{7}{16}$	7·6576	4·6664	$6\frac{3}{4}$	21·20	35·78
$\frac{1}{4}$	0·7854	0·04909	$2\frac{1}{2}$	7·854	4·9087	7	21·99	38·48
$\frac{5}{16}$	0·9817	0·0767	$2\frac{9}{16}$	8·0503	5·1573	$7\frac{1}{4}$	22·77	41·28
$\frac{3}{8}$	1·1781	0·1104	$2\frac{5}{8}$	8·2467	5·4119	$7\frac{1}{2}$	23·56	44·17
$\frac{7}{16}$	1·3744	0·1503	$2\frac{11}{16}$	8·443	5·6723	$7\frac{3}{4}$	24·34	47·17
$\frac{1}{2}$	1·5708	0·1963	$2\frac{3}{4}$	8·6394	5·9395	8	25·13	50·26
$\frac{9}{16}$	1·7771	0·2485	$2\frac{13}{16}$	8·8357	6·2126	$8\frac{1}{4}$	25·91	53·45
$\frac{5}{8}$	1·9635	0·3068	$2\frac{7}{8}$	9·0321	6·4918	$8\frac{1}{2}$	26·70	56·74
$\frac{11}{16}$	2·1598	0·3712	$2\frac{15}{16}$	9·2284	6·7772	$8\frac{3}{4}$	27·49	60·13
$\frac{3}{4}$	2·3562	0·4417	3	9·4248	7·0686	9	28·27	63·62
$\frac{13}{16}$	2·5525	0·5185	$3\frac{1}{8}$	9·8175	7·6699	$9\frac{1}{4}$	29·06	67·20
$\frac{7}{8}$	2·7489	0·6013	$3\frac{1}{4}$	10·21	8·2957	$9\frac{1}{2}$	29·84	70·88
$\frac{15}{16}$	2·9452	0·6903	$3\frac{3}{8}$	10·602	8·9462	$9\frac{3}{4}$	30·63	74·66
1	3·1416	0·7854	$3\frac{1}{2}$	10·995	9·6211	10	31·41	78·54
$1\frac{1}{16}$	3·3379	0·8866	$3\frac{5}{8}$	11·388	10·32	$10\frac{1}{2}$	32·98	86·59
$1\frac{1}{8}$	3·5343	0·994	$3\frac{3}{4}$	11·781	11·044	11	34·56	95·03
$1\frac{3}{16}$	3·7306	1·1075	$3\frac{7}{8}$	12·173	11·793	$11\frac{1}{2}$	36·13	103·87
$1\frac{1}{4}$	3·927	1·2271	4	12·566	12·566	12	37·69	113·09
$1\frac{5}{16}$	4·1233	1·353	$4\frac{1}{8}$	12·959	13·364	$12\frac{1}{2}$	39·27	122·71
$1\frac{3}{8}$	4·3197	1·4848	$4\frac{1}{4}$	13·351	14·186	13	40·84	132·73
$1\frac{7}{16}$	4·516	1·6229	$4\frac{3}{8}$	13·744	15·033	$13\frac{1}{2}$	42·41	143·13
$1\frac{1}{2}$	4·7124	1·7671	$4\frac{1}{2}$	14·137	15·904	14	43·98	153·93
$1\frac{9}{16}$	4·9087	1·9175	$4\frac{5}{8}$	14·529	16·8	$14\frac{1}{2}$	45·55	165·13
$1\frac{5}{8}$	5·1051	2·0739	$4\frac{3}{4}$	14·922	17·72	15	47·12	176·71
$1\frac{11}{16}$	5·3014	2·2365	$4\frac{7}{8}$	15·315	18·665	$15\frac{1}{2}$	48·69	188·69
$1\frac{3}{4}$	5·4978	2·4052	5	15·708	19·635	16	50·26	201·06
$1\frac{13}{16}$	5·6941	2·58	$5\frac{1}{8}$	16·1	20·629	$16\frac{1}{2}$	51·83	213·82
$1\frac{7}{8}$	5·8905	2·7611	$5\frac{1}{4}$	16·493	21·647	17	53·40	226·98
$1\frac{15}{16}$	6·0868	2·9483	$5\frac{3}{8}$	16·886	22·69	$17\frac{1}{2}$	54·97	240·52
2	6·2832	3·1416	$5\frac{1}{2}$	17·278	23·758	18	56·54	254·47
$2\frac{1}{16}$	6·4795	3·3410	$5\frac{5}{8}$	17·671	24·85	$18\frac{1}{2}$	58·12	268·80
$2\frac{1}{8}$	6·6759	3·5465	$5\frac{3}{4}$	18·064	25·967	19	59·69	283·53
$2\frac{3}{16}$	6·8722	3·7584	$5\frac{7}{8}$	18·457	27·108	$19\frac{1}{2}$	61·26	298·64
$2\frac{1}{4}$	7·0686	3·976	6	18·85	28·27	20	62·83	314·16

Section II

DIMENSIONS OF RADIATORS, TUBES AND FITTINGS

C = CAPACITIES IN GALLONS.
DIA. = DIAMETERS IN FT. & INS.

L = LENGTH
W = WIDTH
H = HEIGHT. } IN FT. & INS.

INDIRECT CYLINDERS COPPER & GALVANIZED. HORIZONTAL & VERTICAL			GALVANIZED FEED & EXPANSION TANKS FOR SMALL HEATING INSTALLATIONS			
C	DIA.	L	C	L	W	H
24	1–6	2–6	7	1–6	0–5	1–0
30	1–6	3–3	10	1–6	1–0	1–0
35	1–6	3–6¾	15	2–0	1–0	1–3
40	1–6	4–0	20	2–0	1–0	1–8
50	1–8	4–2	25	2–0	1–0	2–0
60	1–8	4–10	30	2–0	1–3	2–0
80	2–0	4–6	40	2–0	2–1	1–7
100	2–0	5–9	50	2–0	2–0	2–0
150	2–6	5–5½	70	3–0	2–0	1–11
200	2–8	6–4½				

GALVANIZED HOT WATER CYLINDERS

C.	DIA.	L.	C.	DIA.	L.
20	1–3	2–6	37	1–8	2–6
	1–6	2–0	40	1–6	3–6
21	1–3	2–9	42	1–6	3–9
			42	1–8	3–0
23	1–3	3–0	45	1–6	4–0
25	1–6	2–3	48	1–8	3–6
	1–3	3–3			
			56	1–8	4–0
28	1–6	2–6	60	1–8	4–3
	1–3	3–6			
			65	1–10	4–0
31	1–8	2–3	75	2–0	4–0
	1–6	2–9	85	2–0	4–6
34	1–6	3–0	100	2–0	5–4
37	1–6	3–3			

GALVANIZED HOT WATER TANKS

C.	L.	W.	H.	C.	L.	W.	H.
20	2–0	1–4	1–3	50	2–5	1–10	1–10
	1–6	1–6	1–6		2–0	2–0	2–0
	2–0	2–0	0–10				
25	1–7	1–7	1–7	60	2–6	1–11	2–0
	2–0	1–5	1–5		2–2	2–2	2–2
	2–0	2–0	1–0				
				70	3–0	2–0	1–11
30	2–0	1–6	1–7		2–3	2–3	2–3
	1–8	1–8	1–8				
	2–0	2–0	1–3	80	3–0	2–2	2–0
					2–4	2–4	2–4
40	2–0	1–3	2–0				
	2–3	1–8	1–8	100	3–2	2–3	2–3
	1–10	1–10	1–10		2–6	2–6	2–6

GALVANIZED OPEN TOP CISTERNS

C.	L.	W.	H.	C.	L.	W.	H.	C.	L.	W.	H.
20	2–0	1–0	1–8	60	2–6	1–11	2–0	350	6–6	3–3	2–8
	2–0	1–4	1–3		3–0	2–0	1–8		5–0	3–9	3–0
	1–6	1–6	1–6	70	3–0	2–0	1–11	400	7–0	3–6	2–8
25	2–0	1–5	1–5		2–8	2–2	2–0		4–0	4–0	4–0
	2–0	1–0	2–0	80	3–0	2–2	2–0		6–0	3–7	3–0
	2–0	1–8	1–3	100	3–0	2–6	2–2	500	8–0	3–9	2–8
30	2–0	1–6	1–7		4–0	2–0	2–0		5–0	4–0	4–0
	1–8	1–8	1–8		3–2	2–3	2–3		6–0	4–0	3–4
	2–0	2–0	1–3	125	3–2	2–6	2–7	600	8–0	4–0	3–0
40	2–3	1–8	1–8	150	3–7	2–10	2–5		6–0	4–0	4–0
	2–0	2–0	1–7	200	4–0	3–0	2–8	700	7–0	4–0	4–0
	1–10	1–10	1–10		3–10	2–11	2–11	800	8–0	4–0	4–0
50	2–0	2–0	2–0	250	5–0	3–0	2–8	900	9–0	4–0	4–0
	2–5	1–10	1–10	300	6–0	3–0	2–8	1,000	8–0	5–0	4–0
	2–7	2–0	1–7		4–6	3–7	3–0				

CONTENTS OF STORAGE CYLINDERS (in gallons)

LENGTH (feet and inches)

Dia.	1–0	1–3	1–6	2–0	2–6	3–0	3–6	4–0	4–6	5–0	6–0	7–0
1–0	4·9	6·1	7·3	9·8	12	15	17	19	22	25	29	34
1–3	7·7	9·6	11·5	15	19	23	27	30	34	38	46	53
1–6	11·0	13·8	16·5	22	27	33	38	44	49	55	66	77
2–0	19·6	24	29	39	49	59	68	78	88	98	118	137
2–6		38	46	61	76	91	107	122	138	153	184	214
3–0			66	88	110	132	152	176	198	220	264	308
3–6				120	150	180	210	240	270	300	360	420
4–0					196	235	275	314	353	392	470	549
4–6						288	347	398	447	496	596	695
5–0							428	490	550	612	734	857
5–6								592	667	746	889	1040
6–0									794	882	1060	1230
7–0										1210	1450	1680

IMPERIAL STANDARD WIRE GAUGE

No.	Diameter		Sectional Area sq. in.	Weight of Iron-plates lb. per sq. ft.	No.	Diameter		Sectional Area sq. in.	Weight of Iron-plates lb. per sq. ft.
	in.	mm.				in.	mm.		
7/0	0·500	12·700	0·1963	20·0	12	0·104	2·642	0·0085	4·36
6/0	0·464	11·785	0·1691	18·6	13	0·092	2·337	0·0066	3·80
5/0	0·432	10·973	0·1466	17·3	14	0·080	2·032	0·0050	3·32
4/0	0·400	10·160	0·1257	16·0	15	0·072	1·829	0·0041	2·88
3/0	0·372	9·449	0·1087	14·9	16	0·064	1·626	0·0032	2·60
2/0	·0348	8·839	0·0951	13·9	17	0·056	1·422	0·0025	2·32
0	0·324	8·229	0·0824	13·1	18	0·048	1·219	0·0018	1·96
1	0·300	7·620	0·0707	12·0	19	0·040	1·016	0·0013	1·68
2	0·276	7·010	0·0598	11·36	20	0·036	0·914	0·0010	1·40
3	0·252	6·401	0·0499	10·36	21	0·032	0·813	0·0008	1·28
4	0·232	5·893	0·0423	9·52	22	0·028	0·711	0·000616	1·12
5	0·212	5·385	0·0353	8·80	23	0·024	0·610	0·000452	1·00
6	0·192	4·877	0·0290	8·12	24	0·022	0·559	0·000380	0·88
7	0·176	4·470	0·0243	7·20	25	0·020	0·508	0·000314	0·80
8	0·160	4·064	0·0201	6·60	26	0·018	0·457	0·000254	0·72
9	0·144	3·658	0·0163	5·92	27	0·0164	0·4166	0·000211	0·64
10	0·128	3·251	0·0129	5·36	28	0·0148	0·3759	0·000172	0·56
11	0·116	2·946	0·0106	4·80	29	0·0136	0·3454	0·000145	0·52
					30	0·0124	0·3150	0·000121	0·48

GENERAL DIMENSIONS OF STEEL TUBES TO B.S. 1387 : 1957

(Subject to standard tolerances and usual working allowances)

Nominal Bore in.	Outside Diameter in.	Thickness (S.W.G.)			Weight, lb. per ft. (Black)						Weight, cwt. per 100 ft. (Black)						Approximate ft. per ton (Screwed & Socketed)			Nominal Bore in.
					Screwed & Socketed			Plain Ends			Screwed & Socketed			Plain Ends						
		Light	Medium	Heavy	Light	Medium	Heavy	Light	Medium	Heavy	Light	Medium	Heavy	Light	Medium	Heavy	Light	Medium	Heavy	
1/8	13/32	15	14	12	0·245	0·275	0·333	0·243	0·273	0·331	0·219	0·246	0·297	0·217	0·244	0·296	9143	8146	6727	1/8
1/4	17/32	15	13	11	0·350	0·440	0·520	0·347	0·437	0·517	0·313	0·393	0·464	0·310	0·390	0·462	6400	5091	4308	1/4
3/8	11/16	15	13	11	0·457	0·577	0·690	0·453	0·573	0·686	0·408	0·515	0·616	0·404	0·512	0·613	4902	3882	3246	3/8
1/2	27/32	14	12	10	0·646	0·828	0·983	0·640	0·822	0·977	0·577	0·739	0·878	0·571	0·734	0·872	3467	2705	2279	1/2
3/4	1 1/16	13	12	10	0·954	1·07	1·28	0·944	1·06	1·27	0·852	0·955	1·143	0·843	0·946	1·134	2348	2093	1750	3/4
1	1 11/32	12	10	8	1·36	1·65	2·01	1·35	1·64	2·00	1·214	1·473	1·795	1·205	1·464	1·786	1647	1358	1115	1
1 1/4	1 11/16	12	10	8	1·75	2·13	2·60	1·73	2·11	2·58	1·563	1·902	2·322	1·545	1·884	2·304	1280	1052	862	1 1/4
1 1/2	1 29/32	11	10	8	2·22	2·46	3·01	2·19	2·43	2·98	1·982	2·197	2·688	1·955	2·170	2·661	1009	911	744	1 1/2
2	2 3/8	11	9	7	2·81	3·47	4·19	2·76	3·42	4·14	2·509	3·098	3·741	2·464	3·054	3·697	797	646	535	2
2 1/2	3	10	9	7	3·98	4·46	5·39	3·90	4·38	5·31	3·554	3·982	4·813	3·482	3·911	4·741	563	502	416	2 1/2
3	3 1/2	10	8	6	4·69	5·80	6·87	4·58	5·69	6·76	4·188	5·179	6·134	4·089	5·081	6·036	478	386	326	3
3 1/2	4	9	8	6	6·00	6·65	7·88	5·88	6·53	7·76	5·357	5·938	7·036	5·250	5·831	6·929	373	337	284	3 1/2
4	4 1/2	9	7	5	6·84	8·34	9·91	6·64	8·14	9·71	6·107	7·447	8·849	5·929	7·268	8·670	327	269	226	4
5	5 1/2	—	6	5	—	11·2	12·3	—	10·9	12·0	—	10·00	10·98	—	9·733	10·72	—	200	182	5
6	6 1/2	—	6	5	—	13·3	14·7	—	12·9	14·3	—	11·88	13·13	—	11·52	12·77	—	168	152	6

SUGGESTED MAXIMUM WORKING PRESSURES
(Water, Saturated Steam and Compressed Air)

The pressures given below can be taken as being conservative estimates for tubes screwed taper with sockets tapped parallel under normal (non-shock) conditions.

		⅛ to 1 in.	1¼ & 1½ in.	2 & 2½ in.	3 in.	3½ & 4 in.	5 in.	6 in.
Water Pressure (lb. p.s.i.)	Light	150	125	100	100	80	—	—
	Medium	300	250	200	200	150	150	125
	Heavy	350	300	250	250	200	200	150
S/Steam or Air Pressure (lb. p.s.i.)	Medium	150	125	100	100	80	80	60
	Heavy	175	150	125	125	100	100	80

The following increased working pressures are allowable for end-to-end welding of plain end tubes used for steam or compressed air.

	Medium	*Heavy*
⅛ to 1¼ in. Bore	250	300 lb. p.s.i.
1½ to 2½ in. Bore	200	300 lb. p.s.i.
2½ to 5 in. Bore	150	200 lb. p.s.i.
6 in. Bore	125	175 lb. p.s.i.

COLOURING OF TUBES: Light... BROWN; Medium... BLUE; Heavy... RED.

SURFACES, AREAS AND CONTENTS OF TUBES

Brit. Standard Dia. in. Nom. Bore.	*Exter-nal dia.*	*Surface sq. ft. per ft.*	*Area sq. in.*	*Content Gal. p. per ft.*	*Brit. Standard Dia. in.* Nom. Bore.	*Exter-nal dia.*	*Surface sq. ft. per ft.*	*Area sq. in.*	*Content Gal p. per ft.*
⅛	11/32	0·11	0·023	0·0005	4	4½	1·18	12·55	0·5426
¼	17/32	0·14	0·049	0·0021	5	5½	1·44	19·65	0·8480
⅜	11/16	0·18	0·11	0·0048	6	6½	1·70	28·3	1·2210
½	27/32	0·22	0·19	0·0084	7	7½	1·96	38·48	1·67
¾	1 1/16	0·28	0·44	0·0190	8	8½	2·23	50·27	2·37
1	1 11/32	0·35	0·78	0·0339	9	9½	2·49	63·62	2·75
1¼	1 11/16	0·44	1·23	0·0530	10	10½	2·74	77·50	3·35
1½	1 29/32	0·50	1·77	0·0763	11	11½	3·01	91·20	3·95
2	2⅜	0·62	3·14	0·1356	12	12½	3·27	110·70	4·77
2½	3	0·78	4·92	0·2120					
3	3½	1·05	7·05	0·3053					
3½	4	1·05	9·62	0·4156					

EQUIVALENT LENGTHS OF FITTINGS TO BE ADDED TO THE ACTUAL LENGTH

Pipe size in inches	*Elbows*	*Tees*	*90° bends*
½ to I ...	2	2	1
1¼ and 1½	3	3	1
2 ...	5	5	2
3 ...	8	8	3

SURFACE OF PIPE INSULATIONS IN SQ. FT. PER FT. LIN.

Size of Pipe Nom.Bore in.	External Pipe Dia. in.	Total Thickness of Insulation in.						
		½"	⅝"	¾"	1"	1¼"	1½"	2"
⅜"	11/16	0·44	0·52	0·59	0·72	0·85	0·98	1·24
½	27/32	0·48	0·56	0·62	0·75	0·88	1·02	1·27
¾	1 1/16	0·54	0·61	0·67	0·80	0·94	1·06	1·33
1	1 11/32	0·61	0·69	0·75	0·88	1·02	1·14	1·41
1¼	1 11/16	0·70	0·78	0·85	0·98	1·11	1·24	1·51
1½	1 29/32	0·76	0·82	0·89	1·02	1·15	1·28	1·54
2	2⅜	0·88	0·95	1·02	1·14	1·28	1·41	1·67
2½	3	1·05	1·11	1·18	1·31	1·44	1·57	1·84
3	3½	1·18	1·24	1·31	1·44	1·57	1·70	1·97
3½	4	1·31	1·37	1·44	1·57	1·70	1·84	2·10
4	4½	1·44	1·50	1·57	1·70	1·84	1·97	2·23
5	5½	1·70	1·77	1·83	1·97	2·10	2·23	2·49
6	6½	1·96	2·03	2·09	2·23	2·36	2·49	2·75
7	7½	2·22	2·29	2·35	2·49	2·62	2·75	3·02
8	8½	2·48	2·55	2·62	2·75	2·88	3·02	3·28
9	9½	2·74	2·81	2·88	3·02	3·15	3·28	3·54
10	10½	3·01	3·08	3·14	3·28	3·41	3·54	3·80
12	12½	3·53	3·60	3·66	3·80	3·80	4·07	4·32

MOST ECONOMICAL THICKNESS OF INSULATION

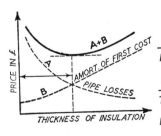

PRICE IN £ — A+B — AMORT. OF FIRST COST — PIPE LOSSES — A — B — THICKNESS OF INSULATION

	Temperature Difference between Pipe and Air.									
	90°F.				180°F.					
Pipe Size Nom. Bore in.	½–1¼	1½–2½	2½–4	Plate	½–¾	1–1¼	1½–2	2½–3	3–4	Plate
Thickness of insulation in inches	¾	1¼	1½	2	¾	1¼	1½	2	2⅜	3

AMOUNT OF EXPANSION

$e = KLt.$

e = Amount of Expansion, in in.
L = Length of Piping under consideration, in ft.
t = Maximum Temperature Variation, in °F.
K = 0·000085 for Temperatures from 0°F. to 500°F.

See also IV. 1 and IV. 20

Range of temp. from 60°F. to	100°	150°	200°	250°	300°	350°	400°	500°
Expansion in in. per 100 ft. of Tube	0·5	0·75	1·34	1·6	2·05	2·5	2·9	3·75

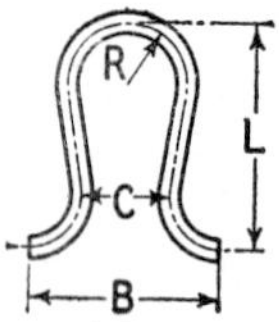

Fig. 1

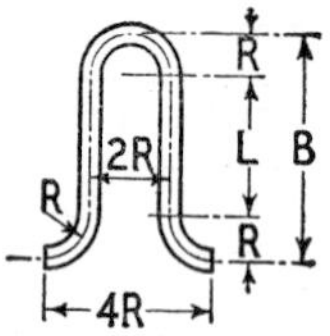

Fig. 2

DIMENSIONS OF EXPANSION LOOPS:

	Dia. of Tube in. Nom.	External	Dimensions in ft. and in. L	B	C	R_1	R_2	Total Travel in.	Cold Draw in.	Load at Anchors at Max. ColdDraw
Fig. 1	1	1 11/32	2 0	1 6	5¼	4	6	0·9	0·45	170
	1¼	1 11/16	2-2	1-8	5½	4½	6½	0·9	0·45	290
	1½	1 29/32	2 3	1-9	6	5	7	0·9	0·45	400
	2	2⅜	2-6	2-0	7	5½	8	1·05	0·50	600
	2½	3	2 9	2-3	8	6½	9	1·05	0·50	1130
	3	3½	3 0	2 6	9	7	10	1·25	0·60	1390
	3½	4	3-3	2-11	10½	8½	11	1·35	0·70	1660
	4	4½	3-6	3-4	1-0	10	1-0	1·45	0·75	1870
	5	5½	4 2	4-2	1-1½	1-0½	1-2	1·85	1·00	2000
	6	6½	5-0	4-10	1-3	1-3	1-4	2·10	1·20	2890
	7	7½	6-0	5-4	1-6	1-6	1-5	2·70	1·55	3000
	8	8½	7-0	6-0	1-9	1-8	1-7	3·35	1·90	3030
	9	9½	9-0	8-0	2-3	2-3	2-0	4·80	2·75	4040
	10	10½	9-9	9-6	2-9	2-6	2-10	5·35	3·10	4590
	11	11½	11-6	10-6	3-3	2-9	3-3	6·95	3·95	4540
	12	12½	13-4	11-6	3-6	3-0	3-6	8·35	4·80	4390
Fig. 2	1	1 11/32	3-0	3-8		4		2·0	1·0	
	1¼	1 11/16	3-6	4-4		5		2·2	1·1	
	1½	1 29/32	4-0	5-0		6		2·5	1·25	
	2	2⅜	4-6	5-6		6		2·5	1·25	
	2½	3	5-0	5-10		5		2·5	1·25	
	3	3½	5 6	6-6		6		2·6	1·3	
	3½	4	5-9	6-7½		5¼		2·5	1·25	
	4	4½	6-0	7-0		6		2·4	1·2	
	5	5½	6-9	7-9½		7½		2·5	1·25	
	6	6½	7-0	8-6		9		3·00	1·5	
	7	7½	8-0	9-9½		10½		2·55	1·3	
	8	8½	9-0	11-0		1-0		2·70	1·35	
	9	9½	9-6	11-8½		1-1½		2·85	1·42	
	10	10½	10-0	12-6		1-3		2·85	1·42	
	11	11½	11-0	13-9		1-4½		3·15	1·60	
	12	12½	12-0	15-0		1-6		3·5	1·80	

FACING OF FLANGES

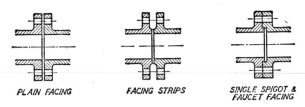

PLAIN FACING   *FACING STRIPS*   *SINGLE SPIGOT &*
                                                 FAUCET FACING

DIMENSIONS OF BRITISH STANDARD PIPE FLANGES—SEE TABLES II. 11–14

Water pipes in which the water temperature does not exceed 450°F. may be fitted with flanges to the next lower Table than that required for steam at the same pressure and a maximum temperature of 800°F.

WELDED PIPE JOINTS

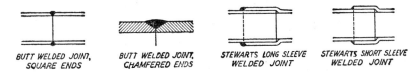

BUTT WELDED JOINT,   *BUTT WELDED JOINT,*   *STEWARTS LONG SLEEVE*   *STEWARTS SHORT SLEEVE*
SQUARE ENDS   *CHAMFERED ENDS*   *WELDED JOINT*   *WELDED JOINT*

HIGH PRESSURE FLANGES, METHODS OF FIXING

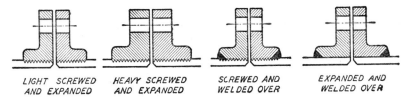

LIGHT SCREWED   *HEAVY SCREWED*   *SCREWED AND*   *EXPANDED AND*
AND EXPANDED   *AND EXPANDED*   *WELDED OVER*   *WELDED OVER*

PIPE HANGERS (Usual Dimensions in inches)

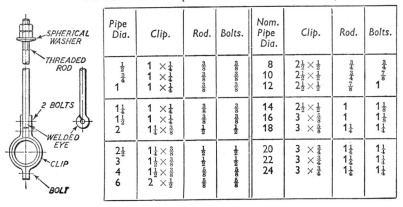

Pipe Dia.	Clip.	Rod.	Bolts.	Nom. Pipe Dia.	Clip.	Rod.	Bolts.
½	1 × ¼	⅜	⅜	8	2½ × ½	¾	¾
¾	1 × ¼	⅜	⅜	10	2½ × ½	¾	⅞
1	1 × ¼	⅜	⅜	12	2½ × ½	⅞	1
1¼	1 × ¼	⅜	⅜	14	2½ × ½	1	1⅛
1½	1 × ¼	⅜	⅜	16	3 × ⅝	1	1⅛
2	1¼ × ⅜	½	½	18	3 × ⅝	1¼	1¼
2½	1¼ × ⅜	½	½	20	3 × ¾	1¼	1¼
3	1½ × ⅜	½	½	22	3 × ¾	1¼	1¼
4	1½ × ⅜	⅝	⅝	24	3 × ¾	1¼	1¼
6	2 × ½	⅝	⅝				

SPHERICAL WASHER
THREADED ROD
2 BOLTS
WELDED EYE
CLIP
BOLT

BRITISH STANDARD TABLES OF PIPE FLANGES (FOR LAND USE).

TABLE D (superseding Table I of Report No. 10-1904). Flanges for Pipes, Valves, and Fittings for working steam pressures up to 50 lb. per sq. in.

1	1a	2	3	4	5	6(a)	6(b)	6(c)
Nominal Pipe Size	Actual Outside Dia. of Wrought Pipe	Dia. of Flange	Dia. of Bolt Circle	Number of Bolts	Diam. of Bolts	Thickness of Flange		
						Cast Iron	Cast Steel & Bronze	Iron or Steel (Stamped or Forged) Screwed or riveted on with boss or welded on with fillet
in.	in.	in.	in.		in.	in.	in.	in.
1/2	27/32	3 3/4	2 5/8	4	1/2	1/2	3/8	3/16
3/4	1 1/16	4	2 7/8	4	1/2	1/2	3/8	3/16
1	1 11/32	4 1/2	3 1/4	4	1/2	1/2	3/8	3/16
1 1/4	1 11/16	4 3/4	3 7/16	4	1/2	5/8	1/2	1/4
1 1/2	1 29/32	5 1/4	3 7/8	4	1/2	5/8	1/2	1/4
2	2 3/8	6	4 1/2	4	5/8	3/4	9/16	5/16
2 1/2	3	6 1/2	5	4	5/8	3/4	9/16	5/16
3	3 1/2	7 1/4	5 3/4	4	5/8	3/4	9/16	3/8
3 1/2	4	8	6 1/2	4	5/8	3/4	9/16	3/8
4	4 1/2	8 1/2	7	4	5/8	7/8	11/16	3/8
*4 1/2	5	9	7 1/2	8	5/8	7/8	11/16	7/16
5	5 1/2	10	8 1/4	8	5/8	7/8	11/16	1/2
6	6 1/2	11	9 1/4	8	5/8	7/8	11/16	1/2
7	7 1/2	12	10 1/2	8	5/8	1	3/4	1/2
8	8 1/2	13 1/4	11 1/2	8	5/8	1	3/4	1/2
9	9 1/2	14 1/2	12 3/4	8	5/8	1	3/4	5/8
10	10 1/2	16	14	8	3/4	1	3/4	5/8
*11	11 1/2	17	15	8	3/4	1 1/8	7/8	5/8
12	12 1/2	18	16	12	3/4	1 1/8	7/8	5/8
*13	14	19 1/4	17 1/2	12	3/4	1 1/8	7/8	3/4
14	15	20 3/4	18 1/2	12	7/8	1 1/4	1	3/4
15	16	21 1/4	19 1/2	12	7/8	1 1/4	1	3/4
16	17	22 3/4	20 1/2	12	7/8	1 1/4	1	3/4
*17	18	24	21 3/4	12	7/8	1 3/8	1 1/8	7/8
18	19	25 1/4	23	12	7/8	1 3/8	1 1/8	7/8
*19	20	26 1/2	24	12	7/8	1 3/8	1 1/8	7/8
20	21	27 3/4	25 1/4	16	7/8	1 1/2	1 1/4	1
21	22	29	26 1/2	16	7/8	1 1/2	1 1/4	1
*22	23	30	27 1/2	16	1	1 1/2	1 1/4	1
*23	24	31	28 1/2	16	1	1 5/8	1 3/8	1 1/8
24	25	32 1/2	29 3/4	16	1	1 5/8	1 3/8	1 1/8

* The Institution recommends that the use of these sizes be avoided.

Thicknesses.—The thicknesses given in this Table include a raised face of not more than 1/16 in. high if such is used. **Bolt Holes.**—For 1/2 in. and 5/8 in. Bolts the diameter of the holes to be 1/16 in. larger than the diameter of the Bolts, and for larger sizes of Bolts, 1/8 in. Bolt Holes to be drilled off centre lines.

BRITISH STANDARD TABLES OF PIPE FLANGES (FOR LAND USE)

TABLE E (superseding Table 2 of Report No. 10-1904). Flanges for Pipes, Valves, and Fittings, for working steam pressure above 50 lb. and up to 100 lb. per sq. in.

1	1a	2	3	4	5	6(a)	6(b)	6(c)
Nominal Pipe Size	*Actual Outside Dia. of Wrought Pipe*	*Dia. of Flange*	*Dia. of Bolt Circle*	*Number of Bolts*	*Diam. of Bolts*	*Thickness of Flange*		
						Cast Iron	*Cast Steel & Bronze*	*Iron or Steel (Stamped or Forged) Screwed or Riveted on with boss, or welded on with fillet*
in.	*in.*	*in.*	*in.*		*in.*	*in.*	*in.*	*in.*
1/2	27/32	3 3/4	2 5/8	4	1/2	1/2	3/8	1/4
3/4	1 1/16	4	2 7/8	4	1/2	1/2	3/8	1/4
1	1 11/32	4 1/2	3 1/4	4	1/2	1/2	3/8	9/32
1 1/4	1 11/16	4 3/4	3 7/16	4	1/2	5/8	1/2	5/16
1 1/2	1 29/32	5 1/4	3 7/8	4	1/2	5/8	1/2	11/32
2	2 3/8	6	4 1/2	4	5/8	3/4	9/16	3/8
2 1/2	3	6 1/2	5	4	5/8	3/4	9/16	13/32
3	3 1/2	7 1/4	5 3/4	4	5/8	3/4	9/16	7/16
3 1/2	4	8	6 1/2	8	5/8	3/4	9/16	15/32
4	4 1/2	8 1/2	7	8	5/8	7/8	11/16	1/2
*4 1/2	5	9	7 1/2	8	5/8	7/8	11/16	1/2
5	5 1/2	10	8 1/4	8	5/8	7/8	11/16	9/16
6	6 1/2	11	9 1/4	8	3/4	7/8	11/16	11/16
7	7 1/2	12	10 1/4	8	3/4	1	3/4	3/4
8	8 1/2	13 1/4	11 1/2	8	3/4	1	3/4	3/4
9	9 1/2	14 1/2	12 3/4	12	3/4	1	13/16	13/16
10	10 1/2	16	14	12	3/4	1	7/8	7/8
*11	11 1/2	17	15	12	3/4	1 1/8	15/16	15/16
12	12 1/2	18	16	12	7/8	1 1/8	1	1
*13	14	19 1/4	17 1/4	12	7/8	1 1/8	1	1
14	15	20 3/4	18 1/2	12	7/8	1 1/4	1	1
15	16	21 3/4	19 1/2	12	7/8	1 1/4	1	1
16	17	22 3/4	20 1/2	12	7/8	1 1/4	1	1
*17	18	24	21 3/4	12	7/8	1 3/8	1 1/8	1 1/8
18	19	25 1/4	23	16	7/8	1 3/8	1 1/8	1 1/8
*19	20	26 1/2	24	16	7/8	1 3/8	1 1/4	1 1/4
20	21	27 3/4	25 1/4	16	7/8	1 1/2	1 1/4	1 1/4
21	22	29	26 1/2	16	1	1 1/2	1 3/8	1 3/8
*22	23	30	27 1/2	16	1	1 1/2	1 3/8	1 3/8
*23	24	31	28 1/2	16	1	1 5/8	1 3/8	1 3/8
24	25	32 1/2	29 3/4	16	1	1 5/8	1 1/2	1 1/2

* The Institution recommends that the use of these sizes be avoided.

Thicknesses.—The thicknesses given in this Table include a raised face of not more than 1/16 in. high if such be used. **Bolt Holes.**—For 1/2 in. and 5/8 in. Bolts the diameters of the holes to be 1/16 in. larger than the diameters of the Bolts, and for larger sizes 1/8 in. Bolt Holes to be drilled off centre lines.

BRITISH STANDARD TABLES OF PIPE FLANGES (FOR LAND USE)
TABLE F (superseding Table 2 of Report No. 10-1904). Flanges for Pipes, Valves, and Fittings, for working steam pressure above 100 lb. and up to 150 lb. per sq. in.

1	1(a)	2	3	4	5	6(a)	6(b)
Nominal Pipe Size	Actual Outside Dia. of Wrought Pipe	Dia. of Flange	Dia. of Bolt Circle	Number of Bolts	Diam. of Bolts	Thickness of Flange	
						Cast Iron	Cast Steel Bronze, Iron or Steel (Stamped or Forged) Screwed or Riveted on with boss or welded on with fillet.
in.	in.	in.	in.		in.	in.	in.
$\frac{1}{2}$	$\frac{27}{32}$	$3\frac{3}{4}$	$2\frac{5}{8}$	4	$\frac{1}{2}$	$\frac{1}{2}$	$\frac{3}{8}$
$\frac{3}{4}$	$1\frac{1}{16}$	4	$2\frac{7}{8}$	4	$\frac{1}{2}$	$\frac{1}{2}$	$\frac{3}{8}$
1	$1\frac{11}{32}$	$4\frac{3}{4}$	$3\frac{7}{16}$	4	$\frac{5}{8}$	$\frac{1}{2}$	$\frac{3}{8}$
$1\frac{1}{4}$	$1\frac{11}{16}$	$5\frac{1}{4}$	$3\frac{7}{8}$	4	$\frac{5}{8}$	$\frac{5}{8}$	$\frac{1}{2}$
$1\frac{1}{2}$	$1\frac{29}{32}$	$5\frac{1}{2}$	$4\frac{1}{8}$	4	$\frac{5}{8}$	$\frac{5}{8}$	$\frac{1}{2}$
2	$2\frac{3}{8}$	$6\frac{1}{2}$	5	4	$\frac{5}{8}$	$\frac{3}{4}$	$\frac{5}{8}$
$2\frac{1}{2}$	3	$7\frac{1}{4}$	$5\frac{3}{4}$	8	$\frac{5}{8}$	$\frac{3}{4}$	$\frac{5}{8}$
3	$3\frac{1}{2}$	8	$6\frac{1}{2}$	8	$\frac{5}{8}$	$\frac{3}{4}$	$\frac{5}{8}$
$3\frac{1}{2}$	4	$8\frac{1}{2}$	7	8	$\frac{5}{8}$	$\frac{7}{8}$	$\frac{3}{4}$
4	$4\frac{1}{2}$	9	$7\frac{1}{2}$	8	$\frac{5}{8}$	$\frac{7}{8}$	$\frac{3}{4}$
*$4\frac{1}{2}$	5	10	$8\frac{1}{4}$	8	$\frac{3}{4}$	$\frac{7}{8}$	$\frac{3}{4}$
5	$5\frac{1}{2}$	11	$9\frac{1}{4}$	8	$\frac{3}{4}$	1	$\frac{7}{8}$
6	$6\frac{1}{2}$	12	$10\frac{1}{4}$	12	$\frac{3}{4}$	1	$\frac{7}{8}$
7	$7\frac{1}{2}$	$13\frac{1}{2}$	$11\frac{1}{2}$	12	$\frac{3}{4}$	1	$\frac{7}{8}$
8	$8\frac{1}{2}$	$14\frac{1}{2}$	$12\frac{3}{4}$	12	$\frac{3}{4}$	$1\frac{1}{8}$	1
9	$9\frac{1}{2}$	16	14	12	$\frac{7}{8}$	$1\frac{1}{8}$	1
10	$10\frac{1}{2}$	17	15	12	$\frac{7}{8}$	$1\frac{1}{8}$	1
*11	$11\frac{1}{2}$	18	16	16	$\frac{7}{8}$	$1\frac{1}{4}$	$1\frac{1}{8}$
12	$12\frac{1}{2}$	$19\frac{1}{4}$	$17\frac{1}{4}$	16	$\frac{7}{8}$	$1\frac{1}{4}$	$1\frac{1}{8}$
*13	14	$20\frac{3}{4}$	$18\frac{1}{2}$	16	1	$1\frac{1}{4}$	$1\frac{1}{8}$
14	15	$21\frac{3}{4}$	$19\frac{1}{2}$	16	1	$1\frac{3}{8}$	$1\frac{1}{4}$
15	16	$22\frac{3}{4}$	$20\frac{1}{2}$	16	1	$1\frac{3}{8}$	$1\frac{1}{4}$
16	17	24	$21\frac{3}{4}$	20	1	$1\frac{3}{8}$	$1\frac{1}{4}$
*17	18	$25\frac{1}{4}$	23	20	1	$1\frac{1}{2}$	$1\frac{3}{8}$
18	19	$26\frac{1}{2}$	24	20	$1\frac{1}{8}$	$1\frac{1}{2}$	$1\frac{3}{8}$
*19	20	$27\frac{3}{4}$	$25\frac{1}{4}$	20	$1\frac{1}{8}$	$1\frac{1}{2}$	$1\frac{3}{8}$
20	21	29	$26\frac{1}{2}$	24	$1\frac{1}{8}$	$1\frac{5}{8}$	$1\frac{1}{2}$
21	22	30	$27\frac{1}{2}$	24	$1\frac{1}{8}$	$1\frac{5}{8}$	$1\frac{1}{2}$
*22	23	31	$28\frac{1}{2}$	24	$1\frac{1}{8}$	$1\frac{5}{8}$	$1\frac{1}{2}$
*23	24	$32\frac{1}{2}$	$29\frac{3}{4}$	24	$1\frac{1}{4}$	$1\frac{3}{4}$	$1\frac{5}{8}$
24	25	$33\frac{1}{2}$	$30\frac{3}{4}$	24	$1\frac{1}{4}$	$1\frac{3}{4}$	$1\frac{5}{8}$

* The Institution recommends that the use of these sizes be avoided.

Thicknesses.—The thicknesses given in this Table include a raised face of not more than $\frac{1}{16}$ in. high if such be used. **Bolt Holes.**—For $\frac{1}{2}$ in. and $\frac{5}{8}$ in. Bolts the diameters of the holes to be $\frac{1}{16}$ in. larger than the diameters of the Bolts, and for larger sizes of Bolts $\frac{1}{8}$ in. Bolt Holes to be drilled off centre lines.

BRITISH STANDARD TABLES OF PIPE FLANGES (FOR LAND USE).

TABLE H (superseding Table 2 of Report No. 10-1904). Flanges for Pipes, Valves, and Fittings, for working steam pressure above 150 lb. and up to 250 lb. per sq. in.

1	1(a)	2	3	4	5	6
Nominal Dia. of Pipe	Actual Outside Dia. of Wrought Pipe	Diameter of Flange	Diameter of Bolt Circle	Number of Bolts	Diameter of Bolts	Thickness of Flange
						Cast Steel and Bronze, Steel (Stamped or Forged) Screwed or Riveted on with Boss, or welded on with fillet
in.	in.	in.	in.		in.	in.
$\frac{1}{2}$	$\frac{27}{32}$	$4\frac{1}{2}$	$3\frac{1}{4}$	4	$\frac{5}{8}$	$\frac{1}{2}$
$\frac{3}{4}$	$1\frac{1}{16}$	$4\frac{1}{2}$	$3\frac{1}{4}$	4	$\frac{5}{8}$	$\frac{1}{2}$
1	$1\frac{11}{32}$	$4\frac{3}{4}$	$3\frac{7}{16}$	4	$\frac{5}{8}$	$\frac{9}{16}$
$1\frac{1}{4}$	$1\frac{11}{16}$	$5\frac{1}{4}$	$3\frac{7}{8}$	4	$\frac{5}{8}$	$\frac{11}{16}$
$1\frac{1}{2}$	$1\frac{29}{32}$	$5\frac{1}{2}$	$4\frac{1}{8}$	4	$\frac{5}{8}$	$\frac{11}{16}$
2	$2\frac{3}{8}$	$6\frac{1}{2}$	5	4	$\frac{5}{8}$	$\frac{3}{4}$
$2\frac{1}{2}$	3	$7\frac{1}{4}$	$5\frac{3}{4}$	8	$\frac{5}{8}$	$\frac{3}{4}$
3	$3\frac{1}{2}$	8	$6\frac{1}{2}$	8	$\frac{5}{8}$	$\frac{7}{8}$
$3\frac{1}{2}$	4	$8\frac{1}{2}$	7	8	$\frac{5}{8}$	$\frac{7}{8}$
4	$4\frac{1}{2}$	9	$7\frac{1}{2}$	8	$\frac{5}{8}$	1
*$4\frac{1}{2}$	5	10	$8\frac{1}{4}$	8	$\frac{3}{4}$	1
5	$5\frac{1}{2}$	11	$9\frac{1}{4}$	8	$\frac{3}{4}$	$1\frac{1}{8}$
6	$6\frac{1}{2}$	12	$10\frac{1}{4}$	12	$\frac{3}{4}$	$1\frac{1}{8}$
7	$7\frac{1}{2}$	$13\frac{1}{2}$	$11\frac{1}{2}$	12	$\frac{3}{4}$	$1\frac{1}{4}$
8	$8\frac{1}{2}$	$14\frac{1}{2}$	$12\frac{3}{4}$	12	$\frac{3}{4}$	$1\frac{1}{4}$
9	$9\frac{1}{2}$	16	14	12	$\frac{7}{8}$	$1\frac{3}{8}$
10	$10\frac{1}{2}$	17	15	12	$\frac{7}{8}$	$1\frac{3}{8}$
*11	$11\frac{1}{2}$	18	16	16	$\frac{7}{8}$	$1\frac{1}{2}$
12	$12\frac{1}{2}$	$19\frac{1}{4}$	$17\frac{1}{4}$	16	$\frac{7}{8}$	$1\frac{1}{2}$
*13	14	$20\frac{3}{4}$	$18\frac{1}{2}$	16	1	$1\frac{5}{8}$
14	15	$21\frac{3}{4}$	$19\frac{1}{2}$	16	1	$1\frac{5}{8}$
15	16	$22\frac{3}{4}$	$20\frac{1}{2}$	16	1	$1\frac{3}{4}$
16	17	24	$21\frac{3}{4}$	20	1	$1\frac{3}{4}$
*17	18	$25\frac{1}{4}$	23	20	1	$1\frac{7}{8}$
18	19	$26\frac{1}{3}$	24	20	$1\frac{1}{8}$	$1\frac{7}{8}$
*19	20	$27\frac{3}{4}$	$25\frac{1}{4}$	20	$1\frac{1}{8}$	2
20	21	29	$26\frac{1}{2}$	24	$1\frac{1}{8}$	2
21	22	30	$27\frac{1}{2}$	24	$1\frac{1}{8}$	$2\frac{1}{8}$
*22	23	31	$28\frac{1}{2}$	24	$1\frac{1}{8}$	$2\frac{1}{8}$
*23	24	$32\frac{1}{2}$	$29\frac{1}{4}$	24	$1\frac{1}{4}$	$2\frac{1}{4}$
24	25	$33\frac{1}{2}$	$30\frac{3}{4}$	24	$1\frac{1}{4}$	$2\frac{1}{4}$

* The Institution recommends that the use of these sizes be avoided.

Thicknesses.—The thicknesses given in this Table include a raised face of not more than $\frac{1}{16}$ in. high if such be used. **Bolt Holes.**—For $\frac{1}{2}$ in. and $\frac{5}{8}$ in. Bolts the diameters of the Holes to be $\frac{1}{16}$ in. larger than the diameter of the Bolts, and for larger sizes of Bolts $\frac{1}{8}$ in. Bolt Holes to be drilled off centre lines.

STEEL FLANGES (Weights in lb.)

Nom. Bore.	British Standard Table.					
	D.	E.	F.	H.	J.	K.
$\frac{1}{2}$	0·62	0·88	1·20	2·50	3·12	3·75
$\frac{3}{4}$	0·75	1·00	1·38	2·50	3·12	3·75
1	1·00	1·30	2·00	3·12	4·00	5·38
$1\frac{1}{4}$	1·30	1·62	3·00	4·38	4·88	5·62
$1\frac{1}{2}$	1·62	2·25	3·38	4·75	6·00	8·50
2	2·5	2·88	5·50	7·25	9·62	9·62
$2\frac{1}{2}$	2·75	3·50	6·62	8·50	11·38	12·75
3	3·88	4·62	8·00	11·62	16·75	16·75
$3\frac{1}{2}$	4·62	5·75	10·38	12·88	18·25	21·25
4	5·25	6·75	11·38	15·75	21·50	24·88
$4\frac{1}{2}$	6·88	7·75	13·88	19·50	26·12	29·00
5	9·50	10·38	19·25	26·25	35·25	38·00
6	11·88	15·50	23·25	29·50	39·62	43·00
7	13·50	18·75	27·25	39·00		
8	16·75	22·50	36·38	44·75		
9	22·38	28·50	43·00	59·12		
10	27·12	35·75	46·75	63·50		
12	32·50	47·50	62·75	80·38		

AREAS OF CIRCLES IN SQ. INS.

Diameters in inches and $\frac{1}{4}$ths.

Diameter in Inches.	0 in.	$\frac{1}{4}$ in.	$\frac{1}{2}$ in.	$\frac{3}{4}$ in.
0	0·0	0·0490	0·1963	0·4417
1	0·7854	1·227	1·767	2·405
2	3·141	3·976	4·908	5·939
3	7·068	8·295	9·621	11·04
4	12·56	14·18	15·90	17·72
5	19·63	21·64	23·75	25·96
6	28·27	30·67	33·18	35·78
7	38·48	41·28	44·17	47·17
8	50·26	53·45	56·74	60·13
9	63·61	67·20	70·88	74·66
10	78·54	82·51	86·59	90·76
11	95·03	99·40	103·8	108·4
12	113·0	117·8	122·7	127·6

MALLEABLE IRON PIPE FITTINGS, BANDED AND BEADED, BLACK AND GALVANIZED.

Air Tested 100 lb. under water, sizes up to 2 in.; fittings $2\frac{1}{2}$ in. size and over tested 300 lb. hydraulic.

Fitting.	Crane	Ideal "P"	G.F.	Fitting.	Crane	Ideal "P"	G.F.
M & F . Bend	192	P80A	1	Parallel Thread Socket	176	P30	270
Female Bend	193	P80	2	Socket R. & L.	178		271
Elbow, M. & F.	152	P25	92	Hexagonal Nipple Equal	144	P115	281
Elbow	151	P20	90	Hexagonal Bush	140	P110	241
Close Return Bend	211		61	Reducing Socket	179	P27	240
Open Return Bend	213	P61	70	Eccentric Socket	180	P28	260
Wide Return Bend	214		60	Beaded Plug	146	P114	290
Tee	161	P21	130	Cap	185	P31	300
Twin Elbow	197	P81	132	Back Nut	150	P6	312
Pitcher Tee	199	P82	131	Union Elbow Female	246	P70	95
Cross	171	P22	180	Union Elbow M. & F.	247	P71	97
Pitcher Cross	201	P83	181	Standard Union F.	241	P90	330
				Standard Union M. & F.	242	P92	331

BRITISH STANDARD CAST IRON PIPES FOR WATER, GAS, AND SEWAGE. Standard thickness and external diameters for Spigot and Socket and Flange Straight Pipes. Brit. Stand. Spec. No. 78:1938 (Abstract)

DIMENSIONS IN INCHES

Nom. Internal dia. of Pipe.	GAS CLASS A. Test Pressure 200 ft. head.		WATER AND SEWAGE CLASS B. Test Pressure 400 ft. head.		CLASS C. Test Pressure 600 ft. head.		CLASS D. Test Pressure 800 ft. head.		Nom. Internal dia. of Pipe.
	Thick.	Ext. dia.	Thick.	Ext. dia.	Thick.	Ext. dia.	Thick.	Ext. dia.	
3	0·38	3·76	0·38	3·76	0·38	3·76	0·40	3·76	3
4	0·39	4·80	0·39	4·80	0·40	4·38	0·46	4·80	4
5	0·41	5·90	0·41	5·90	0·45	5·90	0·52	5·90	5
6	0·43	6·98	0·43	6·98	0·49	6·98	0·57	6·98	6
7	0·45	8·06	0·45	8·06	0·53	8·06	0·61	8·06	7
8	0·47	9·14	0·47	9·14	0·57	9·14	0·65	9·14	8
9	0·49	10·20	0·49	10·20	0·60	10·20	0·69	10·20	9
10	0·52	11·26	0·52	11·26	0·63	11·26	0·73	11·26	10
12	0·55	13·14	0·57	13·14	0·69	13·60	0·80	13·60	12

BASIC SIZES FOR B.S. PIPE THREADS
Abstract from Table I, B.S.21 : 1938

1	2	3	4	5	6	7	8	9	10	11	12
B.S.P. Size (Nom. Bore of Tube).	Outside Diameter of Black Tube				No. of Threads per inch.	Pitch	Depth of Thread.	Diameters at Gauge Plane (Basic).			Gauge Length.
	Max.	Min.	Mean.	Tol.				Major (Gauge Diam.)	Effective.	Minor.	
in.	in.	in.	in.	in.		in.	in.	in.	in.	in.	in.
$\frac{1}{8}$	0·412	0·387	0·400	0·025	28	0·03571	0·0229	0·383	0·3601	0·3372	0·1563
$\frac{1}{4}$	0·550	0·525	0·538	0·025	19	0·05263	0·0337	0·518	0·4843	0·4506	0·2367
$\frac{3}{8}$	0·688	0·663	0·676	0·025	19	0·05263	0·0337	0·656	0·6223	0·5886	0·2500
$\frac{1}{2}$	0·859	0·834	0·847	0·025	14	0·07143	0·0457	0·825	0·7793	0·7336	0·3214
$\frac{3}{4}$	1·075	1·050	1·063	0·025	14	0·07143	0·0457	1·041	0·9953	0·9496	0·3750
1	1·351	1·320	1·336	0·031	11	0·09091	0·0582	1·309	1·2508	1·1926	0·4091
$1\frac{1}{4}$	1·692	1·661	1·677	0·031	11	0·09091	0·0582	1·650	1·5918	1·5336	0·5000
$1\frac{1}{2}$	1·924	1·893	1·909	0·031	11	0·09091	0·0582	1·882	1·8238	1·7656	0·5000
2	2·403	2·358	2·381	0·045	11	0·09091	0·0582	2·347	2·2888	2·2306	0·6250
$2\frac{1}{2}$	3·021	2·971	2·996	0·050	11	0·09091	0·0582	2·960	2·9018	2·8436	0·6875
3	3·526	3·471	3·499	0·055	11	0·09091	0·0582	3·460	3·4018	3·3436	0·8125
$3\frac{1}{2}$	4·021	3·961	3·991	0·060	11	0·09091	0·0582	3·950	3·8918	3·8336	0·8750
4	4·526	4·461	4·494	0·065	11	0·09091	0·0582	4·450	4·3918	4·3336	1·0000
5	5·536	5·461	5·498	0·075	11	0·09091	0·0582	5·450	5·3918	5·3336	1·1250
6	6·541	6·461	6·501	0·080	11	0·09091	0·0582	6·450	6·3918	6·3336	1·1250

WEIGHT OF SHEET AND ROUND AND SQUARE STEEL BARS.

Density = 486 lb. per cu. ft.   Spec. gravity = 7·8.   Weight of Iron Plates.
see also II. 3

Thickness or dia. in.	Weight in lb. of			Thickness or dia. in.	Weight in lb. of		
	Sheet per sq. ft.	Square per ft.	Round per ft.		Sheet per sq. ft.	Square per ft.	Round per ft.
$\frac{1}{16}$	2·55						
$\frac{1}{8}$	5·10	0·053	0·042	$1\frac{1}{8}$	45·9	4·31	3·38
$\frac{3}{16}$	7·65	0·120	0·094	$1\frac{1}{4}$	51·0	5·32	4·17
$\frac{1}{4}$	10·20	0·213	0·167	$1\frac{3}{8}$	56·1	6·43	5·05
$\frac{5}{16}$	12·75	0·332	0·261	$1\frac{1}{2}$	61·2	7·71	6·01
$\frac{3}{8}$	15·30	0·479	0·376	$1\frac{5}{8}$	66·3	8·99	7·05
$\frac{7}{16}$	17·85	0·651	0·511	$1\frac{3}{4}$	71·4	10·4	8·19
$\frac{1}{2}$	20·40	0·851	0·658	$1\frac{7}{8}$	76·5	12·0	9·39
$\frac{9}{16}$	22·95	1·08	0·845	2	81·6	13·6	10·7
$\frac{5}{8}$	25·50	1·33	1·04	$2\frac{1}{4}$	91·8	17·2	13·6
$\frac{11}{16}$	28·05	1·61	1·29	$2\frac{1}{2}$	102·2	21·3	16·8
$\frac{3}{4}$	30·60	1·91	1·50	$2\frac{3}{4}$	112·4	25·7	20·2
$\frac{13}{16}$	33·15	2·25	1·77	3	122·4	30·6	24·1
$\frac{7}{8}$	35·70	2·61	2·04	4	163·2	54·4	42·8
$\frac{15}{16}$	38·25	2·99	2·35	5	204·0	85·1	66·9
1	40·80	3·40	2·68	6	324·8	122·5	96·2

WEIGHT OF FLAT IRON in lb. per ft. run.

Width in inches	Thickness in inches.						
	$\frac{1}{4}$	$\frac{3}{8}$	$\frac{1}{2}$	$\frac{5}{8}$	$\frac{3}{4}$	$\frac{7}{8}$	1
$\frac{3}{4}$	0·625	0·938	1·251	1·564	1·876	2·189	2·502
1	0·834	1·251	1·668	2·085	2·502	2·919	3·336
$1\frac{1}{4}$	1·042	1·564	2·085	2·606	3·127	3·649	4·170
$1\frac{1}{2}$	1·251	1·876	2·502	3·127	3·753	4·378	5·004
$1\frac{3}{4}$	1·459	2·189	2·919	3·649	4·378	5·108	5·835
2	1·668	2·502	3·336	4·170	5·004	5·838	6·672
$2\frac{1}{4}$	1·876	2·815	3·753	4·691	5·629	6·568	7·506
$2\frac{1}{2}$	2·085	3·127	4·170	5·212	6·255	7·297	8·340
$2\frac{3}{4}$	2·293	3·440	4·587	5·734	6·880	8·027	9·174
3	2·502	3·753	5·004	6·255	7·506	8·757	10·008

WHITWORTH STANDARD BOLTS AND NUTS

Dia. of Bolt in.	Threads per inch.	Dia. at Bottom of Thread. in.	Area at Bottom of Thread. sq. in.	Width across Flats. in.	Width across Corners. in.	Thickness of Bolt Head. in.	Thickness of Nut in.
$\frac{1}{4}$	20	0·1860	0·027	0·525	0·6062	0·2187	$\frac{1}{4}$
$\frac{5}{16}$	18	0·2414	0·046	0·6014	0·6944	0·2734	$\frac{5}{16}$
$\frac{3}{8}$	16	0·2950	0·068	0·7094	0·8191	0·3281	$\frac{3}{8}$
$\frac{7}{16}$	14	0·3460	0·094	0·8204	0·9473	0·3828	$\frac{7}{16}$
$\frac{1}{2}$	12	0·3933	0·121	0·9191	1·0612	0·4375	$\frac{1}{2}$
$\frac{9}{16}$	12	0·4558	0·164	1·011	1·1674	0·4921	$\frac{9}{16}$
$\frac{5}{8}$	11	0·5086	0·203	1·101	1·2713	0·5468	$\frac{5}{8}$
$\frac{11}{16}$	11	0·5711	0·256	1·2011	1·3869	0·6015	$\frac{11}{16}$
$\frac{3}{4}$	10	0·6219	0·304	1·3012	1·5024	0·6562	$\frac{3}{4}$
$\frac{13}{16}$	10	0·6844	0·367	1·39	1·6050	0·7109	$\frac{13}{16}$
$\frac{7}{8}$	9	0·7327	0·422	1·4788	1·7075	0·7656	$\frac{7}{8}$
1	8	0·8399	0·554	1·6701	1·9284	0·875	1
$1\frac{1}{4}$	7	1·0670	0·894	2·0483	2·3651	1·0937	$1\frac{1}{4}$
$1\frac{1}{2}$	6	1·2866	1·3	2·4134	2·7867	1·3125	$1\frac{1}{2}$
$1\frac{3}{4}$	5	1·4938	1·753	2·7578	3·1844	1·5312	$1\frac{3}{4}$
2	4·5	1·7154	2·31	3·1491	3·6362	1·75	2
3	3·5	2·6341	5·45	4·531	5·2319	2·625	3
4	3	3·5731	10·027	5·95	6·8704	3·5	4
5	2·75	4·534	16·15	7·8	9·0066	4·375	5

WEIGHT OF FLAT STEEL SHEETS

Gauge B.G. Number.	Thickness in			Weight per Super Foot.
	Fractions of an Inch.	Decimals of an Inch.	Millimetres.	Black.
10	$\frac{1}{8}$	0·125	3·175	5·10
12	—	0·0991	2·517	4·04
14	—	0·0785	1·994	3·20
16	$\frac{1}{16}$	0·0625	1·587	2·55
18	—	0·0495	1·257	2·02
20	—	0·0392	0·996	1·59
22	$\frac{1}{32}$	0·0312	0·794	1·27
24	—	0·0247	0·629	1·00
26	—	0·0196	0·498	0·79
28	$\frac{1}{64}$	0·0156	0·397	0·63

HEAVY GAUGE COPPER TUBES : B.S.S. No. 61

Nominal Bore in.	Low Pressure Tubes		Medium Pressure Tubes		High Pressure Tubes		Nominal Bore in.
	Thickness S.W.G.	Weight lb./ft.	Thickness S.W.G.	Weight lb./ft.	Thickness S.W.G.	Weight lb./ft.	
$\frac{1}{2}$	15	0·50	14	0·53	12	0·91	$\frac{1}{2}$
$\frac{3}{4}$	15	0·72	13	0·89	11	1·30	$\frac{3}{4}$
1	14	1·04	12	1·33	10	1·84	1
$1\frac{1}{4}$	14	1·29	12	1·64	9	2·63	$1\frac{1}{4}$
$1\frac{1}{2}$	14	1·52	12	1·96	9	3·04	$1\frac{1}{2}$
2	13	2·33	12	2·61	9	3·85	2
$2\frac{1}{2}$	13	2·88	11	3·60	7	5·94	$2\frac{1}{2}$
3	12	3·90	10	4·77	6	7·60	3
$3\frac{1}{2}$	11	5·07	9	6·25	5	9·60	$3\frac{1}{2}$
4	10	6·39	8	7·93	4	11·85	4

LIGHT GAUGE COPPER TUBES, B.S.S. No. 659

Nom. Bore in.	Outside dia in.	Thickness		Weight lb./ft.
		S.W.G.	in.	
$\frac{1}{8}$	0·205	22	0·028	0·06
$\frac{3}{16}$	0·283	21	0·032	0·10
$\frac{1}{4}$	0·346	20	0·036	0·13
$\frac{3}{8}$	0·471	20	0·036	0·19
$\frac{1}{2}$	0·596	19	0·040	0·27
$\frac{3}{4}$	0·846	19	0·040	0·39
1	1·112	18	0·048	0·62
$1\frac{1}{4}$	1·362	18	0·048	0·76
$1\frac{1}{2}$	1·612	18	0·048	0·91
2	2·128	17	0·056	1·40
$2\frac{1}{2}$	2·628	17	0·056	1·74
3	3·144	16	0·064	2·38
$3\frac{1}{2}$	3·660	15	0·072	3·12
4	4·184	14	0·080	3·97
5	5·125	13	0·092	5·60
6	6·125	12	0·104	7·58

COPPER, SOIL, WASTE & VENTILATING PIPES
(LONDON C.C. BYE-LAWS)

Internal dia. in.	Thickness S.W.G.	Weight lb./yard
$1\frac{1}{4}$	18	2·25
$1\frac{1}{2}$	18	2·70
2	17	4·17
$2\frac{1}{2}$	17	5·19
3	16	7·11
$3\frac{1}{2}$	15	9·33
4	14	11·85
$4\frac{1}{2}$	14	13·29
5	14	14·76
6	14	17·64

DIMENSIONS OF FLANGED FITTINGS

STANDARD DIMENSIONS OF FLANGED FITTINGS

Nominal Bore	A	B	C	D	E	F	G	H	J
ins.	ins.	ins.	ins.	ins.	ins.	ins.	ft. ins.	ft. ins.	ft. ins.
1	4	5½	3	6	3	4	1 5	1 6	0 9
2	5	6½	3½	9½	6	5	2 0	2 1	1 3
2½	5½	7½	4	11½	7½	5½	2 3	2 6	1 6
3	6	8½	4½	13	9	6	2 6	2 9	1 9
3½	6½	9½	4½	15½	10½	6½	2 9	3 3	2 0
4	7	10½	5	17	12	7	3 1	3 7	2 3
5	8	11½	5½	21	15	8	4 2	4 8	3 0
6	9	12½	6	25	18	9	4 6	5 3	3 6
7	10	13½	6½	31½	24½	10	5 6	6 6	4 1
8	11	15	7	36	28	11	6 6	7 5	4 8
9	12	16½	7½	39½	31½	12	7 8	8 4	5 3
10	13	18	8	49	40	13	9 7	10 6	6 8
12	15	21	9	58	48	15	12 1	12 10	8 0

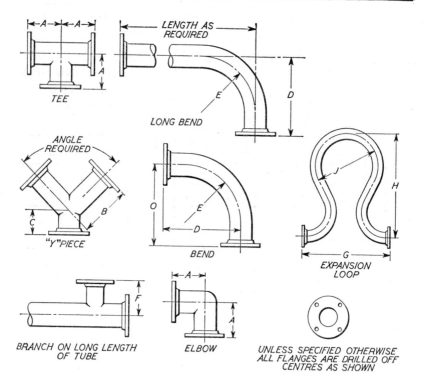

TEE

LONG BEND

"Y" PIECE

BEND

EXPANSION LOOP

BRANCH ON LONG LENGTH OF TUBE

ELBOW

UNLESS SPECIFIED OTHERWISE ALL FLANGES ARE DRILLED OFF CENTRES AS SHOWN

FLANGED FITTINGS

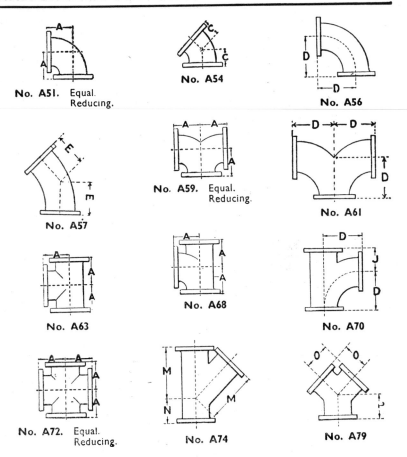

No. A51. Equal. Reducing.

No. A54

No. A56

No. A57

No. A59. Equal. Reducing.

No. A61

No. A63

No. A68

No. A70

No. A72. Equal. Reducing.

No. A74

No. A79

CRANE CAST IRON FLANGED FITTINGS
Flanges to B.S.T. "D" and "E" diameter
General Dimensions

Size	in. 2	in. $2\frac{1}{2}$	in. 3	in. $3\frac{1}{2}$	in. 4	in. 5	in. 6	in. 7	in. 8
A	5	$5\frac{1}{2}$	6	$6\frac{1}{2}$	7	8	9	10	11
C	$2\frac{1}{2}$	3	3	$3\frac{1}{2}$	4	$4\frac{1}{2}$	5	$5\frac{1}{2}$	$5\frac{1}{2}$
D	10	10	12	14	14	15	16	16	18
E	5	$5\frac{1}{2}$	6	8	8	9	10	11	11
J	3	$3\frac{1}{2}$	4	4	4	5	6	6	7
M	8	$9\frac{1}{2}$	10	$11\frac{1}{2}$	12	$13\frac{1}{2}$	$14\frac{1}{2}$	$16\frac{1}{2}$	$17\frac{1}{2}$
N	$2\frac{1}{2}$	$2\frac{1}{2}$	3	3	3	$3\frac{1}{2}$	$3\frac{1}{2}$	4	$4\frac{1}{2}$
O	5	$5\frac{1}{2}$	6	$6\frac{1}{2}$	7	8	9	10	$11\frac{1}{2}$
P	$2\frac{1}{2}$	$2\frac{3}{4}$	3	$3\frac{1}{4}$	$3\frac{1}{2}$	4	$4\frac{1}{2}$	5	$5\frac{1}{2}$

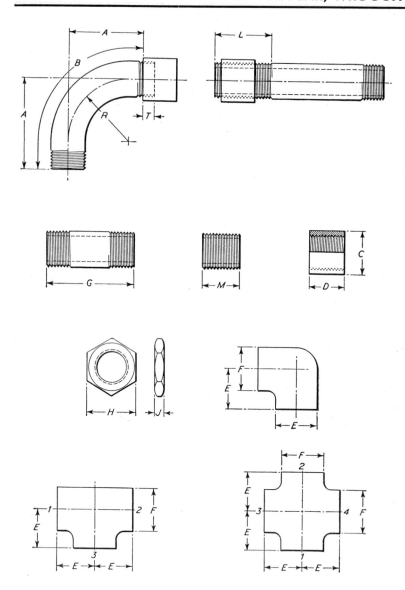

SPECIFY OUTLETS OF TEES AND CROSSES IN
ORDER AS NUMBERED ABOVE

APPROXIMATE DIMENSIONS (in inches) OF STEEL TUBULAR FITTINGS TO B.S. 1387 : 1957, WROUGHT (Heavyweight) FITTINGS TO B.S. 1740 and MALLEABLE FITTINGS TO B.S. 1256.

(Subject to standard tolerances)

		Size:	1/8 in.	1/4 in.	3/8 in.	1/2 in.	3/4 in.	1 in.	1 1/4 in.	1 1/2 in.	2 in.	2 1/2 in.	3 in.	3 1/2 in.	4 in.	5 in.	6 in.
90° Bends, Centre to Face	Mild Steel	A	2 1/8	2 1/2	2 7/8	3 1/4	4	4 3/4	6	6 3/4	8	9 3/4	11 1/2	13 1/4	15	21	24 1/2
	Malleable	A	—	1 3/16	1 7/16	1 3/4	2	2 1/2	3	3 1/2	4	4 1/2	5	5 3/4	6 1/2	7 1/2	9
90° Bends, Radius of M.S. Bends No. 6		R	1 1/4	1 5/8	1 7/8	2 1/4	2 7/8	3 1/2	4 1/4	5	6 1/4	7 3/4	9 1/8	10 5/8	12 1/8	18	21
90° Bends No. 6 and Springs Nos. 7, 8 and 9, Contents ...		B	3 3/4	4 1/4	4 7/8	5 1/2	6 3/4	8	10 1/8	11 3/8	13 1/4	16 1/4	19	22	24 3/4	34 1/4	40
M.S. Sockets, No. 16 (Equal) ... ... (Connector Sockets may be 1/8 in. shorter)	Outside Dia.	C	19/32	3/4	29/32	1 3/32	1 11/32	1 21/32	2 1/32	2 9/32	2 25/32	3 7/16	4	4 1/2	5 1/16	6 1/8	7 1/4
	Length	D	3/4	1	1 1/8	1 1/2	1 5/8	1 7/8	2 1/8	2 1/4	2 1/2	2 3/4	3	3 1/4	3 1/2	3 3/4	3 3/4
Malleable Sockets No. 112 (Equal)	Length	D	31/32	1 1/16	1 5/32	1 11/32	1 17/32	1 11/16	1 15/16	2 5/32	2 17/32	2 7/8	3 3/16	3 7/16	3 11/16	4 1/4	4 3/4
Elbows, Tees and Crosses, Centre to Face ...	Wrought	E	5/8	7/8	15/16	1 1/4	1 3/8	1 11/16	2	2 1/16	2 1/2	3	3 1/2	4	4 1/2	5 1/2	6 1/4
	Malleable	E	11/16	13/16	15/16	1 1/8	1 5/16	1 1/2	1 3/4	1 15/16	2 1/4	2 11/16	3 3/32	3 7/16	3 25/32	4 1/2	5 1/8
Elbows, Tees and Crosses, Outside Diameter	Wrought	F	21/32	25/32	15/16	1 1/8	1 11/32	1 5/8	2	2 1/4	2 3/4	3 13/32	3 15/16	4 7/16	4 31/32	6 1/16	7 1/8
	Malleable (Plain)	F	9/16	11/16	27/32	1	1 1/4	1 17/32	1 29/32	2 1/16	2 11/16	3 5/16	3 27/32	4 3/8	4 29/32	6	7 1/16
M.S. Barrel Nipples No. 23	Length	G	1 3/8	1 3/4	1 3/4	2 1/4	2 1/4	2 1/2	3	3	3	3 1/2	3 1/2	4	4	4 1/2	5
M.S. Backnuts, No. 21	Across Flats	H	3/4	7/8	1 1/16	1 1/4	1 7/16	1 13/16	2 3/8	2 1/2	3 1/16	3 13/16	4 1/2	5 1/8	5 1/2	6 3/4	7 3/4
	Thickness	J	1/4	1/4	9/32	5/16	11/32	3/8	7/16	15/32	17/32	11/16	13/16	13/16	7/8	15/16	1
Connectors, Nos. 4 and 5	Length of Effective Thread	L	1 1/16	1 11/32	1 9/16	2 1/32	2 3/16	2 1/2	2 7/8	3 1/32	3 11/32	3 7/8	4 1/4	4 1/2	4 13/16	5 1/8	5 1/8
Running Nipples, No. 22	Length	M	1/2	3/4	13/16	1 1/16	1 3/16	1 5/16	1 1/2	1 1/2	1 7/8	2	2 1/4	2 3/8	2 3/4	3 1/16	3 1/16
Approx. Thread Engagement when wrench tight		T	5/16	13/32	7/16	1/2	5/8	11/16	3/4	13/16	7/8	1 1/16	1 1/8	1 1/4	1 3/8	1 9/16	1 5/8

PRICE LIST OF SCREWED & SOCKETED STEEL TUBES & WROUGHT FITTINGS

TUBES: B.S. 1387   FITTINGS: B.S. 1740

Internal Diameter (nominal)	in inches	⅛ & ¼	⅜	½	¾	1	1¼	1½	2	2½	3	4	5	6
TUBES														
Tubes, 2 ft. long and over	per foot	9¾d.	10d.	1/-	1/2½	1/9	2/3	2/8	3/9	5/-	6/6	9/3	13/-	16/-
Pieces, 12 to 23½ in. long	each	2/-	2/2	2/4	3/1	4/4	5/7	6/6	9/9	14/1	21/-	32/5	52/-	69/4
Pieces, 4 to 11½ in. long	each	1/5	1/7	1/8	2/-	2/10	3/6	4/2	6/2	9/3	13/6	22/6	39/-	54/-
Longscrews, 12 to 23½ in. long	each	2/3	2/4	2/9	3/5	4/11	5/11	7/3	10/9	15/11	24/-	35/7	57/5	75/9
Longscrews, 3 to 11½ in. long	each	1/7	1/9	1/10	2/4	3/3	4/-	4/10	7/2	11/6	17/-	27/3	43/4	59/9
Barrel Nipples	each	1/-	1/-	1/1	1/3	1/8	2/1	2/7	3/7	5/3	8/-	14/8	27/-	42/8
Bends	each	1/7	1/9	2/-	2/6	3/8	5/5	6/2	10/7	21/6	36/-	67/9	226/6	319/-
Springs, not Socketed	each	1/1	1/3	1/4	1/8	2/8	4/1	4/5	8/1	16/6	29/-	55/9	202/6	283/-
FITTINGS														
Socket Union, Pipe Union	each	4/-	5/-	6/-	8/-	11/-	13/6	16/-	20/-	35/-	45/-	70/-	132/-	210/-
Elbows, Square	each	1/8	1/10	2/2	2/6	3/-	4/4	5/2	8/6	19/-	28/-	56/-	190/-	300/-
Elbows, Round	each	1/10	2/-	2/4	2/10	3/4	4/8	5/8	9/4	21/-	32/-	60/-	190/-	300/-
Tees	each	2/-	2/2	2/6	3/2	3/8	5/-	6/2	10/2	23/-	36/-	64/-	196/-	310/-
Crosses	each	4/4	4/8	5/6	6/6	8/2	11/-	13/2	21/-	44/-	80/-	133/4	440/-	700/-
Sockets, Plain	each	6d.	6d.	8d.	10d.	1/-	1/4	1/9	2/6	5/-	7/-	12/-	24/-	36/-
Sockets, Diminished	each	8d.	10d.	1/-	1/2	1/6	2/-	2/8	4/-	10/-	14/-	22/-	70/-	110/-
Flanges	each	1/6	1/8	2/-	2/4	2/8	3/6	4/-	5/6	10/-	17/-	23/-	36/-	54/-
Caps	each	7d.	7d.	10d.	1/-	1/4	2/-	2/6	4/-	8/8	12/-	21/-	60/-	90/-
Plugs	each	6d.	6d.	8d.	10d.	1/-	1/4	1/8	2/6	5/-	9/6	20/-	60/-	96/-
Backnuts	each	4d.	4d.	6d.	7d.	10d.	1/-	1/4	2/2	4/6	7/-	11/-	36/-	52/-
Nipples	each	4d.	4d.	6d.	7d.	8d.	1/-	1/4	2/-	4/6	7/-	11/-	36/-	52/-
Union Bends	each	5/-	6/-	7/6	10/-	12/6	17/-	20/-	27/-	54/-	74/-	116/-	200/-	320/-

List prices ruling at 1st September, 1962—Subject to trade discounts

WEIGHTS OF WROUGHT FITTINGS EQUAL SIZES
Approximate (for estimating only)

Nominal Bore of Tube (ins.)	Weight shown is Unit of	Longscrews with Sockets Mean Lengths without Nuts — Unders App. 18 in (lbs.)	(ozs.)	Overs App. 18 in (lbs.)	(ozs.)	Bends (lbs.)	(ozs.)	Elbows (lbs.)	(ozs.)	Tees (lbs.)	(ozs.)	Crosses (lbs.)	(ozs.)	Sockets (lbs.)	(ozs.)	Flanges Table 'E' (lbs.)	(ozs.)	Caps (lbs.)	(ozs.)	Plugs (lbs.)	(ozs.)	Back Nuts (lbs.)	(ozs.)	Nipples (lbs.)	(ozs.)
⅛	10	1	14	2	9	1	8	1	1	1	3	1	5	0	8	—	—	0	4	0	3	0	5	0	4
¼	10	3	2	6	0	2	4	1	10	1	12	2	0	0	12	—	—	0	9½	0	7	0	9	0	6
⅜	10	5	0	9	14	3	6	1	15	2	3	3	0	1	2	—	—	1	4	1	14	0	12	0	8
½	10	7	8	14	9	5	8	3	0	3	10	4	6	1	12	9	4	2	6	1	5	1	10	0	11
¾	10	11	14	24	3	8	14	5	5	5	14	7	4	2	8	9	15	3	6	2	6	1	3	1	0
1	10	16	4	31	9	17	0	7	10	9	9	10	11	4	3	12	6	5	8	3	12	2	15	1	10
1¼	10	21	4	39	11	27	14	11	14	13	12	15	0	6	8	17	0	8	6	5	8	3	6	2	8
1½	10	29	12	55	3	36	14	16	6	17	10	18	15	9	6	24	2	11	0	7	10	5	13	3	10
2	10	39	6	73	9	59	6	25	8	32	4	33	12	12	0	31	7	16	8	8	0	4	10	4	12
2½	5	26	4	46	0	46	0	22	8	26	8	28	12	10	6	18	8	14	3	6	2	6	10	4	0
3	5	32	3	53	4	68	0	31	4	38	2	41	0	15	4	28	0	20	8	8	2	8	13	8	2
3½	5	40	12	69	12	86	0	44	8	51	0	54	4	17	10	32	8	27	8	12	0	9	3	8	8
4	5	49	8	83	4	110	0	57	8	63	12	67	3	22	0	37	0	32	12	16	0	13	8	8	10
5	1	12	9	19	3	51	0	24	8	28	0	32	0	7	4	10	3	10	2	6	6	4	0	2	0
6	1	19	8	29	12	65	0	31	8	37	8	41	0	11	6	13	4	14	9	7	0	6	0	2	2

SINGLE PANEL WALL RADIATORS (I IN. DEEP) (Belcon Ltd)

Sq. ft. and heat emission in B.t.u./hr. Heat transfer coefficient K quoted in B.t.u./hr./100°F.

No. of Sections	Overall Length in.	Height 12 (K 197) Sq. ft.	B.t.u.	Height 18 (K 194) Sq. ft.	B.t.u.	Height 20 (K 193) Sq. ft.	B.t.u.	Height 24 (K 192) Sq. ft.	B.t.u.	Height 30 (K 191) Sq. ft.	B.t.u.	Height 40 (K 190) Sq. ft.	B.t.u.
10	15¾	3·6	700	4·9	950	5·8	1,100	6·5	1,250	8·2	1,550	10·5	2,000
12	18⅞	4·3	850	5·9	1,150	7·0	1,350	7·8	1,500	9·8	1,850	12·6	2,400
14	22	5·0	1,000	6·9	1,350	8·1	1,550	9·1	1,750	11·5	2,200	14·7	2,800
16	25¼	5·8	1,150	7·8	1,500	9·3	1,800	10·4	2,000	13·1	2,500	16·8	3,200
18	28⅜	6·5	1,300	8·8	1,700	10·4	2,000	11·7	2,250	14·8	2,850	18·9	3,600
20	31	7·2	1,400	9·8	1,900	11·6	2,250	13·0	2,500	16·4	3,150	21·0	4,000
22	34⅝	7·9	1,550	10·8	2,100	12·8	2,450	14·3	2,750	18·0	3,450	23·1	4,400
24	37⅝	8·6	1,700	11·8	2,300	13·9	2,700	15·6	3,000	19·7	3,800	25·2	4,800
26	41	9·4	1,850	12·7	2,450	15·0	2,900	16·9	3,250	21·3	4,050	27·3	5,200
28	44⅛	10·1	2,000	13·7	2,650	16·2	3,150	18·2	3,500	22·9	4,350	29·4	5,600
30	47¼	10·8	2,150	14·7	2,850	17·4	3,350	19·5	3,750	24·6	4,700	31·5	6,000
32	50⅜	11·5	2,250	15·7	3,050	18·6	3,600	20·8	4,000	26·2	5,000	33·6	6,400
34	53⅛	12·2	2,400	16·7	3,250	19·7	3,800	22·1	4,250	27·9	5,350	35·7	6,880
36	56¾	13·0	2,550	17·6	3,400	20·9	4,050	23·4	4,500	29·5	5,650	37·8	7,200
38	59⅝	13·7	2,700	18·6	3,600	22·0	4,250	24·7	4,750	31·2	5,950	39·9	7,600
40	63	14·4	2,850	19·6	3,800	23·2	4,500	26·0	5,000	32·8	6,250	42·0	8,000
42	66⅛	15·1	3,950	20·6	4,000	24·4	4,700	27·3	5,250	34·5	6,600	44·1	8,400
44	69¼	15·8	3,100	21·6	4,200	25·5	4,900	28·6	5,500	36·0	6,900	46·2	8,800
46	72⅛	16·5	3,250	22·5	4,350	26·7	5,150	29·9	5,750	37·7	7,200	48·3	9,200
48	75⅝	17·3	3,400	23·5	4,550	27·8	5,350	31·2	6,000	39·3	7,500	50·4	9,600
50	78½	18·0	8,550	24·5	4,750	29·0	5,600	32·5	6,250	41·0	7,850	52·5	10,000
60	94⅛	21·6	4,250	29·4	5,700	34·8	6,700	39·0	7,500	49·2	9,400	63·0	12,000
70	110¼	25·2	4,950	34·3	6,650	40·6	7,850	45·5	8,750	57·4	10,950	73·5	13,950
80	126	28·8	5,650	39·2	7,600	46·4	8,950	52·0	10,000	65·6	12,550	84·0	15,950
90	141¾	32·4	6,400	44·1	8,550	52·2	10,100	58·5	11,250	73·8	14,100	94·5	17,950
100	157½	36·0	7,100	49·0	9,500	58·0	11,200	65·0	12,500	82·0	15,650	105·0	19,950

DOUBLE PANEL WALL RADIATORS ($2\frac{3}{8}$ IN. DEEP) (Belcon Ltd)

Height—in.		40		30		24		20		18		12	
K		162		165		166		167		170		178	
		Sq. ft. and heat emission in B.t.u./hr. Heat transfer coefficient K quoted in B.t.u./hr./100° F.											
No. of Sections	Overall Length in.	Sq. ft.	B.t.u.	Sq. ft.	B.t.u.	Sq. ft.	B.t.u.	Sq. ft.	B.t.u.	Sq. ft.	B.t.u.	Sq. ft.	B.t.u.
10	15¾	21·0	3,400	16·3	2,700	13·0	2,150	11·6	1,950	9·8	1,650	7·2	1,300
12	18⅞	25·2	4,100	19·6	3,200	15·6	2,600	14·0	2,350	11·8	2,000	8·6	1,550
14	22	29·4	4,750	22·8	3,750	18·2	3,000	16·2	2,700	13·8	2,350	10·0	1,800
16	25¼	33·6	5,450	26·1	4,300	20·8	3,450	18·6	3,100	15·6	2,650	11·6	2,050
18	28⅜	37·8	6,150	29·4	4,850	23·4	3,900	20·8	3,450	17·6	3,000	13·0	2,300
20	31½	42·0	6,800	32·6	5,400	26·0	4,300	23·2	3,850	19·6	3,350	14·4	2,550
22	34⅝	46·2	7,500	35·9	5,900	28·6	4,750	25·6	4,300	21·6	3,650	15·8	2,800
24	37¾	50·4	8,150	39·1	6,450	31·2	5,200	27·8	4,650	23·6	4,000	17·2	3,050
26	41	54·6	8,850	42·4	7,000	33·8	5,600	30·0	5,000	25·4	4,300	18·8	3,350
28	44⅛	58·8	9,550	45·6	7,500	36·4	6,050	32·4	5,400	27·4	4,650	20·2	3,600
30	47¼	63·0	10,200	48·8	8,050	39·0	6,450	34·8	5,800	29·4	5,000	21·6	3,850
32	50⅜	67·2	10,900	52·1	8,600	41·6	6,900	37·2	6,200	31·4	5,350	23·0	4,100
34	53½	71·4	11,550	55·4	9,150	44·2	7,350	39·4	6,600	33·4	5,700	24·4	4,350
36	56¾	75·6	12,250	58·7	9,700	46·8	7,750	41·8	7,000	35·2	6,000	26·0	4,650
38	59⅞	79·8	12,950	62·0	10,250	49·4	8,200	44·0	7,350	37·2	6,300	27·4	4,900
40	63	84·0	13,600	65·2	10,750	52·0	8,650	46·4	7,750	39·2	6,650	28·8	5,150
42	66⅛	88·2	14,300	68·5	11,300	54·6	9,050	48·8	8,150	41·2	7,000	30·2	5,400
44	69¼	92·4	14,850	71·7	11,850	57·2	9,500	51·0	8,500	43·2	7,350	31·6	5,600
46	72½	96·6	15,650	75·0	12,350	59·8	9,950	53·4	8,900	45·0	7,650	33·0	5,850
48	75⅝	100·8	16,350	78·2	12,900	62·4	10,350	55·6	9,300	47·0	8,000	34·6	6,150
50	78¾	105·0	17,000	81·5	13,450	65·0	10,800	58·0	9,700	49·0	8,350	36·0	6,400
60	94½	126·0	20,400	97·8	16,150	78·0	12,950	69·6	11,600	58·8	10,000	43·2	7,700
70	110¼	147·0	23,800	114·1	18,850	91·0	15,100	81·0	13,550	68·6	11,650	50·4	8,950
80	126	168·0	27,200	130·4	21,500	104·0	17,250	92·8	15,500	78·4	13,350	57·6	10,250
90	141¾	189·0	30,600	146·7	24,200	117·0	19,400	104·4	17,450	88·2	15,000	64·8	11,550
100	157½	210·0	34,000	163·0	26,900	130·0	21,600	116·0	19,350	98·0	16,650	72·0	12,800

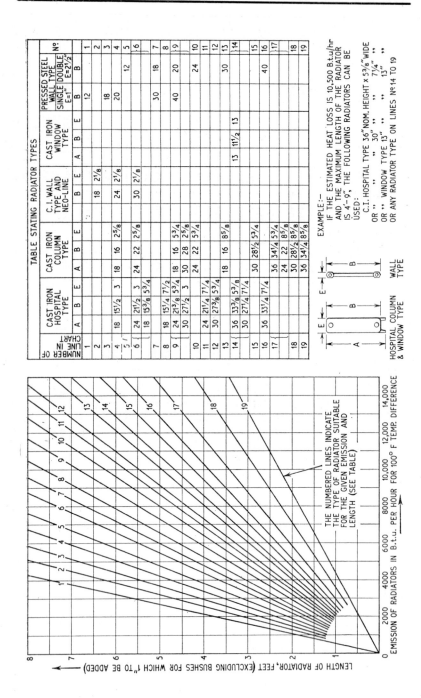

TABLE STATING RADIATOR TYPES

EXAMPLE:—
IF THE ESTIMATED HEAT LOSS IS 10,500 B.t.u/hr
AND THE MAXIMUM LENGTH OF THE RADIATOR
IS 4'-9", THE FOLLOWING RADIATORS CAN BE
USED:

C.I. HOSPITAL TYPE 36" NOM. HEIGHT x 53/8" WIDE
OR " "   "   30"   "   "   71/4" "
OR " WINDOW TYPE 13" "   "   13" "
OR ANY RADIATOR TYPE ON LINES N°14 TO 19

WALL TYPE

HOSPITAL COLUMN & WINDOW TYPE

THE NUMBERED LINES INDICATE
THE TYPE OF RADIATOR SUITABLE
FOR THE GIVEN EMISSION AND
LENGTH (SEE TABLE)

EMISSION OF RADIATORS IN B.t.u. PER HOUR FOR 100° F TEMP. DIFFERENCE

LENGTH OF RADIATOR, FEET (EXCLUDING BUSHES FOR WHICH 1" TO BE ADDED)

2⅝ in. wide

Heat Transmission		185 B.t.u. per sq. ft. per hour					
Nominal Height—in.		18		24		3	
Height without ft.—in.		16⅛		22		28	
No. of Sections	Length in.*	Heating Surface and Emission					
		sq. ft.	B.t.u./hr.	sq. ft.	B.t.u./hr.	sq. ft.	B.t.u./hr.
3	6	2·25	400	3	550	4·0	750
4	8	3·0	550	4	750	5·3	1,000
5	10	3·75	700	5	900	6·2	1,250
6	12	4·5	850	6	1,100	8·0	1,450
7	14	5·25	950	7	1,300	9·33	1,750
8	16	6·0	1,100	8	1,450	10·66	1,950
9	18	6·75	1,250	9	1,650	12·0	2,200
10	20	7·5	1,400	10	1,850	13·33	2,450
11	22	8·25	1,500	11	2,000	14·66	2,700
12	24	9·0	1,650	12	2,200	16·0	2,950
13	26	9·75	1,800	13	2,400	17·33	3,150
14	28	10·5	1,950	14	2,600	18·66	3,500
15	30	11·25	2,100	15	2,800	20·0	3,700
16	32	12·0	2,200	16	2,950	21·33	3,950
17	34	12·75	2,350	17	3,150	22·66	4,200
18	36	13·5	2,500	18	3,300	24·0	4,450
19	38	14·25	2,650	19	3,500	25·33	4,700
20	40	15·0	2,800	20	3,700	26·66	4,950
21	42	15·75	2,950	21	3,900	28·0	5,200
22	44	16·5	3,050	22	4,050	29·33	5,400
23	46	17·25	3,200	23	4,250	30·66	5,700
24	48	18·0	3,300	24	4,450	32·0	5,900
25	50	18·75	3,450	25	4,650	33·33	6,150
26	52	19·5	3,600	26	4,800	34·66	6,400
27	54	20·25	3,750	27	5,000	36·0	6,650
28	56	21·0	3,900	28	5,200	37·33	6,900
29	58	21·75	4,000	29	5,350	38·66	7,150
30	60	22·5	4,150	30	5,550	40·0	7,400
31	62	23·25	4,300	31	5,750	41·33	7,550
32	64	24·0	4,450	32	5,900	42·66	7,900
33	66	24·75	4,550	33	6,100	44·0	8,150
34	68	25·5	4,700	34	6,300	45·33	8,400
35	70	26·25	4,850	35	6,500	46·66	8,700
36	72	27·0	5,000	36	6,650	48·0	8,900
37	74	27·75	5,100	37	6,850	49·33	9,100
38	76	28·5	5,250	38	7,050	50·66	9,350
39	78	29·25	5,400	39	7,200	52·0	9,600
40	80	30·0	5,550	40	7,400	53·66	9,950

* Add 1 in. for bushes.

CAST IRON COLUMN

5⅜ in. wide

Heat Transmission		170 B.t.u. per sq. ft. per hour							
Nominal Height—in.		18		24			30		36
Height without ft—in.		16		22			28⅜		34¼
No. of Sections	Length in.*	sq. ft.	B.t.u./hr.	sq. ft.	B.t.u./hr.	Length in.	sq. ft.	B.t.u./hr.	sq. ft.	B.t.u./hr.
3	6	4·2	700	6	1,000	6½	7·8	1,300	9·6	1,600
4	8	5·6	950	8	1,350	7	10·4	1,750	12·8	2,200
5	10	7·0	1,200	10	1,700	11	13·0	2,200	16·0	2,700
6	12	8·4	1,450	12	2,050	13½	15·6	2,650	19·2	3,300
7	14	9·8	1,650	14	2,400	15½	18·2	3,100	22·4	3,800
8	16	11·2	1,900	16	2,700	16	20·8	3,550	25·6	4,350
9	18	12·6	2,150	18	3,050	20	23·4	4,000	28·8	4,900
10	20	14·0	2,400	20	3,400	22½	26·0	4,400	32·0	5,450
11	22	15·4	2,600	22	3,700	24½	28·6	4,850	35·2	6,000
12	24	16·8	2,850	24	4,100	27	31·2	5,300	38·4	6,550
13	26	18·2	3,100	26	4,400	29	33·8	5,750	41·6	7,100
14	28	19·6	3,350	28	4,750	31½	36·4	6,200	44·8	7,600
15	30	21·0	3,550	30	5,100	33½	39·0	6,650	48·0	8,150
16	32	22·4	3,800	32	5,400	36	41·6	7,100	51·2	8,700
17	34	23·8	4,050	34	5,750	38	44·2	7,500	54·4	9,250
18	36	25·2	4,300	36	6,100	40½	46·8	7,950	57·6	9,800
19	38	26·6	4,500	38	6,450	42½	49·4	8,400	60·8	10,300
20	40	28·0	4,750	40	6,800	45	52·0	8,850	64·0	10,900
21	42	29·4	5,000	42	7,150	47½	54·6	9,300	67·2	11,450
22	44	30·8	5,250	44	7,500	49	57·2	9,700	70·4	11,950
23	46	32·2	5,500	46	7,800	51½	59·8	10,150	73·6	12,500
24	48	33·6	5,700	48	8,150	54	62·4	10,600	76·8	13,000
25	50	35·0	5,950	50	8,500	56	65·0	11,000	80·0	13,600
26	52	36·4	6,200	52	8,850	58	67·0	11,400	83·2	14,150
27	54	37·8	6,400	54	9,200	60½	70·2	11,950	86·4	14,700
28	56	39·2	6,750	56	9,500	63	72·8	12,400	89·6	15,250
29	58	40·6	6,900	58	9,850	65	75·4	12,800	92·8	15,800
30	60	42·0	7,150	60	10,200	67	78·0	13,250	96·0	16,300
31	62	43·4	7,300	62	10,500	69½	80·6	13,700	99·2	16,900
32	64	44·8	7,600	64	10,900	72	83·2	14,150	102·4	17,400
33	66	46·2	7,850	66	11,200	74	85·8	14,600	105·6	18,000
34	68	47·6	8,100	68	11,550	76	88·4	15,000	108·8	18,500
35	70	49·0	8,300	70	11,900	78½	91·0	15,450	112·0	19,000
36	72	50·4	8,050	72	12,200	81	93·6	15,900	115·2	19,600
37	74	51·8	8,800	74	12,600	83	96·2	16,400	118·4	20,200
38	76	53·2	9,050	76	12,900	85	98·8	16,900	121·6	20,700
39	78	54·6	9,300	78	13,300	87½	101·4	17,300	124·8	21,200
40	80	56·0	9,500	80	13,600	90	104·0	17,700	128·0	21,800

* Add 1 in. for bushes.

8⅝ in. wide

Heat Transmsn.		160 B.t.u. per sq. ft. per hr.						

Heat Transmsn.		160 B.t.u. per sq. ft. per hr.						
Nominal Height—in.		18		24		30		36
Height without ft—in.		16⅛		22		28¾		34¼
No. of Sections	Length in.*	Heating Surface and Emission						
		sq. ft.	B.t.u./hr.	sq. ft.	B.t.u./hr.	sq. ft.	B.t.u./hr.	sq. ft.	B.t.u./hr.
3	6	6·3	1,000	9	1,450	12·3	1,950	15	2,400
4	8	8·4	1,400	12	1,900	16·4	2,600	20	3,200
5	10	10·5	1,650	15	2,400	20·5	3,300	25	4,000
6	12	12·6	1,950	18	2,900	24·6	3,950	30	4,800
7	14	14·7	2,350	21	3,350	28·7	4,600	35	5,600
8	16	16·8	2,700	24	3,850	32·8	5,250	40	6,400
9	18	18·9	3,000	27	4,300	36·9	5,950	45	7,200
10	20	21·0	3,350	30	4,800	41·0	6,550	50	8,000
11	22	23·1	3,700	33	5,300	45·1	7,200	55	8,800
12	24	25·2	4,000	36	5,750	49·2	7,850	60	9,600
13	26	27·3	4,350	39	6,250	53·3	8,500	65	10,400
14	28	29·4	4,700	42	6,700	57·4	9,200	70	11,200
15	30	31·5	5,000	45	7,200	61·5	9,850	75	12,000
16	32	33·6	5,400	48	7,700	65·6	10,500	80	12,800
17	34	35·7	5,700	51	8,150	69·7	11,150	85	13,600
18	36	37·8	6,050	54	8,650	73·8	11,800	90	14,400
19	38	39·9	6,400	57	9,100	77·9	12,500	95	15,200
20	40	42·0	6,700	60	9,600	82·0	13,100	100	16,000
21	42	44·1	7,500	63	10,100	86·1	13,800	105	16,800
22	44	46·2	7,400	66	10,600	90·2	14,400	110	17,600
23	46	48·3	7,700	69	11,000	94·3	15,100	115	18,500
24	48	50·4	8,100	72	11,500	98·4	15,750	120	19,200
25	50	52·5	8,400	75	12,000	102·5	16,400	125	20,000
26	52	54·6	8,750	78	12,500	106·6	17,100	130	20,800
27	54	56·7	9,100	81	13,000	110·7	17,700	135	21,600
28	56	58·8	9,400	84	13,500	114·8	18,400	140	22,400
29	58	60·9	9,750	87	13,900	118·9	19,000	145	23,200
30	60	63·0	10,100	90	14,400	123·0	19,700	150	24,000
31	62	65·1	10,400	93	14,900	127·1	20,400	155	24,800
32	64	67·2	10,750	96	15,400	131·2	21,000	160	25,600
33	66	69·3	11,100	99	16,850	135·3	21,700	165	26,400
34	68	71·4	11,400	102	16,300	139·4	22,400	170	27,200
35	70	73·5	11,750	105	16,800	143·5	23,000	175	28,000
36	72	75·6	12,100	108	17,300	147·6	23,700	180	28,800
37	74	77·7	12,400	111	17,800	151·7	24,300	185	29,600
38	76	79·8	12,800	114	18,300	155·8	25,000	190	30,400
39	78	81·9	13,100	117	18,700	159·9	25,500	195	31,200
40	80	84·0	13,450	120	19,200	162·0	26,500	200	32,000

* Add 1 in. for bushes.

3 in. wide

Heat Transmission		185 B.t.u. per sq. ft. per hr. per 100° F.					
Nominal Height—in.		18		24		30	
Height without ft—in.		$15\frac{7}{16}$		$21\frac{7}{16}$		$27\frac{7}{16}$	
No. of Sections	Length in.*	Heating Surface and Emission					
		sq. ft.	B.t.u./hr.	sq. ft.	B.t.u./hr.	sq. ft.	B.t.u./hr.
3	6	2·25	400	3	550	3·9	700
4	8	3·00	550	4	750	5·2	950
5	10	3·75	700	5	900	6·5	1,200
6	12	4·5	850	6	1,100	7·8	1,450
7	14	5·25	950	7	1,300	9·1	1,700
8	16	6·00	1,100	8	1,500	10·4	1,900
9	18	6·75	1,250	9	1,650	11·7	2,150
10	20	7·50	1,400	10	1,850	13·0	2,400
11	22	8·25	1,500	11	2,050	14·3	2,650
12	24	9·00	1,650	12	2,200	15·6	2,900
13	26	9·75	1,800	13	2,400	16·9	3,150
14	28	10·50	1,950	14	2,600	18·2	3,400
15	30	11·25	2,100	15	2,750	19·5	3,600
16	32	12·00	2,200	16	2,950	20·8	3,850
17	34	12·75	2,350	17	3,150	22·1	4,100
18	36	13·50	2,500	18	3,350	23·4	4,350
19	38	14·25	2,650	19	3,500	24·7	4,550
20	40	15·00	2,750	20	3,700	26·0	4,800
21	42	15·75	2,900	21	3,900	27·3	5,050
22	44	16·50	3,050	22	4,050	28·6	5,300
23	46	17·25	3,200	23	4,250	29·9	5,550
24	48	18·00	3,350	24	4,450	31·2	5,750
25	50	18·75	3,450	25	4,600	32·5	6,000
26	52	19·50	3,600	26	4,800	33·8	6,250
27	54	20·25	3,750	27	5,000	35·1	6,500
28	56	21·00	3,900	28	5,200	36·4	6,750
29	58	21·75	4,000	29	5,350	37·7	7,000
30	60	22·50	4,150	30	5,550	39·0	7,250
31	62	23·25	4,300	31	5,750	40·3	4,500
32	64	24·00	4,450	32	5,900	41·6	7,700
33	66	24·75	4,600	33	6,100	42·9	7,950
34	68	25·50	4,700	34	6,300	44·2	8,200
35	70	26·25	4,850	35	6,450	45·5	8,400
36	72	27·00	5,000	36	4,650	46·8	8,650
37	74	27·75	5,100	37	4,850	48·1	9,100
38	76	28·50	5,250	38	7,050	49·4	9,200
39	78	29·25	5,400	39	7,200	50·7	9,400
40	80	30·00	5,550	40	7,400	52·0	9,650

* Add 1 in. for bushes.

5¾ in. wide

Heat Transmission		158 B.t.u. per hour per 100°F.							
Nominal Height—in.		18		24		30		36	
Height without ft—in.		15⅜		21⅜		27⅜		33⅜	
No. of Sections	Length in.*	Heating Surface and Emission							
		sq. ft.	B.t.u./hr.	sq. ft.	B.t.u./hr.	sq. ft.	B.t.u./hr.	sq. ft.	B.t.u./hr.
3	7⅝	4·5	700	6	950	7·5	1,200	9	1,400
4	10¼	6·0	950	8	1,250	10·0	1,580	12	1,900
5	12⅞	7·5	1,200	10	1,580	12·5	2,000	15	2,400
6	15½	9·0	1,400	12	1,900	15·0	2,400	18	2,850
7	18⅛	10·5	1,650	14	2,200	17·5	2,800	21	3,300
8	20¾	12·0	1,900	16	2,500	20·0	3,150	24	3,800
9	23⅜	13·5	2,150	18	2,850	22·5	3,600	27	4,250
10	26	15·0	2,350	20	3,160	25·0	3,950	30	4,750
11	28⅝	16·5	2,600	22	3,500	27·5	4,350	33	5,200
12	31¼	18·0	2,750	24	3,800	30·0	4,750	36	5,700
13	33⅞	19·5	3,100	26	4,100	32·5	5,150	39	6,150
14	36½	21·0	3,300	28	4,400	35·0	5,500	42	6,600
15	39⅛	22·5	3,550	30	4,750	37·5	6,100	45	7,100
16	41¾	24·0	3,800	32	5,050	40·0	6,300	48	7,600
17	44⅜	25·5	4,050	34	5,350	42·5	6,700	51	8,050
18	47	27·0	4,250	36	5,700	45·0	7,100	54	8,500
19	49⅝	28·5	4,500	38	6,000	47·5	7,500	57	9,000
20	52¼	30·0	4,700	40	6,300	50·0	7,900	60	9,500
21	54⅞	31·5	5,000	42	6,600	52·5	8,300	63	10,000
22	57½	33·0	5,200	44	7,000	55·0	8,700	66	10,400
23	60⅛	34·5	5,450	46	7,250	57·5	9,100	69	10,900
24	62¾	36·0	5,700	48	7,600	60·0	9,500	72	11,350
25	65⅜	37·5	5,900	50	7,900	62·5	9,900	75	11,850
26	68	39·0	6,150	52	8,200	65·0	11,250	78	12,300
27	70⅝	40·5	6,400	54	8,500	67·5	11,650	81	12,800
28	73¼	42·0	6,650	56	8,850	70·0	11,050	84	13,200
29	75⅞	43·5	6,900	58	9,150	72·5	11,400	87	13,800
30	78½	45·0	7,100	60	9,500	75·0	11,800	90	14,200
31	81⅛	46·5	7,350	62	9,800	77·5	11,200	93	14,700
32	83¾	48·0	7,600	64	10,000	80·0	11,650	96	15,200
33	86⅜	49·5	7,800	66	10,400	82·5	1,300	99	15,650
34	89	51·0	8,050	68	10,700	85·0	13,400	102	16,000
35	91⅝	52·5	8,300	70	11,050	87·5	13,800	105	16,600
36	94¼	54·0	8,550	72	11,350	90·0	14,200	108	17,000
37	96⅞	55·5	8,800	74	11,700	92·5	14,650	111	17,500
38	99½	57·0	9,000	76	12,000	95·0	15,000	114	18,000
39	102⅛	58·5	9,250	78	12,300	97·5	15,400	117	18,500
40	104¾	60·0	9,500	80	12,650	100·0	15,800	120	19,000

* Add 1 in. for bushes.

$7\frac{1}{4}$ in. wide

Heat Transmsn.		150 B.t.u. per sq. ft. per hour per 100°F.							
Nominal Height—in.		18		24		30		36	
Height without Ft.—in.		$15\frac{5}{16}$		$21\frac{5}{16}$		$27\frac{5}{16}$		$33\frac{9}{16}$	
No. of Sects.	Length in.*	Heating Surface and Emission							
		sq. ft.	B.t.u./hr.	sq. ft.	B.t.u./hr.	sq. ft.	B.t.u./hr.	sq. ft.	B.t.u./hr.
3	$7\frac{5}{8}$	5·7	850	7·5	1,000	9·3	1,400	11·1	1,650
4	$10\frac{1}{4}$	7·6	1,050	10·0	1,500	12·4	1,850	14·8	2,200
5	$12\frac{7}{8}$	9·5	1,400	12·5	1,850	15·5	2,300	18·5	2,800
6	$15\frac{1}{2}$	11·4	1,700	15·0	2,250	18·6	2,800	22·2	3,300
7	$18\frac{1}{8}$	13·3	2,000	17·5	2,600	21·7	3,250	25·9	3,900
8	$20\frac{3}{4}$	15·2	2,300	20·0	3,000	24·8	3,700	29·6	4,450
9	$23\frac{3}{8}$	17·1	2,550	22·5	3,400	27·9	4,200	33·3	5,000
10	26	19·0	2,850	25·0	3,750	31·0	4,650	37·0	5,500
11	$28\frac{5}{8}$	20·9	3,100	27·5	4,100	34·1	5,100	40·7	6,100
12	$31\frac{1}{4}$	22·8	3,400	30·0	4,500	37·2	5,600	44·4	6,650
13	$33\frac{7}{8}$	24·7	3,700	32·5	4,900	40·3	6,050	48·1	7,200
14	$36\frac{1}{2}$	26·6	4,000	35·0	5,350	43·4	6,500	51·8	7,800
15	$39\frac{1}{8}$	28·5	4,300	37·5	5,650	46·5	7,000	55·5	8,200
16	$41\frac{3}{4}$	30·4	4,550	40·0	6,000	49·6	7,450	59·2	8,900
17	$44\frac{3}{8}$	32·6	4,900	42·5	6,400	52·7	7,950	62·9	9,450
18	47	34·2	5,100	45·0	6,750	55·8	8,350	66·6	10,000
19	$49\frac{5}{8}$	36·1	5,400	47·5	7,100	58·9	8,850	70·3	10,550
20	$52\frac{1}{4}$	38·0	5,700	50·0	7,500	62·0	9,300	74·0	11,100
21	$54\frac{7}{8}$	39·9	6,000	52·5	7,900	65·1	9,750	77·7	11,650
22	$57\frac{1}{2}$	41·8	6,250	55·0	8,250	68·2	10,250	81·4	12,200
23	$60\frac{1}{4}$	43·7	6,550	57·5	8,600	71·3	10,700	85·1	12,800
24	$62\frac{3}{4}$	45·6	6,800	60·0	9,000	74·4	11,100	88·8	13,350
25	$65\frac{3}{8}$	47·5	7,100	62·5	9,350	77·5	11,600	92·5	13,900
26	68	49·4	7,400	65·0	9,750	80·6	12,100	96·2	14,450
27	$70\frac{5}{8}$	51·3	7,700	67·5	10,100	83·7	12,600	99·9	15,000
28	$73\frac{1}{4}$	53·2	8,000	70·0	10,500	86·8	13,000	103·6	15,500
29	$75\frac{7}{8}$	55·1	8,300	72·5	10,900	89·9	13,500	107·3	16,100
30	$78\frac{1}{2}$	57·0	8,550	75·0	11,200	93·0	13,950	111·0	16,600
31	$81\frac{1}{8}$	58·9	8,850	77·5	11,600	96·1	14,400	114·7	17,200
32	$83\frac{3}{4}$	60·8	9,150	80·0	12,000	99·2	14,900	118·4	17,800
33	$86\frac{3}{8}$	63·0	9,450	82·5	12,400	102·3	15,300	122·1	18,200
34	89	65·2	9,800	85·0	12,800	105·4	15,800	125·8	18,900
35	$91\frac{5}{8}$	66·8	10,000	87·5	13,200	108.5	16,300	129·5	19,500
36	$94\frac{1}{4}$	68·4	10,300	90·0	13,500	111·6	16,700	133·2	20,000
37	$96\frac{7}{8}$	70·3	10,550	92·5	13,900	114·7	17,200	136·9	20,500
38	$99\frac{1}{2}$	72·2	10,850	95·0	14,250	117·8	17,600	140·6	21,100
39	$102\frac{1}{8}$	74·1	11,100	97·5	14,600	120·9	18,100	144·3	21,700
40	$104\frac{3}{4}$	76·0	11,400	100·0	15,000	124·0	18,600	148·0	22,200

* Add 1 in. for bushes.

Section III

FUEL AND COMBUSTION

CLASSES OF FUELS

1. Solid.   2. Liquid.   3. Gaseous.

CLASSIFICATION OF COAL	NAMES AND SIZES OF SOME TRADE SIZES OF COAL
Wood.	
Peat.	Egg ... ... $3\frac{1}{4}$ to $2\frac{3}{8}$ in.
Lignite.	Stove ... ... $2\frac{3}{8}$ to $1\frac{5}{8}$ in.
Bituminous Coal.	Nut ... ... $1\frac{5}{8}$ to $\frac{7}{8}$ in.
Anthracite.	Pea ... ... $\frac{7}{8}$ to $\frac{5}{8}$ in.
	Buck-Wheat No. 1 $\frac{5}{8}$ to $\frac{3}{8}$ in.

BULK OF VARIOUS FUELS

Specific gravity of stowed fuel in lb. per cu. ft. Specific volume of stored fuel in cu. ft. per ton.

Fuel	cu. ft. per ton	lb. per cu. ft.
Wood	90–100	22·5–24
Charcoal, hard wood	240	9·3
Charcoal, soft wood	165	13·5
Anthracite Coal	42–50	45–53
Bituminous Coal	45–52	43–50
Peat	90–115	19·5–25
Coke	72–95	23·5–31

HEAT OF COMBUSTION OF IMPORTANT CHEMICALS

Substance.	Products of Combustion.	Chemical Formula.	Heat of Comb. B.t.u. per lb.
Carbon	Carbon Dioxide ...	$C + O_2 = CO_2$	14,590 Complete Combustion
Carbon	Carbon Monoxide ...	$2C + O_2 = 2CO$ ...	3,960 Incomplete Combustion
Carbon Monoxide	Carbon Dioxide ...	$2CO + O_2 = 2CO_2$ ...	4,367
Hydrogen ...	Water Vapour ...	$2H_2 + O_2 = 2H_2O$ ...	62,000
Sulphur ...	Sulphur Dioxide Vapour	$S + O_2 = SO_2$	3,900
Methane Marsh Gas ...	Carbon Dioxide and Water Vapour ...	$CH_4 + 2O_2 = CO_2 + 2H_2O$	24,017

FUEL SIZE FOR CENTRAL HEATING BOILERS

Output of Boiler in B.t.u. per hr.	Up to 20,000	20,000 to 40,000	40,000 to 120,000	120,000 to 250,000	250,000 up
Size of Coke or Anthracite, in.	¾	¾ to 1¼	¾ to 2	2–3	2–4

COMPARATIVE COSTS OF HEAT
PRODUCED BY VARIOUS FUELS, NOVEMBER 1962

Fuel	Unit	Calorific value of unit B.t.u.	Cost per unit	Approximate efficiency per cent	Cost in pence per useful therm (100,000 B.t.u.)
Electricity ...	kWh.	3,412	1·375d.	100	40·2
Electricity Night Storage	kWh.	3,412	0·50d.	100	14·6
Town Gas ...	Therm	100,000	1s. 6d.	80	22·5
Coke	Ton	28,000,000	220s. 0d.	60	15·7
Coal	Ton	28,672,000	220s. 0d.	60	16·1
Anthracite ...	Ton	32,500,000	300s. 0d.	65	17·0
Domestic Fuel Oil, 35 sec. ...	Gallon	162,000	1s. 6d.	75	14·8
Light Fuel Oil, 200 sec. ...	Gallon	176,000	1s. 3d.	70	12·2
Medium Fuel Oil, 900 sec. ...	Gallon	176,000	1s. 2d.	70	11·4
Kerosene ...	Gallon	159,000	1s. 7d.	70	17·0

THEORETICAL EVAPORATIVE POWER OF FUELS

is the weight of steam theoretically evaporated (without losses) from and at 212° F. by burning 1 lb. of fuel.

$$\text{Theoretical evaporative power} = \frac{\text{calorific value of fuel}}{970}.$$

Actual evaporative power of fuels =

$$\text{Theoretical evaporative power} \times \text{Boiler efficiency}.$$

IGNITION (OR KINDLING) TEMPERATURES OF VARIOUS FUELS

Wood	570° F.	Petroleum ... ... 750° F.
Peat	440° F.	Benzene ... ... 780° F.
Bituminous Coal ...	570° F.	Coal-Tar Oil ... ... 1080° F.
Semi Anthracite Coal ...	750° F.	Producer Gas ... ... 1380° F.
Coke	1290° F.	Light Hydrocarbons ... 1200° F.
Hydrogen	930° F.	Heavy Hydrocarbons ... 1380° F.
Carbon-Monoxide ...	570° F.	Light Gas ... ... 1110° F.
Carbon	1290° F.	Naphtha ... ... 1020° F.

The Heat of Combustion or Calorific Value of a fuel is the heat, expressed in B.t.u., produced by the complete combustion of 1 lb. of the fuel.

The calorific value may be obtained experimentally (Calorimeter), or by calculation from chemical analysis (Dulong's formula).

The Higher or Gross Calorific Value of a fuel is the amount of heat given out in the complete combustion of unit weight of the fuel in oxygen, when the products of combustion are cooled down to the initial temperature (15°C. or 60°F.) at which the oxygen is supplied.

The Lower or Net Calorific Value is the heat obtained by the complete combustion of unit of weight of the fuel in oxygen, when the products are cooled down to 100°C. or 212°F. and the steam is not condensed to water.

Lower Calorific Value=Higher Calorific Value—
Heat of steam formed by combustion=
Higher Calorific Value—$(9H \times 970)$ B.t.u. per lb.

Determination of the Calorific Value of a Fuel

1. *By Calorimeter Test*—Measuring the heat which is liberated by the combustion of a test sample in oxygen.

2. *By Analysis*—Dulong's formula for higher calorific value (approx.)
   $H_h=14,500C.+62,000 (H-\frac{O}{8})+4000S.$
   H_h=Higher Calorific Value in B.t.u. per lb. of fuel.
   C, H, O, S=Weight of carbon, hydrogen, oxygen, sulphur resp. in lb. per 1 lb. of fuel.

Weight of Dry Air theoretically required for the complete combustion:
   $A_{th}=11.47C.+34.28 (H-\frac{O}{8})+4.31S.$ (lb. per 1 lb. of fuel).

Theoretical Weight of Dry Flue Gases:
   $F_{th}=12.47C.+26.28 (H-\frac{O}{8})+5.31S.+N$ (lb. per 1 lb. of fuel).
   C, H, O=Weight in lb. per 1 lb. of fuel.

Actual Air supplied:

$$A_a = X.A_{th} \text{ (lb. per 1 lb. of fuel).}$$
$$X = \text{Excess of air factor.}$$

Actual Weight of Flue Gases:

$$F_a F_{th} + (A_a - A_{th}) \text{ (lb. per 1 lb. of fuel).}$$

Excess of Air:

$$X = \frac{A_a}{A_{th}} = \frac{\text{Actual quantity of Air}}{\text{Theoretically required quantity of air}} =$$
$$\left(\frac{N}{N - 3 \cdot 782 (O - \frac{1}{2}CO)} - 1 \right) \times 100 \text{ (per cent).}$$

N, O, CO=Percentage of nitrogen, etc., by volume in flue gas.

$$X = \frac{\text{Maximum theoretical percentage of } CO_2 \text{ in flue gases}}{\text{Actual percentage of } CO_2 \text{ in flue gases}} \text{(per cent).}$$

Excess of Air for good conditions:

For Anthracite and Coke 40%

For Semi-Anthracite, hand firing ...   ... 70 to 100%

For Semi-Anthracite, with stoker   ... 40 to 70%

For Semi-Anthracite, with travelling grate 30 to 60%

Temperature of Combustion, or Calorific Intensity of Dry Coal with Dry Air:

$$t = t_A + \frac{C_1 W_1}{0 \cdot 24 W_2}$$

t   =Temperature produced in °F.

t_A =Temperature in boiler house in °F.

C_1 =Lower heat value in B.t.u. per lb.

W_1 =Weight of fuel in lb.

W_2 =Weight of combustion products including surplus air in lb.

0·24 =Mean specific heat of combustion products at constant pressure B.t.u. per lb. per °F.

HEAT LOSSES IN A BOILER FURNACE

1. Sensible heat carried away by dry flue gases.
2. Heat lost by free moisture in fuel.
3. Heat lost by incomplete combustion.
4. Heat lost by unburned carbon in the ash.
5. Heat lost by radiation and unaccounted losses.

1. Sensible Heat carried away by Dry Flue Gases:

(in good practice about 15%)

$$L_1 = Wc_p (t_1 - t_A) \text{ (B.t.u. per lb. of fuel).}$$

$$= Wc_p (t_1 - t_A) \frac{100}{CO_2} \text{ (per cent).}$$

W = Weight of combustion products (lb. per lb. of fuel).

t_1 = Temperature of flue gas in °F.

t_A = Temperature in boiler room in °F.

c_p = 0·24 = Mean specific heat of flue gas in B.t.u. per lb.

(See Siegert's Formula, page III. 8).

2. Heat Lost by Free Moisture in Fuel:

$$L_2 = w (H - h) \text{ (B.t.u. per lb. of fuel).}$$

$$= w (H - h) \frac{100}{C_1} \text{ (per cent).}$$

w = Weight of water lb. per lb. of burned fuel.

H = Total heat of superheated steam at temperature t_1 and atmospheric pressure.

h = Sensible heat of water at temperature t_A.

3. Heat Lost by Combustible in the Flue Gas (incomplete combustion):

$$L_3 = 10,220 \frac{CO}{CO_2 + CO} \times C \text{ (B.t.u. per lb. of fuel).}$$

$$= 10,220 \frac{CO}{CO_2 + CO} \times C \times \frac{100}{C_1} \text{ (per cent).}$$

CO, CO_2 = Percentage of carbon-monoxide and carbon-dioxide respectively by volume in flue gas.

C = Weight of carbon in 1 lb. of fuel.

C_1 = Lower calorific value of fuel, B.t.u. per lb.

The heat loss occasioned by CO escaping in the flue gas is approximately 4% to 5% for 1% CO in the flue gas.

4. Heat Lost by Unburned Carbon in the Ash:

$L_4 = W_1 \times$ calorific value of carbon (B.t.u. per lb. of fuel).

$= W_1 \times$ calorific value of carbon $\dfrac{100}{C_1}$ (per cent).

2·5 to 5 per cent for good practice.

$W_1 =$ weight of carbon in ash (lb. per lb. of fuel).

5. Heat Lost by Radiation and Unaccounted Losses

$L_5 =$ Lower calorific value. $-$ (Utilized heat $+ L_1 + L_2 + L_3$).

HEAT BALANCE FOR BOILER FURNACE

$$C_1 = H_u + (L_1 + L_2 + L_3 + L_4 + L_5)$$

$C_1 =$ Lower calorific value of fuel (B.t.u. per lb.).

$H_u =$ Heat utilized from 1 lb. of fuel (B.t.u. per lb.).

$L_1 \ldots L_5 =$ Heat losses B.t.u. per lb.

The Output of a Boiler is generally stated as the equivalent evaporation from and at 212°F.

Equivalent Evaporation: $W_1 = \dfrac{W_s \, (H-h)}{L}$ (lb. per hr.).

Efficiency of Boiler $= \dfrac{\text{Heat in steam supplied}}{\text{Heat in fuel supplied}} = \dfrac{W_s \, (H-h)}{B \times C_1}.$

In which:

$W_1 =$ Equivalent evaporation (lb. per hr.).

$W_s =$ Weight of steam supplied produced at any given temperature and pressure (lb. per hr.).

$H \ \ =$ Total heat of steam raised (B.t.u. per lb.).

$h \ \ =$ Sensible heat of feed water (B.t.u. per lb.).

$L \ \ = 970·7$ latent heat of water at atmospheric pressure (B.t.u. per lb.).

$B \ \ =$ Weight of fuel burned per hour (lb. per hr.).

$C \ \ =$ Lower calorific value of fuel (B.t.u. per lb.).

CONSTITUENTS AND HEATING VALUES OF FUELS

Fuel.	C	H	O + N	S	H_2O	ASH	Theoretically required Air Volume in lb. per lb. of Fuel.	Higher Calorific Value in B.t.u. per lb.
Anthracite ...	83–87	3·5–4·0	3·0–4·7	0·9	1–3	4–6	8·3–8·7	14,000–14,500
Semi-anthracite Coal	63–76	3·5–4·8	8–10	0·5–1·8	5–15	4–14	8·9–10·6	11,500–14,000
Bituminous Coal ...	46–56	3·5–5·0	9–16	0·2–3·0	18–32	2–10	6·0–7·6	7,300–10,000
Lignite	37	7	13·5	0·5	37	5		7,000
Peat	38–49	3·0–4·5	19–28	0·2–1·0	16–29	1–9	4·2–6·7	5,500–8,800
Coke	80–90	0·5–1·5	1·5–5·0	0·5–1·5	1–5	5–12	9·2–10·3	12,000–13,500
Charcoal	84	1	34–42	—	12	3		12,800
Wood (Dry)	35–45	3·0–5·0	34–42	—	7–22	0·3–3·0	4·8–5·7	6,200–7,500
Fuel Oil, Crude	87	11	1	1	—	B.t.u.	per cu. ft.	18,600
Natural Gas								1,004
Coal Gas ...								632
Creosote Pitch ...								16,150

Proximate Analysis in per cent. (columns C, H, O + N, S, H_2O, ASH)

SIEGERT'S FORMULA FOR SENSIBLE HEAT CARRIED AWAY BY DRY FLUE GASES

$$L_1 = k \frac{t_1 - t_A}{CO_2}$$

L_1 = Heat loss in per cent.
CO_2 = Percentage of carbon-dioxide by volume in dry flue gas.
t_1, t_A = Temperature of flue gas and air in boiler room respectively °F.
k = Constant : $k = 0.35$ for coal ; $k = 0.40$ for coke.

DIAGRAM FOR COAL :

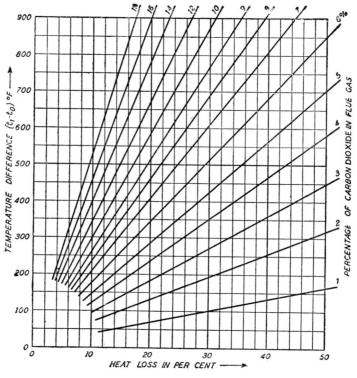

THE RINGELMANN SCALE FOR GRADING DENSITY OF SMOKE

NUMBER	0	1	2	3	4	5
LINES, mm	–	1	2·3	3·7	5·5	ALL BLACK
SQUARES, mm	ALL WHITE	9	7·7	6 3	4·5	–

ORSAT'S APPARATUS FOR ANALYSING FLUE GASES

For the Absorption of Carbon-dioxide, 50 g. of potassium hydrate or a little less sodium hydrate is dissolved in 150 g. of water.

For the Absorption of Oxygen, 17 g. of pyrogallol are dissolved in 35 g. of hot water. After cooling, this solution is mixed with 40 g. of potassium hydrate in 115 g. of water.

For the Absorption of Carbon Monoxide a solution is prepared by boiling a solution of cuprous chloride with metallic copper. When the solution has assumed a very dark colour it is poured into water and the Cu_2Cl_2 is precipitated as a white powder. This is thoroughly washed, out of contact with air if possible, and is dissolved in ammonia or hydrochloric acid to give the absorption solution.

The cuprous chloride and pyrogallol are liable to oxidation, for which reason precautions are taken to exclude the air as much as possible.

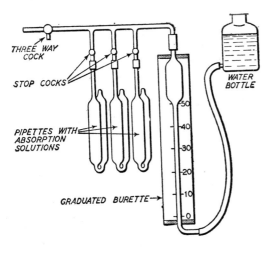

THREE WAY COCK

STOP COCKS

PIPETTES WITH ABSORPTION SOLUTIONS

GRADUATED BURETTE→

WATER BOTTLE

By manipulating the water bottle 100cm³ of fuel gas is drawn into the graduated burette. By again manipulating this 100 cm³ gas sample is passed into the pipette containing the solution absorbing carbon dioxide. After the carbon-dioxide has thus been removed the remainder of the sample is passed back into the burette and measured again.

The decrease in volume indicates the percentage, by volume, of CO_2 in the dry flue gas. In like manner the percentage of carbon-monoxide and oxygen is found.

CHIMNEY CAPACITIES

Chimney Area (Redtenbacher):

$$A = 0.096 \frac{W \cdot w}{\sqrt{H}}$$

Theoretical Draught:

$$h = \frac{H}{0.13} \left(\frac{1}{T_2} - \frac{1}{T_1} \right)$$

A = Cross-sectional area of chimney, sq. ft.
H = Height of chimney above firegrate, ft.
h = Theoretical draught in inches of water.
W = Weight of burned fuel, lb. per hr.
w = Weight of combustion gases in lb. per lb. of fuel.
T_1 = Absolute temperature inside the chimney, °F.
T_2 = Absolute temperature outside the chimney, °F.

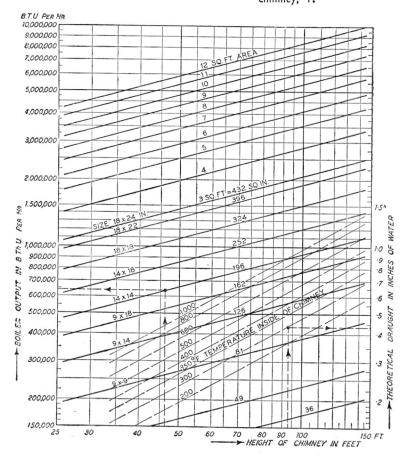

CHART SHOWING CHIMNEY CAPACITIES

COMPARATIVE VOLUMES AND CALORIFIC VALUES OF SOLID AND LIQUID FUELS

Fuel	Approx. gross calorific value B.t.u./lb.	Weight lb. per cu. ft.	Space occupied (cu. ft. per ton)	Calorific value (therms per ton)
Coke	12,500	24	90–95	280
Coal	12,800	45	48–50	287
Anthracite ...	14,850	47	48	333
Domestic Fuel Oil...	19,600	52	43	439
Light Fuel Oil ...	18,800	58	39	421
Kerosene	20,100	49	47	450

SPECIFICATIONS OF FUEL OIL GRADES

	Gas oil	Light fuel oil	Heavy fuel oil	Extra heavy fuel oil
Viscosity Redwood No. 1 at 100°F	35	220	950	3,500
Specific Gravity (Gross Calorific)	0·835	0·935	0·95	0·97
Value, B.t.u./lb.	19,600	18,800	17,000	15,500
Flash-point [Pensky-Martens (closed)] °F.	150	150	150	150
Pour-point, °F. max.	20	35	70	70
Temperature requirements:				
Storage tank	No heating required	45	65	75
Suction line		45	65	100

FLOW OF OIL THROUGH PIPES

Friction Head:

$$E = \frac{0 \cdot 0765 \times T \times V \times L}{D^4}.$$

Where:

E = loss of head in ft. (oil).
  1 ft. = 0·46 lb. per sq. in.
T = oil quantity tons/hour
V = viscosity Redwood No. 1 at mean pumping temperature.
L = length of pipeline in 100 ft. including allowances for bends, valves and fittings.
D = nominal bore of pipeline in inches.

This formula is applied for streamline flow.
The usual velocity in oil-burning installations is below 5 ft. per sec.

For streamline flow:

$$\frac{T}{D \times V} < \frac{1}{30}.$$

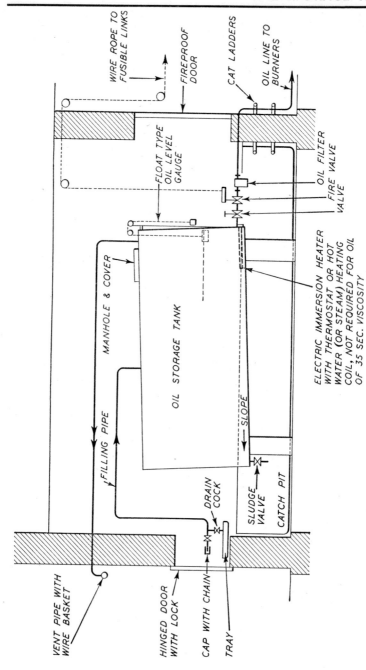

DIAGRAMMATIC ARRANGEMENT OF OIL STORAGE TANK

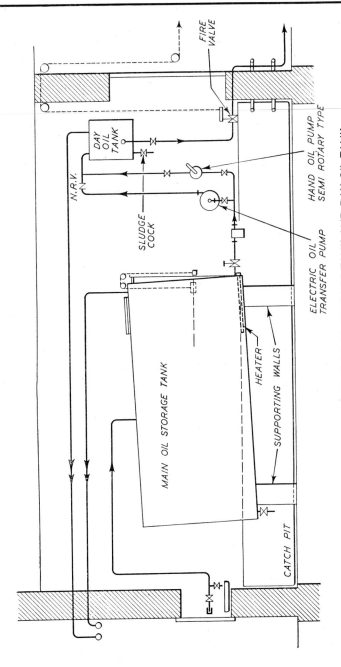

DIAGRAMMATIC ARRANGEMENT OF OIL STORAGE TANK AND DAY OIL TANK

APPROXIMATE CAPACITIES OF CYLINDRICAL TANKS

Approx. capacity in gallons	Internal diameter ft.	in.	Overall length ft.	in.	Thickness of plate in.	Approx. weight in tons Fuel oil	Tank
500	4	6	6	0	$\frac{3}{16}$	2	0·4
650	4	6	7	0	$\frac{3}{16}$	2·6	0·45
750	4	6	8	6	$\frac{3}{16}$	3	0·5
1,000	4	6	11	0	$\frac{3}{16}$	4	0·6
1,250	4	10	11	8	$\frac{3}{16}$	5	0·7
1,500	5	0	13	6	$\frac{3}{16}$	6	0·9
1,500	6	0	9	6	$\frac{1}{4}$	6	1·0
2,000	6	0	12	6	$\frac{1}{4}$	8	1·25
2,000	6	6	10	9	$\frac{1}{4}$	8	1·2
2,500	6	6	13	3	$\frac{1}{4}$	10	1·5
3,000	7	0	13	6	$\frac{1}{4}$	12	1·5
4,000	7	0	17	9	$\frac{1}{4}$	16	1·9
4,000	7	6	15	6	$\frac{1}{4}$	16	1·9
5,000	7	6	19	6	$\frac{1}{4}$	20	2·3
5,000	8	0	15	3	$\frac{1}{4}$	20	2·0
6,000	8	6	18	3	$\frac{1}{4}$	24	2·5
6,000	9	0	16	6	$\frac{1}{4}$	24	2·9
7,000	8	6	21	0	$\frac{1}{4}$	28	2·6
7,000	9	0	19	0	$\frac{1}{4}$	28	2·8
8,000	8	6	24	0	$\frac{1}{4}$	32	3·2
8,000	9	0	21	6	$\frac{1}{4}$	32	3·1
9,000	8	6	27	0	$\frac{1}{4}$	36	3·6
9,000	9	0	24	0	$\frac{1}{4}$	36	3·4
10,000	8	6	30	0	$\frac{1}{4}$	40	3·9
10,000	9	0	27	0	$\frac{1}{4}$	40	3·8

RECTANGULAR TANKS

Approx. capacity in gallons	Length ft. in.	Width ft. in.	Height ft. in.	Thickness of plate (in.)	Approx. weight in tons	
					Fuel oil	Tank
500	5 0	4 0	4 0	$\frac{3}{16}$	2	0·4
625	6 3	4 0	4 0	$\frac{3}{16}$	2½	0·4
750	7 6	4 0	4 0	$\frac{3}{16}$	3	0·45
1,000	8 0	5 0	4 0	$\frac{3}{16}$	4	0·50
1,250	8 0	5 0	5 0	$\frac{3}{16}$	5	0·65
1,500	10 0	5 0	4 10	$\frac{3}{16}$	6	0·70
1,750	10 0	6 0	4 9	$\frac{1}{4}$	7	0·90
2,000	10 0	6 0	5 4	$\frac{1}{4}$	8	1·0
2,500	10 0	8 0	5 0	$\frac{1}{4}$	10	1·05
3,000	12 0	8 0	5 0	$\frac{1}{4}$	12	1·1

HEAT LOSS FROM OIL IN TANK AND PIPE LINES

	Position	Oil temperature °F.	Heat loss B.t.u. per sq. ft. per hour per °F.	
			Unlagged	Lagged
Tank	Sheltered	up to 50 50 to 80 80 to 100	1·2 1·3 1·4	0·3 0·325 0·35
Tank	Exposed	up to 50 50 to 80 80 to 100	1·4 1·5 1·6	0·35 0·375 0·4
Tank	In pit			
Pipe line	Sheltered	up to 80 80 to 260		
Pipe line	Exposed	up to 80 80 to 260		

For maximum heat loss of oil tanks in the open air the ambient temperature should be assumed as 25°F.

The specific heat of heavy fuel oil is 0·45–0·48.

The heat transfer coefficients for coils are:

Steam to oil: approx. 20 B.t.u./sq. ft. hr. °F.
Hot water to oil: approx. 10 B.t.u./sq. ft. hr. °F.

HEAT LOSSES IN FLUE GASES ON OIL FIRED BOILERS

For fuel oil of 200 Sec. Viscosity Red. 1 at 200°F.
19,000 B.t.u./lb. gross cal. value.

Approximate ultimate analysis: per cent

87·4	C
11·0	H
1·45	S
0·15	O

Percentage volume of dry flue gases		Excess air per cent	Heat losses in per cent of the calorific value for various flue gas temperatures in °F.				
CO_2	O_2		360	400	500	600	700
15·9	0	0	10·4	12·4	14·5	16·6	18·7
14·4	2·0	10	10·8	13·0	15·2	17·6	19·9
13·15	3·6	20	11·2	13·6	16·0	18·5	21·0
12·08	5·0	30	11·7	14·2	16·8	19·5	22·2
11·2	6·2	40	12·1	14·8	17·6	20·4	23·3
10·6	7·3	50	12·5	15·4	18·4	21·4	24·5
9·12	9·4	75	13·6	16·9	20·3	23·8	27·3
7·76	10·7	100	14·7	18·4	22·3	26·2	30·2
6·19	12·8	150	16·8	21·4	26·2	31·0	36·0
5·14	14·2	200	19·9	24·4	30·2	35·8	41·7

Heat loss as percentage of gross calorific value

$$= 0.42 \frac{t_1 - t_2}{\% CO_2} \quad \text{where} \quad \begin{array}{l} t_1 = \text{temperature of flue gases °F.} \\ t_2 = \text{temperature of combustion air °F.} \end{array}$$

RECOMMENDED SIZES OF DRAUGHT STABILIZERS FOR OIL FIRING INSTALLATIONS

Cross sectional area of chimney in sq. in.	40–80	80–200	200–300	300–600	600–1,500
Release opening of stabilizer, in. approx	6×9	8×13	13×18	16×24	24×32

Section IV

HEAT AND HEAT TRANSFER

Heat is a Form of Energy

Amount or Quantity of Heat contained in any portion of matter is determined by:

1. The weight of the matter (w) in lb.
2. The specific heat   (c) in B.t.u. per lb. per °F.
3. The temperature   (t) in °F.
4. The pressure (for gases only).

Amount of heat (sensible heat) (H) in B.t.u.: $H = wct$.

One British Thermal Unit (B.t.u.) is the amount of heat required to increase the temperature of 1 lb. of water by 1°F. at atmospheric pressure.

One Centigrade Heat Unit (CHU) or one pound-calorie (lb.-cal.) is the amount of heat required to increase the temperature of 1 lb. of water by 1°C.

One Kilogram Calorie or large calorie (kcal) is the amount of heat required to increase the temperature of 1 kg. of water by 1°C.

1 kilogram calorie (kcal) = 1000 gram calories (cal).

1 B.t.u. = 0·252 kcal.

1 kcal = 3·9683 B.t.u. (See also I. 2).

Temperature is the intensity of heat.

Melting temperature of ice = 32°F. = 0°C. = 0°R. $\left.\right\}$ at atm. pres.
Boiling temperature of water = 212°F. = 100°C. = 80°R.

Absolute temperature: $T = (t + 460)°F.$ (Fahrenheit)
                or $T = (t + 273°C.)$ (Centigrade).

Absolute zero of temperature = −460°F.
                       −273°C.

Conversion of degrees Fahrenheit into Centigrade:

$$°F. = 32 + \frac{9}{5}C.; \quad °C. = \frac{5}{9}(F - 32).$$

(Conversion Table, see pages I. 6 to I. 8)

Expansion by Heat:

1. Linear Expansion is the increase in length
$$L_2 = L_1(1 + et)$$

2. Surface, or superficial expansion is the increase in area.
$$A_2 = A_1(1 + 2et)$$

3. Volumetric expansion is the increase in volume.
$$V_2 = V_1(1 + 3et)$$

where:

t = temperature difference in °F.
$L_1 \ A_1 \ V_1$ = original length, area, volume, respectively.
$L_2 \ A_2 \ V_2$ = final length, area, volume, respectively.
e = coefficient of linear expansion in. per in. per °F.

Thermal Expansion of Gases (see IV. 4).

The Coefficient of linear expansion is the increase in length in inches per inch of original length per °F. temperature difference. (See IV. 15 and II. 8.)

Latent Heat is the heat energy which is required to produce changes in the physical state of a substance:

Latent heat of melting or fusion,

Latent heat of vaporization or evaporation.

Latent heat = Change of State Heat + External Work Heat.

Specific Heat of a Solid or Liquid is the amount of heat in B.t.u. required to raise the temperature of 1 lb. of substance 1°F.

(a) Proper specific heat

(b) Mean specific heat

The specific heat increases with the temperature.

Specific Heat of Gases:

1. Specific heat at constant pressure C_p

2. Specific heat at constant volume C_v

$$\frac{C_p}{C_v} = \gamma \qquad \text{(See \textit{Table} page IV. 19)}$$

Sensible Heat for Heating or Cooling:

$H = cW \ (t_2 - t_1)$ H = Heat   ...   .   B.t.u.

              W = Weight   ...   ...   lb.

              c = Specific heat   ...   ...   B.t.u. per lb. per °F.

              t_1 = Initial temperature   ...   °F.

              t_2 = Final temperature   ...   °F.

The Mechanical Equivalent of Heat is the number of foot-pounds in one British Thermal Unit.

1 B.t.u.   =777·5 ft.-lb.
1 ft.-lb.   =0·00128 B.t.u.
1 kcal   =427 m.kg.
1 h.p.   =42·42 B.t.u. per min.=2,545 B.t.u. per hr.

Pressure is force per unit area :

$$P = \frac{W}{A}$$

P =Pressure   ...   ... lb. per sq. in.
W =Total load of force ... lb.
A =Area   ...   ... sq. in.

Atmospheric Pressure is the pressure which is exerted by the earth's atmosphere.

The atmospheric pressure at sea-level at a temperature of 32°F. is 14·696 lb. per sq. in. = 1 atm.=29·921 ins. Hg.

Absolute Pressure existing at any point in a fluid medium is the true total pressure.

(Absolute pressure)=(Gauge pressure) + (Atmospheric pressure).

Gauge Pressure is the difference between the true pressure and the pressure of the surrounding air.

(Gauge pressure) = (Absolute pressure) — (Atmospheric pressure).

Density is the weight of unit volume, expressed in lb. per cu. ft.

$$\rho = \frac{W}{v} = \frac{\text{Weight in lb.}}{\text{volume in cu. ft.}}$$

Specific Gravity is the ratio of the weight of a body to the weight of an equal volume of pure water at the temperature of maximum density (39°F.).

Specific Volume is the volume of unit weight, expressed in cu. ft. per lb.

$$v = \frac{1}{\rho} = \frac{V}{W} = \frac{\text{volume in cu. ft.}}{\text{weight in lb.}}$$

Mass is the quantity of matter to which the unit of force (1 lb.) will give an acceleration of 1 ft. per sec. per sec.

$$m = \frac{W}{g} = \frac{\text{weight in lb.}}{\text{gravitation of earth in ft. per sec}^2.}$$

First Law of Thermodynamics:

Heat and mechanical energy can be converted one to the other and when thus converted a definite relationship always exists.

Second Law of Thermodynamics:

1. Heat has never been known to flow of its own accord from a cold to a relatively hot body.

2. It is impossible to obtain by cooling any portion of matter below the temperature of the coolest surrounding objects.

THE LAWS OF PERFECT GASES
(These Laws do not apply to Vapours)

(Nearly true for Permanent Gases, such as Oxygen, Nitrogen, Hydrogen, and Atmospheric Air)

Relations between the Volume, Pressure and Temperature:

Normal Temperature and Pressure (N.T.P.): For convenience, the properties of gases are always given on a standard basis of temperature and pressure which is known as normal temperature and pressure.

Normal temperature = 0°C. = 32° F.
Normal pressure   = 14·7 lb. per sq. in. = 1 atm.

Notations:
W = Weight of gas in lb.

$V_1\ V_2$ = Initial and final volume resp. in cu. ft.

$P_1\ P_2$ = Initial and final pressure, resp. in lb. per sq. ft.

$T_1\ T_2$ = Initial and absolute temperature, resp. °F.

R = Gas constant.

Rm = Gas constant for mixtures.

1. Boyle's Law—Temperature Constant:

If the temperature of a given weight of gas is kept constant, the absolute pressure of the gas will vary inversely as its volume.

$V_2 = \dfrac{V_1\,P_1}{P_2}$ Final volume.

$P_2 = \dfrac{V_1\,P_1}{V_2}$ Final abs. pressure.

$\dfrac{P_1}{P_2} = \dfrac{V_2}{V_1}$ (Ratio).

or: $P_1 V_1 = P_2 V_2$.
$PV = $ Constant.

2. Gay-Lussac's Law—Volume Constant:

If the volume of a given weight of gas is kept constant, the absolute pressure will vary directly as the absolute temperature of the gas.

$$\frac{P_1}{P_2} = \frac{T_1}{T_2} \text{ (Ratio)}.$$

$$P_2 = \frac{P_1 T_2}{T_1} \text{ (Final pressure)}.$$

$$T_2 = \frac{T_1 P_2}{P_1} \text{ (Final absolute temperature)}.$$

3. Charles' Law—Pressure Constant:

If the absolute pressure of a given weight of any gas is kept constant its volume will vary directly as the absolute temperature of the gas

$$\frac{V_1}{V_2} = \frac{T_1}{T_2} \text{ (Ratio)}.$$

$$V_2 = \frac{V_1 T_2}{T_1} \text{ (Final volume)}.$$

$$T_2 = T_1 \frac{V_2}{V_1} \text{ (Final absolute temperature)}.$$

The volume of a mass of gas varies by $\frac{1}{492} = 0.002032$ of its volume at 32°F. for every 1°F. change of temperature, the pressure being kept constant.

4. Combined Boyle's, Charles' and Gay-Lussac's Laws:

$$\frac{P_1 V_1}{T_1} = \frac{P_2 V_2}{T_2}.$$

$$P_2 = \frac{P_1 V_1 T_2}{V_2 T_1} \text{ (Final abs. pressure)}.$$

$$V_2 = \frac{P_1 V_1 T_2}{P_2 T_1} \text{ (Final volume)}.$$

$$T_2 = \frac{P_2 V_2 T_1}{P_1 V_1} \text{ (Final abs. temperature)}.$$

5. General Gas Law (the Perfect-Gas Law) states the relation which exists between the pressure, volume, absolute temperature and weight of a perfect gas.

$$PV = wRT \qquad R = \frac{PV}{wT} = \text{Gas constant}.$$

6. Universal Gas Constant (applied for any gas):

$$= \frac{1545}{\text{Molecular weight}}$$

Mixture of Gases:

$$PV = wRmT.$$

$$Rm = \frac{R_1 w_1 + R_2 w_2 + R_n w_n}{w_1 + w_2 + w_n}. \quad \text{Gas constant of mixture.}$$

Dalton's Law of Gases:

Each separate gas, in a mixture of gases, responds to change of pressure, volume, and temperature exactly as though it were entirely isolated from the other gases.

The total pressure of a mixture of gases is equal to the sum of the pressures of all gases in the mixture.

$$P \quad = \text{Pressure of mixture.}$$
$$P_1 \; P_2 = \text{Partial gas or vapour pressure.}$$
$$P \quad = P_1 + P_2.$$

Avogadro's Law:

Equal volumes of all gases at the same temperature and pressure contain the same number of molecules.

METHODS OF HEATING OR EXPANDING GASES (NOT VAPOURS)

Type of Expansion.	Remarks.	Work Done = W	Change of Intl. Energy = E	Heat Absorbed or rejected = H	Final Temp.
Constant Pressure	Isobar	$\dfrac{P(V_2-V_1)}{J}$	$WC_v(T_2-T_1)$	$WC_p(T_2-T_1)$	$T_1\dfrac{V_2}{V_1}$
Constant Temperature	Isotherm Boyle's Law $PV = \text{Constant}$	$\dfrac{P_1 V_1 \log_e \frac{V_2}{V_1}}{J}$	O	W	T_1
Constant Heat	Adiabatic $PV^\gamma = \text{Constant}$	$\dfrac{P_1 V_1 - P_2 V_2}{J(\gamma-1)}$	$WC_v(T_2-T_1)$	O	$\left(\dfrac{V_1}{V_2}\right)^{\gamma-1} = \dfrac{T_2}{T_1}$
Int. Energy & Temp. Change	Polytrope $PV^n = \text{const.}$	$\dfrac{P_1 V_1 - P_2 V_2}{J(n-1)}$	$WC_v(T_2-T_1)$	$W+E$	$\left(\dfrac{V_1}{V_2}\right)^{n-1} = \dfrac{T_2}{T_1}$

in which :
W = External work done by gas.
E = Increase of internal energy of the gas.
H = Total heat absorbed or rejected.
C_p = Specific heat of the gas at constant pressure.
C_v = Specific heat of the gas at constant volume.
$\gamma = \dfrac{C_p}{C_v}.$
J = 778 ft. lb. per B.t.u.
$V_1 \; P_1 \; T_1$ = Initial volume, pressure, temperature, resp.
$V_2 \; P_2 \; T_2$ = Final volume, pressure, temperature, resp.
$n = \dfrac{\log P_1 - \log P_2}{\log V_2 - \log V_1}$ (For indicator diagrams).

ENTROPY OF GASES

Heat energy transfer may be expressed as the product of entropy and
absolute temperature.

Definition :

The change in entropy of a substance, between two thermal conditions,
is the heat energy transferred to the substance, as heat, per degree of
average absolute temperature between the two conditions ;

or : The change in entropy between two thermal conditions is a value
such that when it is multiplied by the proper average of all the absolute
temperatures which the substance experienced during the heat
transfer between the two conditions, it will give as a product the
total energy added or abstracted from the substance—as heat—
during the transfer.

Usual symbol for Entropy=ϕ.

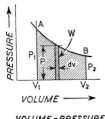

VOLUME - PRESSURE
DIAGRAM

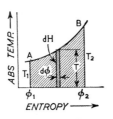

TEMP. - ENTROPY
DIAGRAM

T =Absolute tempera-
        ture.
dH=Small amount of
        heat.
W =Work done.
P =Pressure.
V =Volume.
ϕ =Entropy.
dϕ =Change of Entropy.

General Formulæ :

$$dH = Td\phi.$$

$$d\phi = \frac{dH}{T}.$$

$$\phi_2 - \phi_1 = \int_{T_1}^{T_2}\frac{dH}{T}.$$

$$W = \int_{V_1}^{V_2} PdV.$$

Heat energy change = (Entropy change) $\times$ (Average absolute temperature).

The Critical Temperature of a substance is that temperature above which it cannot exist as a liquid.

The Critical Pressure is the pressure of a saturated vapour at its critical temperature.

CRITICAL TEMPERATURES AND PRESSURES OF VARIOUS SUBSTANCES

Substance.	Critical Temperature °F.	°C.	Critical Pressure Absolute. lb./sq. in.	atm.	Boiling Temp. at Atm. Pres. °F.	°C.
Air	−220	−140	573	39	...	...
Alcohol (C_2H_6O) ...	421	216	956	65	172·4	78
Ammonia (NH_3) ...	266	130	1691	115	− 27·4	−33
Benzol (C_6H_6) ...	554	292	735	50	176	80
Carbon-dioxide (CO_2)	88·2	31	1132	77	−110	− 79
Carbon-monoxide (CO)	−222	−141	528	35·9	−310	−190
Ether ($C_4H_{10}O$) ...	381·2	194	544	37	95	35
Hydrogen (H) ...	−402	−242	294	20	−423	−253
Nitrogen (N) ...	−236	−149	514	35	−321	−195
Oxygen (O_2) ...	−180	−118	735	50	−297	−183
Water (H_2O) ...	706–716	375–380	3200	217·8	212	100

(From Mark's Mech. Eng. Hand.)

ESTIMATIONS OF TEMPERATURES OF INCANDESCENT BODIES

COLOURS OF DIFFERENT TEMPERATURES

Faint red	960°F.	516°C.
Dull red	1290°F.	700°C.
Brilliant red ...	1470°F.	750°C.
Cherry red ...	1650°F.	900°C.
Bright cherry red...	1830°F.	1000°C.
Orange	2010°F.	1100°C.
Bright orange ...	2190°F.	1200°C.
White heat ...	2370°F.	1300°C.
Bright white heat...	2550°F.	1400°C.
Brilliant white heat	2750°F.	1500°C.

TRANSFER OF HEAT MAY OCCUR BY:

1. Conduction.
2. Convection.
3. Radiation.

1. **Conduction** is the transfer of heat through the molecules of a substance.

   (*a*) *Internal Conduction* is transmission within a body.

   (*b*) *External Conduction* is transmission from one body to another, when the two bodies are in contact.

   Thermal Conductivity of a substance is the quantity of heat transferred through a body of one square foot area and one inch of thickness in one hour per one degree F. temp. difference.

   (B.t.u./sq. ft./in./°F. hr.).

   Heat Flow: $H = A \dfrac{K}{X} (t_2 - t_1)$ ...   ...   B.t.u./hr.

   in which: K = Thermal conductivity ...   B.t.u./sq. ft./in./°F. hr.
   A = Area   ...   .   sq. ft.
   X = Thickness   ...   ...   in.
   t_1 = Temperature at Cooler
   Section   ...   ...   °F.
   t_2 = Temperature at Hotter
   Section   ...   ...   °F.

Thermal Resistance is numerically the reciprocal of the thermal conductance.

   Heat Flow: $H = \dfrac{t_2 - t_1}{R}$ ...   ...   B.t.u./hr.

   Thermal resistance $= R = \dfrac{1}{K} \dfrac{X}{A}$

2. **Convection** is the transfer of heat by flow of currents within a fluid body. (Liquid or gas flowing over the surface of a hotter or cooler body.)

   $H = aA (t_2 - t_1) = \dfrac{t_2 - t_1}{R_1}$ (B.t.u. per hr.).

   a = Thermal conductance (B.t.u. per sq. ft. per hr. per °F.).

   $R_1 = \dfrac{1}{aA}$ = Thermal resistance.

   The amount of heat transferred per unit of time is affected by the velocity of moving medium, the area and form of surface and the temp. difference.

3. Radiation is the transfer of heat from one body to another by wave motion.

Stephan-Boltzmann Formula.

$$E = C \left(\frac{T}{100} \right)^4$$

E=Heat emission of a body in B.t.u. per hr.
T=Absolute temperature °F.
C=Radiation constant.

For the absolute black body: C=0·173.
For other materials: C (see Table below).
Quantity of heat transferred between two surfaces:

$$Q_{rad} = CA \left[\left(\frac{T_1}{100} \right)^4 - \left(\frac{T_2}{100} \right)^4 \right] \quad \dots \quad (B.t.u. \text{ per hr.}).$$

A   = Area in sq. ft.

$T_1 \, T_2$ = Absolute temperature of the hot and cold surface resp. °F.

RADIATION CONSTANT OF BUILDING MATERIAL (C)

Black body	... 0·173	Sand ...	... 0·127	Cast Iron, rough	
Cotton...	... 0·128	Shavings	... 0·124	oxidized	...0·154
Glass ...	... 0·155	Silk ...	... 0·130	Copper,	
Wood ...	... 0·126	Water ...	... 0·112	polished	... 0·028
Brick ...	... 0·156	Wool ...	... 0·130	Brass, dull	... 0·036
Oil Paint	... 0·130	Wrought Iron,		Silver ...	... 0·0046
Paper ...	... 0·134	dull oxidized	0·156	Zinc, dull	... 0·036
Plaster	... 0·156	Wrought Iron,		Tin ...	... 0·0077
Lamp Black	... 0·156	polished	... 0·047		

CONDUCTION OF HEAT THROUGH PIPES OR PARTITIONS

Symbols

t_m = Logarithmic Mean temperature difference.

t_{a1} = Initial temperature of heating medium °F.

t_{a2} = Final temperature of heating medium °F.

t_1 = Initial temperature of heated fluid °F.

t_3 = Final temperature of heated fluid °F.

The heat exchange can be classified as follows:

1. Parallel Flow, the fluids flow in the same directions over the separating wall.

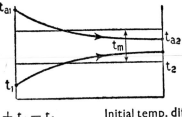

$$t_m = \frac{t_{a1} - t_{a2} + t_2 - t_1}{\log_e \frac{t_{a1} - t_1}{t_{a2} - t_2}} = \frac{\text{Initial temp. dif.} - \text{Final temp. dif.}}{2.3 \log_{10} \frac{\text{Initial temp. dif.}}{\text{Final temp. dif.}}}$$

2. Counter Flow, the directions are opposite.

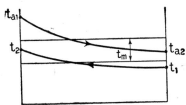

$$t_m = \text{(as before)} = \frac{\text{Initial temp. dif.} - \text{Final temp. dif.}}{2.3 \log_{10} \frac{\text{Initial temp. dif.}}{\text{Final temp. dif.}}}$$

3. Evaporators or Condensers:
One fluid remains at a constant temperature while changing its state.

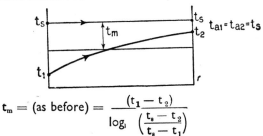

$$t_m = \text{(as before)} = \frac{(t_1 - t_2)}{\log_e \left(\frac{t_s - t_2}{t_s - t_1}\right)}$$

4. Mixed Flow:
One of the fluids takes an irregular direction with respect to the other.

$$t_m = \left(\frac{t_{a1} - t_{a2}}{2}\right) - \left(\frac{t_1 - t_2}{2}\right)$$

Newton's Law of Cooling: In the warming and cooling of bodies, the heat gain or loss respectively, is proportional to the difference between the temperatures of the body and the surroundings.

Let: t_s=Temperature of the cold surroundings in °F.

     t_1=Initial Temperature of the Hot Body.

     t_2=Temperature of the Body.

     C=Thermal Conductivity of the Body.

     P =Density of the Body.

     S =Specific Heat of the Body.

     U=Coefficient of Heat Transfer between the Body and the surroundings, B.t.u. per sq. ft. per °F. per hour.

     R =Radius of a sphere or cylinder, or half thickness of a slab cooled or heated on both faces. Thickness of a slab cooled or heated on one face only.

     $\theta = (\theta_1 - \theta_2)$=Cooling time.

Then : $$\frac{t_2 - t_s}{t_1 - t_s} = e^{-K\theta}$$

     and $\log_e (t_2 - t_s) - \log_e (t_1 - t_s) = -K\theta$.

where : K = Constant which can be found by measuring the temperatures of the body at different times θ_1 and θ_2 and which is :

$$K = \log_e \frac{t_2 - t_s}{t_1 - t_s} \div (\theta_1 - \theta_2).$$

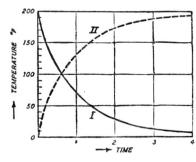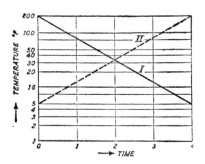

Cooling Curve (I) and Heating Curve (II) showing relation of Temperature and Time on Linear and Semi-logarithmic Paper.

Graphs showing how the Temperature of Cooling or Heated Up Bodies can be plotted on semi-logarithmic paper by introducing the following dimensionless ratios:

$$Y = \frac{t_s - t_1}{t_s - t_2}, \qquad X = \frac{c\theta}{psR^2}, \qquad m = \frac{c}{UR}$$

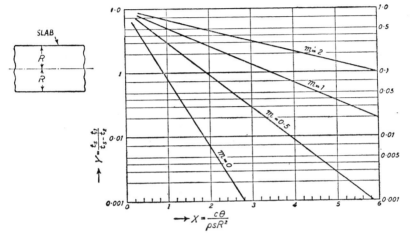

The Increased Heat Loss of Buildings during the heating up period causes a greater heat requirement than the steady state. This additional heat loss depends mainly on the type of building, length of heating interruption and heating up time, and type of heating installation. The allowance for covering the increased heat loss during heating up is usually expressed as a percentage of the heat loss in the steady state.

(See VI. 10, Rietschel's Formula, and VI. 2, Allowances for Intermittent Heating.)

The Temperatures during warming up of bodies are represented graphically by curves which are symmetrical to cooling down curves.

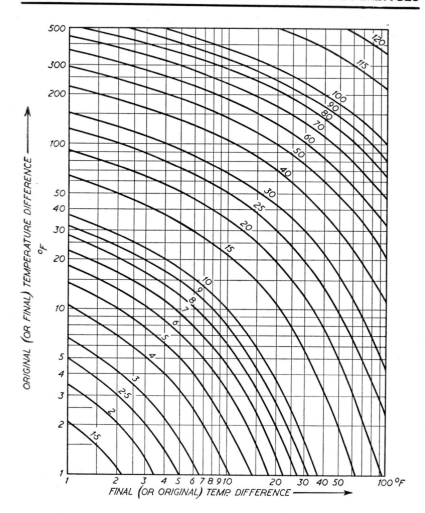

Example of Using the Chart

Water to Water Calorifier with Counter Flow.
Primary flow temperature 180°F. Secondary return temperature 50°F.
Primary return temperature 160°F. Secondary flow temperature 100°F.
Original temperature difference=180—50=130°F.
Final temperature difference=160—100=60°F.
From chart: Log. mean temp. difference=95°F.

HEAT TRANSMISSION COEFFICIENTS FOR METALS

in B.t.u. per sq. ft. per hr. per °F.

Water	...	Cast iron	...	Air or Gas	...	1·4
Water	...	Mild Steel	...	Air or Gas	...	2·0
Water	...	Copper	...	Air or Gas	...	2·25
Water	...	Cast Iron	...	Water	...	40 to 50
Water	...	Mild Steel	...	Water	...	60 to 70
Water	...	Copper	...	Water	...	62 to 80
Air ...	...	Cast Iron	...	Air ...	...	1·0
Air ...	...	Mild Steel	...	Air ...	...	1·4
Steam	...	Cast Iron	...	Air ...	...	2·0
Steam	...	Mild Steel	...	Air ...	...	2·5
Steam	...	Copper	...	Air ...	...	3·0
Steam	...	Cast Iron	...	Water	...	160
Steam	...	Mild Steel	...	Water	...	185
Steam	...	Copper	...	Water	...	205

The above values are average coefficients for practically still fluids.

The coefficients are dependent on velocities of heating and heated mediæ
on type of heating surface, temperature difference and other circumstances. For special cases, see literature, and manufacturers' data

HEAT TRANSMISSION COEFFICIENTS FOR VARIOUS VELOCITIES

The Heat Transmission Coefficients $(U_1 \ U_2)$ are directly proportional to
the square of the air velocity $U_1 : U_2 = V_1^2 : V_2^2$.

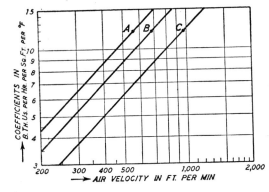

Coefficients for $\frac{3}{4}$ in. dia.
tubes with $1\frac{1}{2}$ in. O.D.
gills, 7 gills per in.,
50 per cent free area.

(a) Heating with steam
5–150.

(b) Cooling with water.
Water velocity 2
f.p.m.

(c) Cooling with direct
expansion.

TRANSMISSION TABLE, B.t.u./sq. ft. hr.

Coefficient B.t.u. /sq. ft. °F. hr.		Heating System	Hot Water						Steam		
		Mean Rad Temp. °F.	160			165			215		
Water.	Steam.	Room Temp. °F.	55	60	65	55	60	65	55	60	65
1·85	2·12	2-Col. Rad. ...	195	185	176	203	195	185	340	328	319
1·70	1·95	4-Col. Rad. ...	178	170	162	187	178	170	312	302	292
1·60	1·84	6-Col. Rad. ...	158	160	152	176	158	160	294	285	276
1·71	1·95	Wall	180	171	163	188	180	171	312	302	292
1·58	1·81	Window ...	166	158	150	174	166	158	290	282	270
1·85	2·12	3″ Hospital ...	195	185	176	203	195	185	340	328	319
1·58	1·80	5¾″ Hospital ...	166	158	150	174	166	158	290	278	270
1·51	1·72	7⅛″ Hospital ...	158	151	144	166	158	151	275	266	258
2·17	2·37	Pipe Coil, 1 row	228	217	206	239	228	217	380	367	356
1·76	1·90	Pipe Coil, 2 rows	185	176	167	191	185	176	304	284	285
1·03	1·13	Gilled Tube 1 row	107	103	98	118	107	103	181	175	170
0·93	1·01	,, 2 rows	98	93	88	108	98	93	160	155	150

Transmissions are based on:

    30″ high Radiators.
    2½″ between Radiator and Wall.

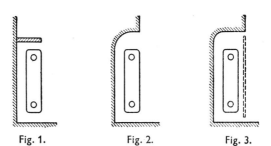

Fig. 1.   Fig. 2.   Fig. 3.

Transmissions are to be reduced by:

    2– 5% for Radiators below Window-sill ... ... Fig. 1.
    5–10% for Radiators in Wall Recess ... ... Fig. 2.
    15–25% for Radiators in Wall Recess, with Grill ... ... Fig. 3.
    25–30% for Radiators, with Aluminium Painting

HEAT TRANSMISSION COEFFICIENTS "K" FOR RADIATORS IN AIR DUCTS

In B.t.u. per sq. ft. per. °F. per hr.

Mean air temperature 32°F. atmospheric pressure, for hot water heating:
170°F. mean water temperature,
and 6 ft./sec. water velocity
or steam heating of 15 to 45 lb. per sq. in. working pressure.
For various air velocities "V" in ft. per minute.

V. Air velocity. ft. per min.	K. Heat tr. coeff. B.t.u./sq. ft. °F. hr.	V. Air velocity. ft./min.	K. Heat tr. coeff. B.t.u./sq. ft. °F. hr.
40	1·48	280	4·82
60	1·90	320	5·22
80	2·23	360	5·60
100	2·56	400	6·00
120	2·87	450	6·44
160	3·42	500	6·86
200	3·92	550	7·30
240	4·38	600	7·70

For water velocities lower than 6 ft. per sec. the values are to be reduced by 5 per cent. The values are to be multiplied by:

0·98 for mean air temperature of 50°F.
0·96   ,,   ,,   68°F.
0·94   ,,   ,,   86°F.
0·92   ,,   ,,   104°F.
0·90   ,,   ,,   122°F.

TABLE OF $n^{1·3}$ For Radiator and Pipe Coefficients in relation to various Temperature Differences.

n	$n^{1·3}$	n	$n^{1·3}$	n	$n^{1·3}$	n	$n^{1·3}$	n	$n^{1·3}$	n	$n^{1·3}$
30	83	70	250	110	450	150	674	190	917	230	1,176
35	102	75	273	115	477	155	704	195	948	235	1,209
40	121	80	298	120	505	160	733	200	980	240	1,242
45	141	85	322	125	533	165	763	205	1,012	245	1,219
50	162	90	347	130	560	170	793	210	1,044	250	1,310
55	183	95	372	135	589	175	824	215	1,075	—	—
60	205	100	398	140	617	180	855	220	1,110	—	—
65	226	105	424	145	645	185	887	225	1,142	—	—

Heat Loss of Steel Pipes:

For various Temperature Differences between Pipe and Air, in B.t.u. per ft. run per hr.

Nom. Bore of Pipe in.	Surface sq. ft. per ft.	Heat Trans. Coefficient.*		Temp. Difference °F. Water.								Steam	
		Water	Steam	60	70	80	90	100	150	200	225	150	145
½	0·21	2·68	2·94	29	35	42	46	56	95	138	160	103	99
¾	0·28	2·5	2·75	36	44	52	63	70	118	172	220	129	123
1	0·33	2·4	2·64	41	50	60	72	80	135	198	230	147	141
1¼	0·43	2·3	2·53	50	61	73	88	98	165	241	261	180	173
1½	0·50	2·2	2·42	57	69	82	99	110	186	270	316	202	194
2	0·62	2·1	2·31	66	81	96	116	129	218	317	370	238	228
2½	0·75	2·05	2·25	79	97	115	138	154	260	380	442	283	272
3	0·92	2·05	2·25	97	118	141	169	188	318	462	540	345	331
3½	1·05	2·0	2·20	107	131	156	187	208	352	512	597	383	367
4	1·19	1·95	2·15	120	146	174	209	232	392	570	665	426	409
5	1·46	1·93	2·12	146	177	221	254	282	477	695	810	522	500
6	1·75	1·90	2·09	171	208	348	298	331	560	815	950	610	585

*The above **Heat Transmission Coefficients** are in B.t.u. per sq. ft. per °F. per hr. when the temperature difference is 100°F. They are for uncovered pipes freely exposed under natural convection in B.t.u. per linear ft. per hr.

The above Heat Transmissions are to be multiplied by: ...

Single Pipe	... ...	Along Skirting or Riser ...	1·0
More than 1 Pipe ...	...	Along Skirting or Riser ...	0·91
Single Pipe	... ...	Along Ceiling	0·73
More than 1 Pipe ...	...	Along Ceiling	0·66
Single Pipe	... ...	Freely Exposed	1·1
More than 1 Pipe ...	...	Freely Exposed	1·0

Heat Loss of Copper Pipes:

For various Temperature Differences between Pipe and Air, in B.t.u. per ft. run per hr.

Pipe Size in.	Temp. Difference °F.		
	70	100	130
½	22	34	47
¾	29	45	63
1	36	56	79
1¼	43	67	93
1½	49	77	108
2	62	97	136
2½	74	116	162
3	87	135	189
3½	99	154	216
4	111	172	241

Heat Loss of Insulated Copper Pipes:

For Temperature Difference 100°F and insulation K=0·3, 1 in. thick. In B.t.u. per ft. run per hour.

Pipe Size—in.	H.
¾	8
1	10
1½	12
2	15
2½	17
3	20

These tables are reproduced by permission from "A Guide to Current Practice", 1959 edition, published by the Institution of Heating and Ventilating Engineers.

SPECIFIC HEAT OF SUBSTANCES between 32° and 212°F. (B.t.u./lb. °F.)

Metals		Metal Alloys				Liquids	
Aluminium	0·218	Bell Metal...	0·086	Coal	... 0·314	Acetic Acid	0·51
Antimony...	0·051	Brass	... 0·090	Concrete	... 0·27	Alcohol	... 0·70
Copper	... 0·093	Bronze	... 0·104	Cork	... 0·485	Benzol	... 0·43
Gold	... 0·031	Nickel Steel	0·109	Glass	... 0·20	Ether	... 0·503
Iron	... 0·110	Solder	... 0·04	Ice ...	... 0·504	Glycerine	... 0·576
Lead	... 0·031			Ind.Rubber	·27–·98	Machine Oil	0·40
Nickel	... 0·108	**Miscellaneous**		Marble	... 0·21	Mercury	... 0·033
Platinum	... 0·032	Asbestos	... 0·20	Paraffin	... 0·69	Petroleum	0·50
Silver	... 0·056	Ashes	... 0·20	Porcelain	... 0·255	Sulph. Acid	0·50
Tin	... 0·055	Brick	... 0·22	Sand	... 0·195	Turpentine	0·472
Zinc	... 0·094	Coke	... 0·203	Wood	0·55–0·65	Water	... 1·000

SPECIFIC HEAT AND WEIGHT OF GASES

Name of Gas.	Chemical Symbol	Mol. Weight	Density at 32°F. and Atm. Press. lb./cu. ft.	Specific Heat B.t.u./lb.		$\gamma = \dfrac{C_p}{C_v}$	Gas Constant. $(C_p - C_v) \times 778$
				C_p	C_v		
Sulphur Dioxide ...	SO_2	64	0·1828	0·154	0·123	1·25	24·10
Carbon Dioxide ...	CO_2	44	0·1234	0·210	0·160	1·31	35·09
Oxygen	O_2	32	0·0892	0·217	0·155	1·40	48·25
Air	—	28	0·0806	0·241	0·171	1·40	53·34
Nitrogen	N_2	28	0·0780	0·247	0·176	1·40	54·99
Ethylene	C_2H_4	28	0·0786	0·400	0·330	1·20	55·08
Carbon Monoxide ...	CO	28	0·0780	0·243	0·172	1·41	55·14
Acetylene	C_2H_2	26	0·0729	0·350	0·270	1·28	59·34
Blast Furnace ...	—	—	0·0780	0·245	0·174	1·40	55·05
Ammonia	NH_3	17	0·0480	0·523	0·399	1·31	90·50
Methane (Marsh Gas)	CH_4	16	0·0447	0·593	0·450	1·32	96·31
Hydrogen	H_2	2	0·0056	3·42	2·44	1·40	765·90
Combustion Products	—	—	—	0·24	—	—	—

LATENT HEATS OF MELTING OF DIFFERENT SUBSTANCES (B.t.u./lb.)

Aluminium	... 138·2	Iron Slag	... 90·0	Platinum	... 49·0
Bismuth ...	... 22·75	Ice ...	... 143·33	Silver ...	... 37·9
Copper ...	... 75·6	Lead ...	... 9·65	Sulphur ...	... 16·87
Iron, Grey Cast...	41·4	Mercury ...	... 5·08	Tin ...	... 25·2
Iron, White Cast	59·4	Nickel ...	... 8·35	Zinc ...	... 50·63

MELTING AND FREEZING POINTS of various substances (°F. at atmospheric pressure)

Alcohol ...	... −143	Calcium Chloride	1,404	Iron (Pure)	...	2,786
Aluminium	... 1,218	Carbon ...	... 6,300	Lead ...	...	621
Antimony	... 1,166	Carbon Dioxide	−706	Mercury ...	...	−38
Barium ...	... 1,562	Carbon Disulphide	−166	Nickel ...	...	2,646
Bismuth ...	... 520	Copper ...	... 1,981	Oxygen ...	...	−360
Borax ...	... 1,366	Glycerine	... 4	Platinum	...	3,191
Calcium ...	... 1,490	Gold ...	... 1,945	Silver ...	...	1,761
Sulphur ...	224–247	Tin ...	... 449	Zinc ...	...	787
Ice (Fresh Water)	32			Wax ...	...	149
Ice (Sea Water)...	27·5					

BOILING TEMPERATURES of various Liquids at atmospheric pressure (°F.)

Zinc .	... **1,680**	Linseed Oil	... 538	Sodium Chloride	
Sulphur ...	... 823	Naphthalene	... 424	(Sat. Sol.) ... 226·4	
Mercury ...	... 675	Aniline ...	... 363	Water ...	... 212
Paraffin ...	... 572	Calcium Chloride		Alcohol ...	... 172·4
Glycerine	... 554	(Sat. Sol.) ...	356	Helium ...	... −450
Phosphorus	... 554	Turpentine	... 320		
		Toluene	... 230		

LATENT HEATS OF VAPORIZATION at atmospheric pressure (B.t.u./lb.)

Acetone ...	... 233	Chloroform	... 110	Nitrogen	... 81·5
Alcohol ...	... 385	Ether ...	... 162	Oxygen ...	... 92
Aniline ...	... 198	Hydrogen	... 222	Sulphur ...	... 650
Benzol ...	... 169	Methyl Chlorine	175	Turpentine	... 126
Chlorine	... 112	Mercury ...	... 122	Water ...	... 970·4

COEFFICIENTS OF LINEAR EXPANSION of some materials. Average Values between 32°F. and 212°F. (ins. per in. per °F × 10^6)

Aluminium	... 12·3	Lead ...	... 15·1	Glass, Hard	... 3·3
Antimony	... 5·8	Silver ...	... 10·7	Glass, Plate	... 5·0
Brass ...	... 10·4	Solder ...	... 13·4	Marble ...	... 6·5
Bronze ...	... 10·0	Nickel Steel	... 7·3	Rubber ...	... 42·8
Copper ...	... 9·3	Type Metal	... 10·8	Wood, Oak	
Gold ...	... 8·2	Zinc ...	... 16·5	Parallel to Grain 2·7	
Iron, Pure	... 6·7	Brick ...	... 3·1	Across Grain ...	3·0
Iron, Cast	... 5·9	Cement ...	... 6·0	Porcelain...	... 1·7
Iron, Forged	... 6·3	Concrete	... 8·0	Masonry ...	2·5 to 5·0
				Graphite	... 4·4

Metals

	Specific Gravity	lb. per cu. ft.		Specific Gravity.	lb. per cu. ft.
Aluminium ...	2·7	168	Iron, wrought...	7·8	486
Antimony ...	6·7	417	Lead	11·34	705
Brass, cast ...	8·1	505	Mercury ...	13·55	840
Brass, yellow ...	8·4	518	Nickel	8·9	551
Bronze, gunmetal	8·5	529	Platinum ...	21·5	1340
Copper ...	8·9	551	Silver	10·5	655
Gold, pure cast	19·3	1,200	Steel	7·9	493
Iron, cast ...	7·5	467			

Liquids

	Specific Gravity	lb. per cu. ft.		Specific Gravity	lb. per cu. ft.
Alcohol, pure 60°F.	0·79	49	Oil, olive ...	0·92	57
Alcohol, 80°F....	0·85	53	Oil, turpentine	0·87	54
Alcohol, 50°F....	0·91	57	Water, distilled	1·0	62
Ether	0·87	54	Water, sea 39°F.	1·03	64
Glycerine, acetic	1·28	79	Milk	1·03	64
Oil, naphtha ...	0·85	53	Beer	1·03	64

Miscellaneous

	Specific Gravity	lb. per cu. ft.		Specific Gravity	lb. per cu. ft.
Asbestos ...	3·07	191	Limestone ...	3·18	198
Atm. air ...	0·00121	0·075	Marble ...	2·65	165
Asphalt ...	1·65	103	Mortar... ...	1·4–1·75	86–109
Cement, Port...	3·0	187	Peat	0·60–	37–83
Cement, Roman	1·56	97		1·33	
Chalk	1·5–2·8	95–175	Plaster ...	1·18	73
Coal	1·5–1·65	95–103	Porcelain ...	2·3	143
Coke	1·0	62	Rubber ...	0·92	67
Concrete, mean	2·24	140	Salt, common ...	2·13	133
Glass, window	2·64	164	Soap	1·07	67
Granitstone ...	2·14	133	Starch ...	0·95	59
Gypsum ...	2·17	135	Sulphur ...	2·03	126
Ice at 32°F. ...	0·92	57	Wax, paraffin	93	58
Lime, hydraulic	2·75	171			

THERMAL CONDUCTIVITY "K" OF VARIOUS MATERIALS
B.t.u. per sq. ft.-in. per °F. per hr.

Metals—Temperature range 32–500°F. :

Aluminium 1,050	Lead 240
Brass, yellow 500	Mercury 48
Brass, red 600	Nickel 400
Copper 2,100	Platinum 480
Gold... 2,150	Silver 2,900
Iron, cast 450	Steel, soft 320
Iron, wrought 400	Zinc 440

Miscellaneous :

Material.	Temp. °F	K.
Air-cell Asbestos	212–572 ...	1·1
Asbestos, 44 lb./cu. ft.	— ...	1·5
Asbestos, 29 lb./cu. ft.	— ...	1·0
Asphalt	68 ...	4·8
Cardboard	— ...	1·4
Cement	95–194 ...	5·5
Charcoal, powdered	32–212 ...	0·4
Cotton	32–220 ...	0·45
Firebrick	32–2400 ...	9·00
Firebrick, powdered	70–212 ...	0·82
Glass, crown, window	— ...	7·00
Ice	— ...	16·00
Linoleum	68 ...	1·25
Marble	— ...	17·00
Paper	— ...	0·90
Porcelain	— ...	7·20
Rubber	— ...	1·30
Scale, boiler	— ...	16·00
Slate	— ...	14·00
Wool, sheep	— ...	0·40
Wool, mineral	— ...	0·42
Water	— ...	4.2
Brine	39 ...	3·3
Ammonia	32–212 ...	0·015
Air	32 ...	0.055

Thermal Conductance:
1 Cal. per hr. per sq. cm. per °C=2·048 B.t.u. per hr. per sq. ft. per °F.
1 B.t.u. per hr. per sq. ft. per °F=0·4882 Cal. per hr. per sq. cm. per °C.

Thermal Conductivity:
1 Cal. per hr. per sq. cm. per cm. per °C=0·0672 B.t.u. per hr. per sq. ft. per ft. per °F.
1 B.t.u. per hr. per sq. ft. per ft. per °F=14·88 Cal. per hr. per sq. cm. per cm. per °C.

CONDUCTIVITIES   K in B.t.u. per sq. ft. per hr. in per °F.

CONDUCTANCES $C = \dfrac{K}{x}$ in B.t.u. per sq. ft. per hr. per °F.

FOR BUILDING MATERIAL

Material.	K.	C.	Material.	K.	C.
			Stucco	12·0	—
Brick, common	5·00	—	Stone, average	12·5	—
Brick, face ...	9·2	—			
Brickwork, wet	10·0	—	Tile, hollow clay 8″	—	0·60
Concrete, average	12·0	—	,, 12″	—	0·40
			,, 16″	—	0·31
Concrete, stone	9·46	—	Tile, hollow clay		
Concrete, cinder	5·20	—	with ½″ cement		
Mortar, cement	8·00	—	plaster on each		
Plaster... ...	3·3	—	side 2″	—	1·00
			Ditto 4″	—	0·60
			Ditto 6″	—	0·47
Plaster, gypsum	5·0	—			
Roofing compos.	—	6·5	Wood across the		
Shingles, asbestos	—	6·0	grain : Cypress...	0·67	—
Shingles, asphalt	—	6·5	Fir ...	0·76	—
			Maple ...	1·10	—
			Yellow Pine	1·03	—
			White Pine	0·78	—

CONDUCTIVITIES K FOR INSULATING MATERIAL
in B.t.u. per sq. ft. per in. per hr. per °F.

Material.	Density lb. per cu. ft.	K.	Material.	Density lb. per cu. ft.	K.
Asbestos, wood, pressed asbestos and cement ...	123·0	2·7	Insulex, dry ...	12·0	0·44
			Insulex, dry ...	30·0	1·00
			Insulite ...	16·9	0·34
Balsam wool ...	2·2	0·27	Rock wool ...	10·0	0·27
Cabot's quilt	3·4	0·25	Rock wool ...	21·0	0·30
Cabot's quilt ...	4·6	0·26	Sawdust ...	—	0·70
Celotex ...	13·2	0·34	Shavings ...	—	0·71
Cork board ...	7·0	0·27	Thermofill ...	19·8	0·35
Cork board ...	14·0	0·34	Thermofill ...	34·0	0·60
Cork, regranulated	8·1	0·31	Thermofill ...	7·3	0·33
Flaxlinum ...	13·0	0·31	Wood, balsa ...	8·8	0·38
Gyplap, ½″ thick	53·5	2·60	across grain...	20·0	0·58
Hair felt ...	12·0	0·26			

MULTIPLYING FACTORS

For determining the capacities of Unit Heaters for various conditions. Based on inlet air temp. 60°F., barometric press. 30 in. Hg.

HOT WATER HEATING (Based on Mean Water Temp. 170°F.)

		Inlet Air Temperature °F.					
		30	40	50	55	60	70
Mean Water Temperature °F.	110	0·73	0·64	0·53	0·50	0·45	0·36
	120	0·82	0·73	0·64	0·59	0·55	0·45
	130	0·91	0·82	0·73	0·68	0·64	0·55
	140	1·00	0·91	0·82	0·77	0·73	0·69
	150	1·10	1·00	0·91	0·86	0·82	0·73
	160	1·18	1·09	1·00	0·95	0·91	0·82
	170	1·27	1·18	1·09	1·05	1·00	0·91
	180	1·36	1·27	1·18	1·14	1·09	1·00
	190	1·46	1·36	1·27	1·23	1·18	1·09

STEAM HEATING (Based on Steam Press. 2 lb. per sq. in.)

Steam Pressure lb. per sq. in.	0	1·190	1·115	1·041	0·994	0·967	0·896
	2	1·226	1·148	1·074	1·037	1·000	0·927
	5	1·286	1·211	1·136	1·098	1·062	0·989
	10	1·368	1·291	1·214	1·177	1·140	1·067
	20	1·496	1·417	1·340	1·302	1·265	1·191
	30	1·596	1·517	1·438	1·401	1·361	1·286
	40	1·677	1·598	1·519	1·480	1·442	1·366
	50	1·751	1·670	1·592	1·552	1·513	1·436
	60	1·812	1·732	1·656	1·612	1·573	1·496
	70	1·871	1·788	1·708	1·669	1·629	1·552
	80	1·923	1·841	1·760	1·720	1·681	1·603
	90	1·969	1·886	1·805	1·770	1·725	1·646
	100	2·015	1·932	1·850	1·809	1·764	1·686

Temp.	Abs. pressure	Density	Specific Gravity	Specific Volume	Specific Heat B.t.u./ lb. °F.	Entropy B.t.u./ lb. °F.	Absolute Viscosity in poises	Total Heat
°F.	lb./sq. in.	lb./cu. ft.		cu. ft./lb.				B.t.u./lb.
32	0·088	62·42	1·000	0·0160	1·0093	0·0000	0·0179	0
40	0·122	62·42	1·000	0·0160	1·0048	0·01615	0·0155	8
50	0·178	62·42	1·000	0·0160	1·0015	0·03595	0·0131	18
60	0·256	62·38	1·000	0·0160	0·9995	0·05765	0·0113	28
62	0·275	62·35	1·000	0·0160	0·9992	0·05919	0·0110	30
70	0·363	62·30	0·999	0·0160	0·9982	0·0754	0·0098	38
80	0·507	62·22	0·998	0·0160	0·9975	0·0929	0·0086	48
90	0·698	62·11	0·996	0·0161	0·9971	0·1112	0·0076	58
100	0·949	61·99	0·994	0·0161	0·9970	0·1292	0·0088	68
110	1·27	61·86	0·992	0·0161	0·9971	0·1469	0·0062	78
120	1·69	61·71	0·990	0·0162	0·9974	0·1641	0·0056	88
130	2·22	61·55	0·987	0·0162	0·9978	0·1816	0·0051	98
140	2·89	61·38	0·984	0·0163	0·9984	0·1981	0·0047	108
150	3·72	61·20	0·982	0·0163	0·9990	0·2147	0·0043	118
160	4·74	61·00	0·979	0·0164	0·9988	0·2309	0·0040	128
170	5·99	60·80	0·975	0·0164	1·0007	0·2472	0·0037	138
180	7·51	60·58	0·971	0·0165	1·0017	0·2629	0·00345	148
190	9·33	60·36	0·969	0·0166	1·0028	0·2787	0·00323	158
200	11·53	60·12	0·965	0·0166	1·0039	0·2938	0·00302	168
210	14·13	59·92	0·958	0·0167	1·0052	0·3089	0·00287	178
212	14·70	59·88	0·957	0·0167	1·0055	0·3119	0·00285	180
220	17·19	59·66	0·955	0·0168	1·0068	0·3237	0·00272	188·1
230	20·77	59·37	0·950	0·0168	1·0087	0·3385	0·00257	198·2
240	24·97	59·17	0·946	0·0169	1·0104	0·3531	0·00254	208·3
250	29·81	58·84	0·941	0·0170	1·0126	0·3676	0·00230	218·4
260	35·42	58·62	0·940	0·0171	1·0148	0·3818	0·00217	228·6
270	41·85	58·25	0·933	0·0172	1·0174	0·3962	0·00208	238·7
280	49·18	58·04	0·929	0·0172	1·0200	0·4097	0·00200	248·9
290	57·55	57·65	0·923	0·0173	1·0230	0·4236	0·00193	259·2
300	67·00	57·41	0·920	0·0174	1·0260	0·4272	0·00186	262·5
310	77·67	57·00	0·913	0·0175	1·0296	0·4507	0·00179	279·8
320	89·63	56·65	0·906	0·0177	1·0332	0·4643	0·00173	290·2
330	103·00	56·31	0·900	0·0178	1·0368	0·4777	0·00188	300·6
340	118·0	55·95	0·897	0·0179	1·0404	0·4908	0·00163	311·1
350	134·6	55·65	0·890	0·0180	1·0440	0·5040	0·00158	321·7
360	153·0	55·19	0·883	0·0181	1·0486	0·5158	0·00153	332·3
370	173·3	54·78	0·876	0·0182	1·0532	0·5292	0·00149	342·9
380	195·6	54·36	0·870	0·0184	1·0578	0·5420	0·00145	353·5
390	220·2	53·96	0·865	0·0187	1·0624	0·5548	0·00141	364·3
400	247·1	53·62	0·834	0·0186	1·0670	0·5677	0·00137	375·3
450	422	51·3	0·821	0·0195	1·0950	0·6298	—	430·2
500	679	48·8	0·781	0·0205	1·1300	0·6907	—	489·1
550	1043	45·7	0·730	0·0219	1·2000	0·7550	—	553·5
600	1540	41·5	0·666	0·0241	1·3620	0·8199	—	623·2
706·1	3226	19·2	0·307	0·0522	—	1·0785	—	925·0

GENERAL DATA, WATER

Maximum density at a temperature of: 39·2°F. or 4°C.

1 cu. ft.	=	6·23 gal.	=	62·355 lb.	⎫
1 lb.	=	0·1 gal.	=	27·72 cu. in.	⎬ at 62°F.
1 gal.	=	0·16 cu. ft.	=	10 lb.	⎭
1 ton	=	35·9674 cu.ft.	=	224 gal.	
1 litre	=	0·22 gal.	=	1 kg.=0·45 lb. at 39·2°F. (4°C.).	

Freezing temperature	...	32°F.	0°C.	⎫
Boiling temperature	...	212°F.	100°C.	⎪ at
Latent heat of melting	...	144 B.t.u./lb.	79·5 kcal/kg.	⎬ atm.
Latent heat of evaporation		977 B.t.u./lb.	539·4 kcal/kg.	⎪ pres.
Critical temperature	...	706–716°F.	380–386°C.	⎭
Critical pressure	...	3,200 lb./sq. in.	217·8 atm.	

Pressure of water:

1 lb. per sq. in.	=	2·31 ft. of water.
	=	27·71 in. of water.
	=	703·03 kg. per m².
	=	703·03 mm. of water.

(See also Conversions Table, page I. 2)

Specific heat of water	= 1·0000 B.t.u./lb.
Specific heat of ice	= 0·504 B.t.u./lb.
Specific heat of water vapour	= 0·477 B.t.u./lb.

Thermal expansion: Water expands in bulk
from 40°F. to 212°F. $\frac{1}{23}$ of its original volume.

Bulk elastic modulus of water = 300,000 lb. per sq. in.

Section V

PROPERTIES OF STEAM AND AIR

PROPERTIES OF STEAM AND OTHER VAPOURS

A Vapour is any substance in the gaseous state which does not even approximately follow the general gas laws.

Highly superheated vapours are gases, if the superheat is sufficiently great, and they then approximately follow the general gas law.

Conditions of Vapours:

1. **Dry Saturated Vapour** is free from unvaporized liquid particles.

2. **Wet Saturated Vapour** carries liquid globules in suspension.

3. **Superheated Vapour** is vapour the temperature of which is higher than that of the boiling point corresponding to the pressure.

Dryness Fraction or Quality of Saturated Vapour (X) is the percentage of dry vapour present in the given amount of the wet saturated vapour.

$$X = \frac{Ws}{Ws + Ww.}$$

Ws = Weight of dry steam in steam considered.
Ww = Weight of water in steam.

The Heat of the Liquid "h" is the heat in B.t.u. per lb. required to raise the temperature of 1 lb. of the liquid from 32°F. to that temperature at which the liquid begins to boil at the given pressure.

$$h = c\,(t - 32).$$

c = Mean specific heat of water.
t = Temperature formation of steam at pressure considered °F.

The Latent Heat of Evaporation "L" is the heat required to change a liquid at a given temperature and pressure into a vapour at the same temperature and pressure. It is divided into two parts:

1. External Latent Heat of Vapour = External Work Heat.
2. Internal Latent Heat of Vapour = Heat due to change of state.

The Total Heat of a Vapour (or Enthalpy) is the amount of heat which must be supplied to 1 lb. of the liquid which is at 32°F. to convert it at constant pressure into vapour at the temperature and pressure considered.

Total Heat of Dry Saturated Vapour:

$$H = h + L \text{ (B.t.u. per lb.)}$$

h = Heat of liquid at the temperature of the wet vapour B.t.u. per lb.
L = Latent heat, B.t.u. per lb.

Total Heat of Wet Saturated Vapour:

$$H_w = h + xL \text{ (B.t.u. per lb.)}$$

x = Dryness Factor.

Total Heat of Superheated Vapour:

$$H_s = h + L + c(t_s - t_1) \text{ (B.t.u. per lb.)}$$

c = Mean specific heat of superheated vapour at the pressure and degrees of superheat considered.
t_s = Temperature of superheat °F.
t_1 = Temperature of formation of steam °F.

Specific Volumes of Wet Vapour:

$$V_w = (1-x) V + xV_D.$$
when x = very small.

$$V_w = xV_D, \quad x = \frac{V_w}{V_D}.$$

V_w = Specific volume of the wet vapour, cu. ft. per lb.
V_D = Specific volume of dry saturated vapour of the same pressure, cu. ft. per lb. (Can be found from the Vapour Tables).

Specific Volume of Superheated Vapour:

Approximate method by using Charles' Law:

$$V = \frac{V_s T_s}{T_1}.$$

ENTROPY OF STEAM

1. Entropy of Water:

Change of Entropy $= \log_e \dfrac{T_1}{T}.$

T_1, T = Absolute temperature °F.

Entropy of water above freezing-point $= \phi_w = \log_e \dfrac{T_1}{492}.$

2. Entropy of Evaporation:

Change of Entropy during evaporation $= \dfrac{dL}{T}.$

Entropy of 1 lb. of wet steam above freezing point: $\phi_s = \phi_w + \dfrac{xL_1}{T_1}.$

3. Entropy of Superheated Steam:

Change of Entropy per lb. of steam during superheating

$$= C_p \log_e \frac{T}{T_1}.$$

Total Entropy of 1 lb. of superheated steam above freezing point

$$= \phi_w + \frac{L_1}{T_1} + C_p \log_e \frac{T_s}{T_1}.$$

L_1 = Latent heat of evaporation at T_1 °F. absolute.
T_1 = Absolute temperature of evaporation.
T_s = Absolute temperature of superheat.

TEMPERATURE—ENTROPY DIAGRAM FOR STEAM

shows the relationship between Pressure, Temperature, Dryness Fraction and Entropy.

When two of these factors are given the two others can be found on the chart.

The ordinates represent the Absolute Temperature and the Entropy.

The chart consists of the following lines:

1. Isothermal Lines.
2. Pressure Lines.
3. Lines of Dryness Fraction.
4. Water Line between Water and Steam.
5. Dry Steam Lines.
6. Constant Volume Lines.

The total heat is given by the area, enclosed by absolute zero base water line and horizontal and vertical line from the respective points.

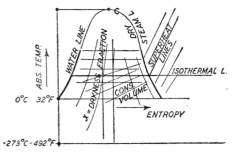

An adiabatic expansion is a vertical line (expansion at Constant Entropy, no transfer of heat).

C = Critical temperature of steam
= 706°F. to 716°F.
= 375°C. to 380°C.

Critical Pressure : 3,200 lb. per sq. in. = 217·8 atm.

MOLLIER OR TOTAL HEAT—ENTROPY CHART

Contains the same lines as the Temperature-Entropy Diagram, but with ordinates representing the Total Heat and Entropy of Steam. This diagram is used to find the drop in the total heat of steam during an adiabatic expansion.

TOTAL HEAT OF SUPERHEATED STEAM (B.t.u. per lb.)

Abs.Pres. lb. per sq.in.	Sat.Temp. °F.	Degrees of Superheat °F.						
		0	40	80	120	160	200	280
20	228	1157·1	1177·2	1197·2	1216·9	1236·6	1256·1	1294·9
30	250·3	1165·5	1185·9	1206·1	1226·1	1245·9	1265·6	1304·7
40	267·2	1171·6	1192·3	1212·9	1233·0	1253·0	1272·8	1312·2
50	280·9	1176·3	1197·3	1218·1	1238·5	1258·6	1278·5	1317·9
60	292·6	1180·1	1201·4	1222·2	1242·8	1263·1	1283·2	1322·9
70	302·8	1183·3	1204·7	1225·8	1246·6	1266·9	1287·2	1327·1
80	311·9	1186·1	1207·9	1229·1	1250·0	1270·5	1290·9	1330·8
90	320·2	1188·5	1210·5	1232·1	1253·0	1273·7	1294·0	1334·2
100	327·9	1190·7	1212·9	1234·6	1255·7	1276·5	1297·0	1337·3
120	341·3	1194·3	1216·9	1239·0	1260·4	1281·3	1302·0	1342·6
140	353·0	1197·2	1220·2	1242·5	1264·2	1285·5	1306·3	1347·1
160	363·6	1199·7	1222·9	1245·6	1267·6	1289·1	1310·0	1351·1
180	373·1	1201·7	1225·5	1248·3	1270·7	1292·2	1313·2	1354·6
200	381·8	1203·5	1227·6	1250·7	1273·1	1295·0	1316·2	1358·0
250	401·0	1207·0	1231·7	1255·7	1278·9	1301·2	1322·6	1364·9
300	417·4	1209·4	1235·0	1259·5	1283·2	1305·8	1327·6	1370·3
400	444·7	1212·1	1239·6	1265·4	1289·9	1313·3	1335·8	1379·6
500	467·1	1213·2	1242·2	1269·1	1294·7	1318·8	1341·9	1386.6

ENTROPY OF SUPERHEATED STEAM (B.t.u. per °F.)

Abs.Pres. lb. per sq.in.	Sat.Temp. °F.	Degrees of Superheat °F.						
		0	40	80	120	160	200	280
20	228	1·7333	1·7617	1·7883	1·8134	1·8372	1·8596	1·9017
30	250·3	1·7017	1·7298	1·7560	1·7807	1·8041	1·8261	1·8472
40	267·2	1·6793	1 7071	1·7331	1·7575	1·7806	1·8025	1·8233
50	280·9	1·6619	1·6895	1·7153	1·7397	1·7626	1·7843	1·8049
60	292·6	1·6477	1·6752	1·7010	1·7253	1·7480	1·7694	1·7899
70	302·8	1·6357	1·6632	1·6889	1·7130	1·7357	1·7570	1·7774
80	311·9	1·6254	1·6527	1·6784	1·7024	1·7251	1·7463	1·7665
90	320·2	1·6161	1·6436	1·6692	1·6931	1·7157	1·7367	1·7569
100	327·9	1·6079	1·6353	1·6608	1·6847	1·7073	1·7283	1·7484
120	341·3	1·5935	1·6210	1·6467	1·6705	1·6928	1·7138	1·7337
140	353·0	1 5813	1·6088	1·6345	1·6583	1·6805	1·7014	1·7212
160	363·6	1·5706	1·5983	1·6240	1·6479	1·6701	1·6909	1·7107
180	373·1	1·5610	1·5890	1·6148	1·6386	1·6607	1·6815	1·7013
200	381·8	1·5525	1·5806	1·6063	1·6301	1·6523	1·6730	1·6929
250	401·0	1·5342	1·5628	1·5886	1·6125	1·6347	1·6554	1·6751
300	417·4	1·5190	1·5479	1·5740	1·5980	1·6203	1·6410	1·6607
400	444·7	1·4941	1·5240	1·5506	1·5749	1·5973	1·6181	1·6379
500	467·1	1·4740	1·5049	1·5322	1·5568	1·5795	1·6004	1·6201

(Based on Callendar's Values)

Abs. Pres. p. lb./sq. in.	Temp. t. °F.	Specific Volume. v. cu. ft./lb.	Density. w. lb./cu. ft.	Heat of			Entropy S. B.t.u./lb.°F.
				Liquid. h. B.t.u./lb.	Evap. L. B.t.u./lb.	Sat. Vap. H. B.t.u./lb.	
0·5	79·5	640·5	0·00156	47·4	1045	1092	2·0299
1	101·7	333·1	0·0030	69·5	1033	1102	1·9724
2	126·1	173·5	0·0058	93·9	1020	1114	1·9159
3	141·5	118·6	0·0085	109·3	1012	1121	1·8833
4	153·0	90·5	0·0111	120·8	1005	1126	1·8600
5	162·3	73·4	0·0136	130·1	1000	1130	1·8422
6	170·1	61·9	0·0162	137·9	995	1133	1·8277
7	176·9	53·6	0·0187	144·8	991	1136	1·8156
8	182·9	47·3	0·0212	150·8	988	1139	1·8049
9	188·3	42·4	0·0236	156·3	985	1141	1·7956
10	193·2	38·4	0·0261	161·1	982	1143	1·7874
12	202·0	32·4	0·0309	169·9	977	1147	1·7731
14	209·6	28·0	0·0357	177·6	972	1150	1·7611
14·7	212·0	26·8	0·0373	180·0	970	1151	1·7573
16	216·3	24·7	0·0404	184·4	968	1152·5	1·7506
18	222·4	22·2	0·0451	190·5	964	1155	1·7414
20	228·0	20·1	0·0498	196·1	961	1157	1·7333
22	233·1	18·37	0·0545	201·3	958	1159	1·7258
24	237·8	16·93	0·0591	206·1	955	1161	1·7189
26	242·2	15·71	0·0636	210·5	952	1162·5	1·7126
28	246·4	14·66	0·0682	214·8	949	1164	1·7069
30	250·3	13·72	0·0728	218·8	947	1165·5	1·7017
35	259·3	11·86	0·8425	228	941	1169	1·6898
40	267·2	10·48	0·0953	236	936	1172	1·6793
45	274·4	9·37	0·1067	243	931	1174	1·6701
50	281·0	8·50	0·1175	250	926	1176	1·6619
55	287·0	7·74	0·1292	256	922	1178	1·6547
60	292·6	7·16	0·1397	262	919	1180	1·6479
65	297·9	6·64	0·1506	267	914	1182	1·6415
70	303·0	6·20	0·1613	272	911	1183	1·6357
75	307·5	5·81	0·1721	277	907	1185	1·6304
80	312·0	5·47	0·1828	282	904	1186	1·6254
85	316·2	5·16	0·1938	286	901	1187	1·6206
90	320·2	4·89	0·2045	290	898	1189	1·6161
95	324·1	4·65	0·2150	295	895	1190	1·6120
100	327·9	4·43	0·2257	298	893	1191	1·6079
105	331·4	4·23	0·2364	302	890	1192	1·6041
110	334·8	4·04	0·2475	306	887	1193	1·6004
115	338·1	3·88	0·2577	309	884	1194	1·5969

| Abs. Pres. | Temp. | Spec. Volume. | Density | Heat of | | | Entropy. |
| | | | | Liquid. h. B.t.u./lb. | Evap. L. B.t.u./lb. | Sat. Vap. H. B.t.u./lb. | |
p. lb./sq. in.	t. °F.	v. cu. ft./lb.	w. lb./cu. ft.				S. B.t.u./lb.°F.
120	341·3	3·73	0·2681	312	882	1194	1·5935
125	344·4	3·59	0·2786	316	879	1195	1·5903
130	347·3	3·46	0·2890	319	877	1196	1·5872
135	350·2	3·33	0·3003	322	875	1197	1·5842
140	353·0	3·22	0·3106	325	872	1197	1·5813
145	355·8	3·12	0·3205	328	870	1198	1·5785
150	358·4	3·02	0·3311	331	868	1199	1·5758
160	363·6	2·84	0·3521	336	864	1200	1·5706
170	368·4	2·68	0·3731	341	860	1201	1·5657
180	373·1	2·54	0·3937	346	856	1202	1·5610
190	377·5	2·41	0·4149	351	852	1203	1·5567
200	382	2·29	0·4347	356	848	1203	1·5525
220	390	2·09	0·4785	364	841	1205	1·5448
240	387	1·93	0·5181	372	834	1206	1·5376
260	404·5	1·78	0·5618	380	827	1207·5	1·5310
280	411·1	1·66	0·6024	387	821	1208·5	1·5241
300	417·4	1·55	0·6452	394	815	1209·4	1·5190
350	431·8	1·34	0·7463	410	801	1211·1	1·5058
400	444·7	1·17	0·8547	425	787·5	1212·1	1·4941
450	456·4	1·04	0·9615	437·8	775	1212·8	1·4836
500	467·1	0·94	1·0638	450·1	763·1	1213·2	1·4740

BOILING POINTS OF WATER AT REDUCED PRESSURES

Absolute Pressure lb. per sq. in.	Vacuum in. of Mercury.	Boiling-point °F.	Volume in cubic ft. per lb. of Steam.
14·7 (Atmospheric Pressure).	0	212	26·79
12	5·49	201·96	32·36
10	9·56	193·22	38·38
7	15·67	176·85	53·56
5	19·74	162·28	73·33
3	23·81	141·52	118·5
2·4	25	133	145·9

PROPERTIES OF AIR

Symbols:
V = Volume of dry air-vapour mixture in cu. ft.

W = Weight of air-vapour mixture in lb.

P_2 = Partial pressure of vapour ⎫

P_{wa} = Actual partial pressure of water vapour ⎬ inches of mercury.

P_{ws} = Saturation pressure of water vapour. ⎭

P = Total pressure of mixture.

t = Dry bulb temperature.

T = $t + 460$ = absolute temperature °F.

ϕ = Relative humidity. per cent.

X = Actual specific humidity, in gr. per lb.

X_s = Specific humidity of saturated air gr. per lb.

d_a = Density of dry air in lb. per cu. ft.

d_w = Actual density of water vapour in lb. per cu. ft.

d = Density of air-water vapour mixture lb. per cu. ft.

R = Gas constant, for dry air = 53·34; for water vapour = 86·00.

1 in. of mercury = 70·59 lb. per sq. ft.

Atmospheric Air is a mixture of dry air and water vapour. It can be considered as an ideal gas without great discrepancies and the gas laws can be applied. (Boyle, Charles, Gay-Lussac, General Gas Law, Dalton, Avogadro, see pages IV. 4-6).

General Gas Law:
$$PV = WRT.$$
$$W = \frac{PV}{T} \cdot \frac{1}{R}.$$

Density of Dry Air:
$$d_a = \frac{70 \cdot 59 P_a}{53 \cdot 34 T} = \frac{1 \cdot 323 P_a}{T} \text{ (lb. per cu. ft.).}$$

Density of Water Vapour:
$$d_w = \frac{70 \cdot 59 P_w}{86 \cdot 0 T} = \frac{0 \cdot 821 P_w}{T} \text{ (lb. per cu. ft.).}$$

Density of Air-Water Vapour Mixture:
$$d = \frac{1 \cdot 323 P_t}{T} - \frac{0 \cdot 503 P_{ws}}{T} \phi \text{ (lb. per cu. ft.).}$$

Air-Water Vapour mixture is always lighter than dry air.

Humidity is the term applied to the quantity of water vapour present in the air.

Absolute Humidity is the actual weight of water vapour in grains or lb. per cu. ft. of a mixture.

Specific Humidity is the actual weight of water vapour in gr. or lb. per 1 lb. of dry air.

$$X = 0.622 \frac{\phi P_{ws}}{P - P_{ws}} \text{ (lb./lb.)} = 4354 \frac{\phi P_{ws}}{P - P_{ws}} \text{ (gr. per lb.).}$$

Specific Humidity of Saturated Air:

$$Xs = 0.622 \frac{P_{ws}}{P - P_{ws}} \text{ (lb./lb.)} = 4354 \frac{P_{ws}}{P - P_{ws}} \text{ (gr. per lb.).}$$

Relative Humidity is either the ratio of the actual partial pressure of water vapour to the vapour pressure at saturation at the existent dry bulb temperature;

or   the ratio of the actual vapour density to the density at saturation at the dry bulb temperature;

or   the ratio of actual amount of moisture in given air volume to amount of moisture required for saturation of that volume.

Usually expressed in per cent.

$$\phi = \frac{P_{wa}}{P_{ws}} = \frac{d_w}{d_{ws}} = \frac{X}{X_s} \text{ (per cent).}$$

Saturated Air holds the maximum amount of water at the given temperature; any lowering of the air temperature will cause condensation of water vapour.

Dry Bulb Temperature is the air temperature as indicated by a thermometer which is not affected by the moisture of the air.

Wet Bulb Temperature is the temperature of adiabatic saturation. It is the lowest temperature indicated by a moistened thermometer bulb when it is exposed to a current of air.

Dew Point Temperature is the temperature to which air with any given moisture content must be cooled to produce saturation of the air and begin condensation of its vapour.

Total Heat of Dry Air:

$$H_1 = 0.24t \text{ (B.t.u./lb.).}$$

Total Heat of Air-Water Vapour Mixture is composed of the sensible heat of air and the latent heat of vaporization of the moisture of vapour in the air.

The total heat is constant for any certain wet-bulb temperature irre- spective of any change in the dry-bulb temperature.

H = 0·24t + X (1059·2 + 0·45t) (B.t.u./lb.).

H = Heat content of the mixture (B.t.u./lb.).

t = Dry-bulb temperature °F.

0·24 = Specific heat of dry air at constant pressure (B.t.u./lb. °F.)

0·45 = Specific heat of water vapour at constant pressure (B.t.u./lb. °F.).

1059 = Latent heat of vaporization of water at 32°F. (B.t.u./lb.).

Thermal Expansion of Air:

Dry air expands or contracts uniformly $\frac{1}{492}$ (= 0·002032) of its volume per °F. difference under constant pressure.

THE HUMIDITY CHART FOR AIR (Mollier)
(See Chart No. 5)

The Chart shows the relationship between:

1. Dry bulb temperature.
2. Wet bulb temperature.
3. Dew point.
4. Relative humidity.
5. Specific humidity.
6. Vapour pressure.
7. Total heat.

When two of these factors are given the others can be found on the chart.

The Chart consists of the following lines:

1. Temperature lines.
2. Constant heat lines (constant wet bulb temperature).
3. Relative humidity lines.
4. Dew point lines (constant moisture).

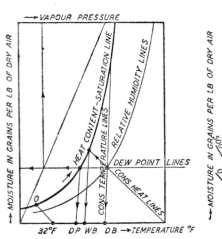
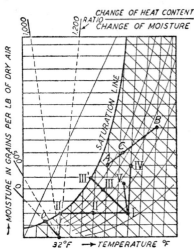

D.P. = Dew Point Temperature.
W.B. = Wet Bulb Temperature.
D.B. = Dry Bulb Temperature.

Change of Condition of Air.	Indicated in above sketch.	Remarks.
Cooling with constant moisture.	From I to II.	Dew point temperature in intersection II', with saturation line.
Adiabatic change.	From I to III, saturation at III'.	No heat is added or extracted.
Temperature constant.	From I to IV.	

Mixing of air, air volume V_A of condition "A" is to be mixed with air volume V_B of condition "B". Condition of mixture is "C"

$$\frac{\text{Distance ``AC''}}{\text{Distance ``BC''}} = \frac{\text{Air Volume } V_B}{\text{Air Volume } V_A}.$$

MAN AND AIR

(a) Respiration

An adult breathes at rest at 16 respirations per minute, about 17·5 cu. ft. of air per hour. When working 3 to 6 times more.

Average condition of expired air:

Oxygen	16·5 per cent
Carbon dioxide	4·0 per cent
Nitrogen and Argon	79·5 per cent

Quantity of expired carbon dioxide in 24 hours—approx. 2·2 lb.

(b) Equilibrium of Heat

Heat is generated within the human body by combustion of food.

Heat is lost from the human body by:

1. Conduction and Convection	about	25 per cent
2. Radiation	about	43 per cent
3. Evaporation		30 per cent
4. Expired Air		2 per cent

Evaporation prevailing in high temperature.

Conduction and convection prevailing in low temperatures.

Heat is liberated at such a rate that the internal body temperature is maintained at about 98·6°F.

PROPORTION OF SENSIBLE AND LATENT HEAT DISSIPATED BY MAN AT FAIRLY HARD WORK

Dry Bulb Temperature °F. ...	55	60	65	70	75	80	85	90
Sensible Heat, per cent	75	68	60	51	42	31	20	10
Latent Heat, per cent	25	32	40	49	58	69	80	90

(c) Heat Loss of Human Body

The total heat loss of an adult (sensible and latent) is approximately 400 B.t.u. per hr. in room temperatures from 65° to 85°F. (see Table, VI. 23).

(d) Comfort Air Conditions

Optimum winter temperature	65°F. to 68°F.
Optimum summer temperature	68°F. to 71°F.
Optimum relative humidity	40% to 65%.

Temperature of heated rooms (see Table VI. 3 et seq.).

DESIRABLE INDOOR AIR CONDITIONS IN SUMMER APPLICABLE
TO EXPOSURES LESS THAN 3 HOURS

Outside Temperature.	Inside Air Conditions with dew point constant at 57°F			
Dry-bulb. °F.	Dry-bulb °F.	Wet-bulb °F.	Rel. Hum.%.	EFF. Temp. °F.
95	80	65	44	73
90	78	64·5	46	72
85	76·5	64	52	71
80	75	63·5	51	70
75	73·5	63	57	69
70	72	62·5	57	68

Thermo-Equivalent Conditions are combinations of temperature, humidity and air movement which produce the same feeling of warmth (effective temperature, equivalent temperature).

British Equivalent Temperature of an environment (B.E.T.) is the temperature of a uniform enclosure in which, in still air, a sizeable black body maintained at a temperature of 75°F. would lose heat at the same rate as in the environment. (Measured by the Eupatheoscope.)

The Effective Temperature (used in America) is an arbitrary index of the degree of warmth or cold felt by the human body in response to temperature, humidity and air movement. It combines the reading of these three values into a single one.

The Numerical Value is that of the temperature of still, saturated air which would induce an identical sensation of warmth.

The Kata-Thermometer (Hill, 1926) is an alcohol thermometer graduated from 95°F. to 100°F. for measuring the effective temperature and especially the velocity of air. It is warmed above 100°F. and the time required for cooling from 100°F. to 95°F. is measured. This time is a scale for the cooling effect of the air.

The Hygrometer (Psychrometer) is an instrument for the determination of relative humidity and dew point by measuring the dry-bulb temperature by an ordinary thermometer and the wet bulb temperature by a thermometer the bulb of which is kept moist.

AIR CONDITIONING

CHART SHOWING RELATION OF EFFECTIVE TEMPERATURE WET-BULB, DRY-BULB TEMPERATURE AND RELATIVE HUMIDITY

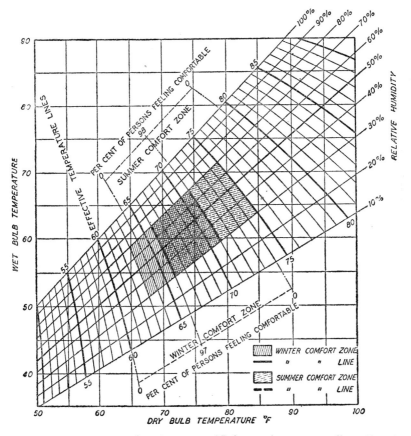

The Chart is for air velocities up to 25 f.p.m. (i.e. practically still air). For an air velocity of 100 f.p.m. the effective temperature decreases by 2°F.

RELATIVE HUMIDITY IN PER CENT

For various Room Temperatures and various Differences between Wet- and Dry-Bulb Temperatures.

(Accurate for Atm. Pressure of 14·25 lb. per sq. in. = 29 in. of Mercury).

Dry-Bulb Temp. °F.	Difference between Dry Bulb and Wet Bulb Temperature. °F.										
	0	2	4	6	8	10	12	14	16	18	20
50	100	87	74	62	50	39	28	17	7	0	0
52	100	88	75	63	52	41	30	20	10	0	0
54	100	88	76	65	54	43	33	23	14	5	0
56	100	88	77	66	55	45	35	26	17	8	0
58	100	88	77	67	57	47	38	28	20	11	3
60	100	89	78	68	58	49	40	31	22	14	6
62	100	89	79	69	60	50	41	33	25	17	9
64	100	90	79	70	61	52	43	35	27	20	12
66	100	90	80	71	62	53	45	37	29	22	15
68	100	90	81	72	63	55	47	39	31	24	17
70	100	90	81	72	64	56	48	40	33	26	20
72	100	91	82	73	65	57	49	42	35	28	22
74	100	91	82	74	66	58	51	44	37	30	24
76	100	91	83	74	67	59	52	45	38	32	26
78	100	91	83	75	67	60	53	46	40	34	28
80	100	91	83	76	68	61	54	47	41	35	29
82	100	92	84	76	69	62	55	49	43	37	31
84	100	92	84	77	70	63	56	50	44	38	32
86	100	92	85	77	70	63	57	51	45	39	34
88	100	92	85	78	71	64	58	52	46	41	35
90	100	92	85	78	71	65	59	53	47	42	37
92	100	92	85	78	72	65	59	54	48	43	38
94	100	93	86	79	72	66	60	54	49	44	39
96	100	93	86	79	73	67	61	55	50	45	40
98	100	93	86	79	73	67	61	56	51	46	41
100	100	93	86	80	74	68	62	57	52	47	42

HEAT REQUIRED TO WARM AIR

From 32°F. to various Room Temperatures, for Various Air Changes
in B.t.u. per cu. ft. of room spaces.

Air Change per hr.	40	45	50	55	60	65	70	75
1	0·164	0·266	0·369	0·471	0·574	0·676	0·779	0·881
1½	0·246	0·399	0·554	0·707	0·861	1·014	1·169	1·322
2	0·328	0·532	0·678	0·942	1·148	1·352	1·558	1·762
2½	0·410	0·665	0·863	1·178	1·435	1·690	1·948	2·203
3	0·492	0·798	1·107	1·413	1·722	2·028	2·337	2·643
3½	0·574	0·831	1·290	1·649	2·009	2·366	2·727	3·084
4	0·656	1·064	1·476	1·884	2·296	2·704	3·116	3·524
5	0·820	1·330	1·845	2·355	2·870	3·380	3·895	4·405

DENSITY AND SPECIFIC VOLUME OF DRY AIR
AT ATMOSPHERIC PRESSURE

Temp. °F.	Density lb. per cu. ft.	Specific Volume cu. ft. per lb.	Temp. °F.	Density lb. per cu. ft.	Specific Volume cu. ft. per lb.
0	0·08633	11·58	180	0·06203	16·12
10	0·08449	11·83	200	0·06015	16·62
20	0·08273	12·08	220	0·05838	17·13
30	0·08104	12·34	240	0·05671	17·63
40	0·07942	12·59	260	0·05514	18·14
50	0·07785	12·84	280	0·05364	18·64
60	0·07636	13·09	300	0·05223	19·14
70	0·07492	13·34	350	0·04901	20·40
80	0·07353	13·59	400	0·04615	21·67
90	0·07219	13·85	450	0·04362	22·92
100	0·07090	14·10	500	0·04135	24·18
110	0·06966	14·35	550	0·03930	25·44
120	0·06845	14·60	600	0·03744	26·70
130	0·06729	14·85	700	0·03422	29·22
140	0·06617	15·11	800	0·3150	31·75
150	0·06509	15·36	900	0·02911	34·35
160	0·06403	15·61	1000	0·02718	36·79

Temp.	Press. of Sat. Vapour.	Weight of Sat. Vapour.		Volume in cu. ft.		Heat Content of Mixture.
		per cu. ft. Grains.	per lb. of Dry Air. Grains.	of 1 lb. of Dry Air.	of 1 lb. of Dry Air. & Vapour to	
°F.	in. of Hg.	per cu. ft.	per lb.		saturate.	B.t.u./lb.
0	0·0375	0·472	5·47	11·58	11·59	0·852
10	0·00628	0·772	9·16	11·83	11·58	3·831
20	0·01027	1·238	15·01	12·09	12·13	7·137
30	0·1646	1·943	24·11	12·34	12·41	10·933
32	0·1806	2·124	26·47	12·39	12·47	11·83
33	0·1880	2·206	27·57	12·41	12·49	12·18
34	0·1957	2·292	28·70	12·44	12·52	12·60
35	0·2036	2·380	29·88	12·47	12·55	13·02
36	0·2119	2·471	31·09	12·49	12·58	13·44
37	0·2204	2·566	32·35	12·52	12·61	13·87
38	0·2292	2·663	33·66	12·54	12·64	14·31
39	0·2384	2·764	35·01	12·57	12·67	14·76
40	0·2478	2·868	36·41	12·59	12·70	15·21
41	0·2576	2·976	37·87	12·62	12·73	15·67
42	0·2678	3·087	39·38	12·64	12·76	16·14
43	0·2783	3·201	40·93	12·67	12·79	16·62
44	0·2897	3·319	42·55	12·69	12·82	17·10
45	0·3003	3·442	44·21	12·72	12·85	17·59
46	0·3120	3·568	45·94	12·74	12·88	18·09
47	0·3240	3·698	47·73	12·77	12·91	18·60
48	0·3364	3·832	49·58	12·79	12·94	19·12
49	0·3492	3·970	51·49	12·82	12·97	19·65
50	0·3624	4·113	53·47	12·84	13·00	20·19
51	0·3761	4·260	55·52	12·87	13·03	20·74
52	0·3903	4·411	57·64	12·89	13·07	21·30
53	0·4049	4·568	59·83	12·92	13·10	21·87
54	0·4200	4·729	62·09	12·95	13·13	22·45
55	0·4356	4·895	64·43	12·97	13·16	23·04
56	0·4517	5·066	66·85	13·00	13·20	23·64
57	0·4684	5·242	69·35	13·02	13·23	24·25
58	0·4855	5·424	71·93	13·05	13·26	24·88
59	0·5032	5·611	74·60	13·07	13·30	25·52
60	0·5214	5·804	77·30	13·10	13·33	26·18

| Temp. | Press. of Sat. Vap. | Weight of Sat. Vap. | | Volume in cu. ft. | | Heat Content of Mixture. |
| | | | | of 1 lb. of Dry Air. | of 1 lb. of Dry Air & Vapour to saturate. | |
°F.	in. of Hg.	Grains. per cu. ft.	Grains. per lb.			B.t.u./lb.
61	0·5403	6·003	80·2	13·12	13·36	26·84
62	0·5597	6·208	83·2	13·15	13·40	27·52
63	0·5798	6·418	86·2	13·17	13·43	28·22
64	0·6005	6·633	89·3	13·20	13·47	28·93
65	0·6218	6·855	92·6	13·22	13·50	29·65
66	0·6438	7·084	95·9	13·25	13·54	30·39
67	0·6664	7·320	99·4	13·27	13·58	31·15
68	0·6898	7·563	103·0	13·30	13·61	31·92
69	0·7139	7·813	106·6	13·32	13·65	32·71
70	0·7386	8·069	110·5	13·35	13·69	33·51
71	0·7642	8·332	114·4	13·38	13·73	34·33
72	0·7906	8·603	118·4	13·40	13·76	35·17
73	0·8177	8·882	122·6	13·43	13·80	36·03
74	0·8456	9·168	126·9	13·45	13·84	36·91
75	0·8744	9·46	131·4	13·48	13·88	37·81
76	0·9040	9·76	135·9	13·50	13·92	38·73
77	0·9345	10·07	140·7	13·53	13·96	39·67
78	0·9658	10·39	145·6	13·55	14·00	40·64
79	0·9981	10·72	150·6	13·58	14·05	41·63
80	1·0314	11·06	155·8	13·60	14·09	42·64
85	1·212	12·89	184·4	13·73	14·31	48·04
90	1·421	14·96	217·6	13·86	14·55	54·13
95	1·659	17·32	256·3	13·98	14·80	61·01
100	1·931	19·98	301·3	14·11	15·08	68·79
105	2·241	22·99	354	14·24	15·39	77·63
110	2·594	26·38	415	14·36	15·73	87·69
115	2·993	31·8	486	14·49	16·10	99·10
120	3·444	34·44	569	14·62	16·52	112·37
125	3·952	39·19	667	14·75	16·99	127·54
130	4·523	44·49	780	14·88	17·53	145·06
135	5·163	50·38	913	15·00	18·13	165·34
140	5·878	56·91	1,072	15·13	18·84	189·22
150	7·566	72·10	1,485	15·39	20·60	250·30

COMPOSITION OF AIR

Dry air is a mechanical mixture of gases.

	Dry Air, per cent.		Atmospheric at Sea-level.	
	By Volume.	By Weight.	By Volume.	
Oxygen	21·00	23·2	20·75	
Nitrogen	78·03	75·5	77·08	
Carbon Dioxide	0·03	0·046	0·03	
Hydrogen	0·01	0·007	0·01	
Rare Gases	0·93	1·247	0·93	
Water Vapour	—	—	1·20	

The composition of air is unchanged to the height of approximately 30,000 ft. The average air temperature diminishes at the rate of about 1°F. for each 300 ft. of vertical height.

ALTITUDE-DENSITY TABLE FOR AIR

Altitude in feet.
Barometric pressure in inches of mercury.
Standard air at 0 alt./29·92 in bar./ = density **1**.

Altitude.	Density.	Barometer.	Altitude.	Density.	Barometer.
0	1·000	29·92	3000	0·891	26·68
250	0·990	29·64	3500	0·875	26·18
500	0·981	29·36	4000	0·858	26·58
750	0·972	29·08	4500	0·843	25·20
1000	0·962	28·80	5000	0·826	24·72
1500	0·946	28·31	6000	0·795	23·79
2000	0·926	27·72	7000	0·766	22·90
2500	0·909	27·20	8000	0·737	22·04

Standard air (used for determination of fan capacities) is air weighing
0·07488 lb. per cu. ft.

or : 0·075 lb. per cu. ft. for practical purposes corresponding to:

Bar. Pressure ... ... 29·92 in mercury.
Dry-Bulb Temperature 68°F.
Relative Humidity ... 50 per cent.

Section VI

HEAT LOSSES

BASIC FORMULAE

1. Heat Loss by Conduction and Convection

Through cooling surfaces (Fabric Loss) such as walls, windows, etc.

$$H = AU\ (t_i - t_o)$$

2. Heat loss due to infiltration:

$$H = 0.019\ n.V\ (t_i - t_o)$$

where: H = Heat loss B.t.u. per hour.

A = Cooling surface in sq. ft.

U = Overall heat transmittance coefficient
B.t.u. per sq. ft. per hr. per °F. diff.

n = Number of air changes per hr.

V = Cube of room in cu. ft.

t_1 = Internal temperature °F.

t_o = External temperature °F.

EXAMPLE OF HEAT LOSS CALCULATION

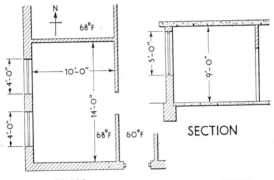

PLAN   EXPOSURE: NORMAL

Aspect	Description	Dimensions, ft.			Volume or Area sq. ft.	U	Rise °F.	B.t.u./hr.
		L	W	H				
S	Cav. wall 11 in.	10		9	90	0·28	38	955
W {	Cav. wall 11 in.	14		9	86	0·29	38	950
	Single glass	2×4		5	40	0·88	38	1,340
	Partition	14		9	126	0·15	8	150
	Floor	10	14		140	0·20	38	1,070
	Flat roof	10	14		140	0·25	38	1,330
	Cube	10	14	9	1260	0·03	38	1,440
	Total:							7,235

Required radiator heating surface

Radiator surface (sq. ft.) $= \dfrac{\text{Heat loss}}{\text{Heat transmission coefficient}}.$

(Continued on p. VI. 2)

For mean water temperature 165° F.
　and room temperature 68° F.
The heat transmission coefficient is 170 B.t.u./hr. sq. ft. for 4-column radiators.
Therefore:

Radiation surface $=\dfrac{7 \cdot 235}{170}=42 \cdot 5$ sq. ft.

APPROXIMATE HEAT LOSSES OF BUILDINGS IN ENGLAND

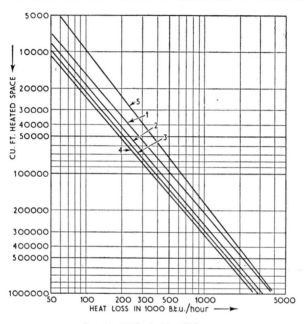

Design temperatures: Outside 30° F. Inside 65° F.
Curve 1 applies for: Single storey buildings, brick walls and flat roof.
Curve 2 applies for: Two-storey buildings, brick walls and flat roof.
Curve 3 applies for: Three-storey buildings, brick walls and flat roof.
Curve 4 applies for: Four-storey buildings, brick walls and flat roof.
Curve 5 applies for: Light factory buildings, single storey.

APPROXIMATE FUEL CONSUMPTION OF CENTRAL HEATING INSTALLATION IN BUILDINGS

H = Heat loss of plant in B.t.u. per hour (nett loss).
　　Assumed heating time 6 a.m. to 10 p.m., 7 days per week.
Coke consumption: in tons per winter = 0·0001 H,
　　　　　　　　　　 or 1 ton per winter for 10,000 B.t.u./hr heat loss.
Oil consumption: in gallons per winter = 0·02 H,
　　　　　　　　　　 or 250 gallons per winter for 10,000 B.t.u./hr heat loss.
Gas consumption: in therms per winter = 0·025 H,
　　　　　　　　　　 or 250 therms per winter for 10,000 B.t.u./hr. heat loss.

1. HEAT LOSS BY CONDUCTION AND CONVECTION THROUGH
WALLS, WINDOWS, ETC.

2. HEAT LOSS DUE TO INFILTRATION.

---

1. Heat Loss through Walls, Windows, Doors, Ceilings, Floor, etc.

$$H = AU (t_i - t_o).$$

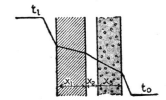

$$U = \cfrac{1}{\cfrac{1}{f_i} + \cfrac{X_1}{K_1} + \cfrac{X_2}{K_2} + \cfrac{X_3}{K_3} + \cfrac{1}{f_o}}$$

H = Heat transmitted   B.t.u. per hr.
A = Area of exposed surface   sq. ft.
t_i = Inside air temperature   °F.
t_o = Outside air temperature   °F.
U = Overall coefficient of heat transmission B.t.u. per sq. ft. per hr.
     per °F.
X = Thickness of material, in.
K = Thermal conductivity in B.t.u. per in. thickness per sq. ft.
     per hr. per °F.
f_i = Surface conductance for inside wall B.t.u. per sq. ft. per hr.
     per °F. ranges from 1·4 to 2·1 for still air conditions with
     different materials, surface conditions, and mean temper-
     atures; commonly taken—f_i = 1·65.
f_o = Surface conductance for outside wall, B.t.u. per sq. ft. per hr.
     per °F. Commonly taken—f_o=6·00.
$C = \dfrac{K}{X}$ = Conductance is the amount of heat in B.t.u. per hr.
     passing through 1 sq. ft. of area of any material of the
     thickness X per °F. difference of the material surface tem-
     peratures B.t.u. per sq. ft. per hr.
$R = \dfrac{X}{K} = \dfrac{1}{C}$ = Thermal resistance or resistivity.

VALUES $\dfrac{X}{K}$ FOR AIR SPACES

Temp. Factor.	Thickness X of Air Space in inches.										
	½	¾	1	1½	2	2½	3	3½	4	4½	5
C = 6	0·76	0·80	0·80	0·85	0·90	0·90	0·94	0·96	0·98	0·99	1·00
Windows 5·5	0·79	0·82	0·85	0·89	0·94	0·97	1·00	1·04	1·06	1·07	1·08
Brickwork 5·0	0·84	0·87	0·90	0·95	1·04	1·04	1·08	1·11	1·14	1·16	1·17

SAFETY ADDITIONS TO HEAT LOSS CALCULATIONS

1. For Aspect: North, East   ...   .   10 per cent

                   West   ...   .   5 per cent

                   To the loss of the respective exposure.

2. For Exposure: 5 to 10 per cent to surface exposed to wind.

3. For Intermittent Heating:

        Buildings heated during day only 10–15%

        Buildings not in use daily 25–30%

        Buildings without heat for long period (Churches) ... up to 50%

4. For Height (rooms over 15 ft. high):

Height (in ft.)	15	18	21	24	27	30	33	36 and above
Percentage ...	$2\frac{1}{2}$	5	$7\frac{1}{2}$	10	$12\frac{1}{2}$	15	$17\frac{1}{2}$	20

Air Movement: Air movement makes any conditions of temperature and humidity feel colder; it lowers the effective temperature. An air velocity of 25 ft. per min. may be considered as practically still air. A slight air movement is desirable for comfort to remove layers of humid and warm air from the surface of the human body. A higher air velocity is required in air of high temperature and high relative humidity than in air of low temperature and low humidity.

The Entering Air Temperature in plenum heating systems must not be too much below the room temperature.

Recommended air entering temperatures:

      for heating, normally, 80–90°F.

      for heating, when good mixing, 100–120°F.

      for cooling, inlets near to occupied zone,   10–15°F. } below room

      for cooling, high velocity jets, diffusion nozzles, 30°F. } temp.

2. Heat Loss of a Room due to Infiltration:

$$H_2 = s.d.n.V\,(t_o - t_i) = 0.019\,n.V.\,(t_o - t_i)$$

in which:

H_2 = Heat loss ... B.t.u./hr.

s = Specific heat

     of air   ... B.t.u./lb.

d = Density of air lb./cu. ft.

$s \times d = 0.019$ B.t.u./cu. ft.

n = Number of air changes per hr.

V = Volume of room   cu. ft.

t_o = Outside temperature °F.

t_i = Inside temperature °F.

Number of Air Changes usually assumed, due to Infiltration
(not for ventilation—Ventilation, see X. 3–6).

Air Changes per hour

Residences	1–2	Halls 3
Offices	1–2	Sitting-rooms ... 2
Factories	1–1½	Bedrooms 1
Large Rooms with small exposure	½–1.	Stores 2–3

Winter Inside Temperatures:

Usually assumed in Building Heating Calculations

Heated Rooms			
Residences ... 65°F.	Churches ... 50°F.	**Unheated Rooms**
Lecture Rooms 65°F.	Museums ... 50°F.	Cellars and
Schoolroom ... 65°F.	Lavatories ... 50°F.	Closed Rooms 32°F.
Offices ... 65°F.	Cloakroom ... 55°F.	Vestibules frequently
Stores ... 62°F.	Prisons ... 50°F.	opened to out-
Bedrooms ... 62°F.	Hot-houses ... 78°F.	side ... 32°F.
Bathrooms ... 70°F.	Warm air baths 120°F	Ditto, not opened
Wards 68–70°F.	Steam Baths... 110°F.	40°F.
Operating-Th. 80°F.	Factories ... 62°F.	Attic under a
Halls ... ... 55°F.		Roof ... 32°F.
Corridors ... 55°F.		Ditto, with com-
Gymnasiums... 55°F.		position covering
		40°F.

Outside Design Temperature in England is 25°F. to 32°F.

(See also Tables VI. 6, VI. 12–14, V. 12, 13)

HEAT LOSS CALCULATIONS FOR HIGH BUILDINGS

Designation	Floor	No. of Air Changes		U—values
		Living-room	Bedroom	
Sheltered ...	Ground and 1st	1	1½	Normal
Normal ...	2nd to 4th	1	1½	Normal
Severe ...	5th to 11th	1½	2	Normal
Very Severe ...	Above 11th	2	2½	Severe

Air Temperatures at various Levels:

Assumption: Increase of air temperature per foot of height above the 5 ft. level is at the rate of 2 per cent of the breathing-line temperature up to ceiling heights of 20 ft.   No further increase above 20 ft.

$$t^1 = t + 0.02 (h - 5)t$$

t^1 = air temperature °F. at a level h ft. above the floor.

t = air temperature °F. at breathing line 5 ft. above the floor.

Temperature of Unheated Spaces:

$$t = \frac{t_i A_c U_c + t_o A_R U_R}{A_c U_c + A_R U_R}.$$

$A_c A_R$ = Areas of ceilings and roof resp. sq. ft.

$U_c U_R$ = Coefficient of heat transmission of ceiling and roof, resp. B.t.u. per sq. ft. per hr. per °F.

t = Temperature of unheated space °F.

t_i = Temperature of adjacent room °F.

t_o = Outside temperature °F.

Combined Coefficient for Ceiling and Roof:

$$U_{CR} = \frac{U_R U_c}{U_R + \dfrac{U_c}{r}} \text{ (B.t.u. per sq. ft. per °F. per hr.).}$$

r = Ratio of roof area to ceiling area.

Allowance for Warming-up (Rietschel):

(a) Rooms heated daily (not by night):

$$H = \frac{0.063 (n-1) H_o}{z} \text{ (B.t.u.).}$$

(b) Rooms not heated daily:

$$H = \frac{0.1 Ht (8+n)}{z} \text{ (B.t.u.).}$$

H = Heat required for warming-up in B.t.u.

H_t = Total heat loss, B.t.u. per hr.

H_o = Heat loss through outside surface, B.t.u. per hr.

n = Interruption of heating in hr.

z = Warming-up time in hr.

CONTRACT TEMPERATURES AND THEIR EQUIVALENTS

Inside temperatures obtained with a certain system with outside temperatures other than for which the system is designed.
(Empirical formula by J. Roger Preston).

$$t_4 = (t_1^{12} - t_2^{12} + t_3^{12})^{\frac{1}{12}}$$

t_1 = Contract inside temperature °F. absolute.
t_2 = Contract outside temperature °F. absolute.
t_3 = Existing outside temperature °F. absolute.
t_4 = Estimated inside temperature °F. absolute.

Table for 30°F. contract outside and 60°F. contract inside:

| Existing Outside temp. °F. | 20 | 22 | 24 | 26 | 28 | **30** | 32 | 34 | 36 | 38 | 40 |
| Inside temp. °F. | 55 | 56 | 57 | 58 | 59 | **60** | 61 | 62 | 63 | 64 | 65 |

MEASUREMENT OF TEMPERATURES

Inside thermometer in the centre of the room 5 ft. above floor.
External thermometer freely exposed on north side of building and not fixed against a wall.

Factors for Multiplying the heat loss for 30°F. outside and 60°F. inside to obtain the heat loss for any other conditions (Walter Jones).

Outside Temp.°F.	Inside Temperature °F.							
	40	45	50	55	60	65	70	75
20	0·50	0·62	0·77	1·00	1·3	1·5	1·8	2·3
25	0·46	0·55	0·68	0·88	1·1	1·3	1·7	2·1
30	0·38	0·48	0·60	0·76	1·0	1·2	1·5	2·0
35	0·34	0·42	0·54	0·68	0·88	1·1	1·4	1·8
40	—	0·36	0·46	0·60	0·76	1·0	1·3	1·6
45	—	—	0·40	0·50	0·65	0·88	1·12	1·5
50	—	—	—	0·44	0·53	0·75	1·0	1·3

HEAT TRANSMITTANCE COEFFICIENTS

The data and tables on pages VI. 8 to VI. 10 are reprinted from **A Guide to Current Practice, 1955,** by courtesy of the publishers, the Institution of Heating and Ventilating Engineers.

SURFACE RESISTANCES

Surface resistances: Internal, R_{S_1}, and External, R_{S_2}, for walls, floors and roofs; sq. ft. h. deg. F./B.t.u.

Note: The following data are applicable to plain surfaces but not to bright metallic surfaces. The resistance of a corrugated surface is less than that of a plain one, generally by about 20 per cent.

INTERNAL RESISTANCES, R_{S_1}

Walls	0·70
Floors or Ceilings	
heat flow upwards	0·60
heat flow downwards	0·85
Roofs, flat or sloping	0·60

EXTERNAL RESISTANCES, R_{S_2}

		Sheltered	Normal	Severe
Walls	S.	0·73	0·57	0·43
	W., SW. or SE.	0·57	0·43	0·30
	NW.	0·43	0·30	0·18
	N., NE. or E.	0·43	0·30	0·07
Roofs	... ...	0·40	0·25	0·10

These figures, in conjunction with the following values, were used in computing the overall coefficients in the tables on pages VI. 17 to VI. 20.

		Conductivity k	Resistivity $\dfrac{1}{k}$
Brickwork	... ...	8·0	0·125
Plaster ...	... ...	4·0	0·25
Concrete	... ...	10·0	0·10
Stone ...	... ...	12·0	0·083
Wood ...	... ...	1·0	1·0

The Calculation of Overall Coefficients

Conductivities and resistivities of various materials given on the following pages enable overall transmittance factors to be calculated for composite walls, floors and roofs, or by the following formulae:

$$U = \frac{1}{R_{S_1} + R_{S_2} + r_1 L_1 + r_2 L_2, \text{ etc.,} + R_a + R_h}$$

or

$$U = \frac{1}{R_{S_1} + R_{S_2} + \dfrac{L_1}{k_1} + \dfrac{L_2}{k_2}, \text{ etc.,} + R_a + R_h}$$

COEFFICIENTS FOR WALLS
Thermal Transmittance, U B.t.u./sq. ft. h. deg. F.

Orientation		Exposure to Wind					
	S.	Sheltered	Normal	Severe	—	—	—
	W. SW. SE.	—	Sheltered	Normal	Severe	—	—
	NW.	—	—	Sheltered	Normal	Severe	—
	N. NE. E.	—	—	Sheltered	Normal	—	Severe
Brickwork		A	B	C	D	E	F
Solid, unplastered	4½ in.	0·50	0·55	0·59	0·64	0·69	0·75
	9 in.	0·39	0·42	0·44	0·47	0·50	0·53
	13½ in.	0·32	0·34	0·35	0·37	0·39	0·41
Solid, plastered	4½ in.	0·46	0·49	0·53	0·57	0·61	0·65
	9 in.	0·36	0·38	0·41	0·43	0·45	0·48
	13½ in.	0·30	0·32	0·33	0·35	0·36	0·38
	18 in.	0·26	0·27	0·28	0·29	0·30	0·31
	22½ in.	0·23	0·23	0·24	0·25	0·26	0·26
Cavity, plastered							
(unventilated)	11 in.	0·27	0·28	0·29	0·30	0·31	0·32
	15½ in.	0·23	0·24	0·25	0·26	0·27	0·27
	20 in.	0·21	0·21	0·22	0·22	0·23	0·24
(ventilated)	11 in.	0·30	0·31	0·33	0·34	0·36	0·37
	15½ in.	0·26	0·27	0·28	0·29	0·30	0·31
	20 in.	0·22	0·23	0·24	0·25	0·25	0·26
Concrete	4 in.	0·55	0·60	0·66	0·71	0·78	0·85
	6 in.	0·49	0·53	0·58	0·63	0·68	0·73
	8 in.	0·45	0·48	0·52	0·56	0·60	0·64
	10 in.	0·41	0·44	0·47	0·50	0·53	0·57
Glass							
Single windows	...	0·70	0·79	0·88	1·00	1·14	1·30
Double windows	...	0·41	0·44	0·47	0·50	0·53	0·56
Stone	12 in.	0·41	0·44	0·47	0·50	0·53	0·56
	18 in.	0·34	0·36	0·38	0·40	0·42	0·44
	24 in.	0·29	0·31	0·32	0·33	0·35	0·36
Wood							
Tongued and	1 in.	0·41	0·44	0·47	0·50	0·53	0·56
grooved	1½ in.	0·34	0·36	0·38	0·40	0·42	0·44
Sheets							
Asbestos	¼ in.	0·64	0·72	0·80	0·89	1·00	1·12
Corrugated asbestos		0·77	0·88	1·00	1·15	1·33	1·56
Corrugated iron 1/16 in.		0·79	0·91	1·04	1·20	1·40	1·67
Corrugated iron on 1-in. t. and g. boards		0·34	0·36	0·38	0·40	0·42	0·44

COEFFICIENTS FOR ROOFS
Thermal Transmittance, U B.t.u./sq. ft. h. deg. F.

Construction of Roof	Sheltered	Normal	Severe
Flat Roofs—			
Asphalt on 6 in. concrete	0·58	0·64	0·70
Asphalt on 6 in. concrete, plastered ...	0·51	0·55	0·61
Asphalt on 6 in. concrete with 1 in. cork	0·21	0·22	0·22
Asphalt on 6 in. concrete with 1 in. cork, plastered	0·20	0·21	0·21
Asphalt on 6 in. concrete with 2 in. cork	0·13	0·13	0·13
Asphalt on 6 in. concrete with 2 in. cork, plastered	0·12	0·12	0·13
Asphalt on 6 in. thick hollow tile ...	0·45	0·48	0·52
Asphalt on 6 in. thick hollow tile, plastered	0·41	0·44	0·47
Asphalt on 6 in. hollow tile with 1 in. cork	0·19	0·20	0·21
Asphalt on 6 in. hollow tile with 1 in. cork, plastered	0·18	0·19	0·20
Asphalt on 6 in. hollow tile with 2 in. cork	0·12	0·12	0·12
Asphalt on 6 in. hollow tile with 2 in. cork, plastered	0·12	0·12	0·12
Asphalt, 1 in. cork, 1¼ in. boards, joists and plaster ceiling	0·16	0·16	0·16
Pitched Roofs—			
Corrugated aluminium (bright) ...	0·90	1·15	1·45
Corrugated asbestos	1·20	1·40	1·70
Corrugated asbestos lined ½ in. boards	0·47	0·50	0·53
Corrugated iron	1·25	1·50	1·80
Corrugated iron lined 1 in. boards and felt	0·33	0·35	0·37
Tiles on boards and felt	0·33	0·35	0·37
Tiles on battens	1·22	1·50	2·00
Tiles on battens, felted	0·63	0·70	0·78
Tiles on feather-edged boarding ...	0·87	1·00	1·17
Plaster ceiling with roof space above—			
(a) with tiles and battens	0·50	0·56	0·64
(b) with tiles or slates on boards and felt	0·28	0·30	0·32
Roof Glazing—			
Skylight	1·00	1·20	1·40
Laylight, with lantern over	0·57	0·60	0·63

For Air to Air, in B.t.u. per sq. ft. per °F. per hr.

Partitions—

4-in. stud lath and plaster, one side	0·53
4-in. stud lath and plaster, both sides	0·33
½ in. thick, plain wood	0·52
¾ in. thick, plain wood	0·45
1 in. thick, plain wood	0·41
2 in. thick, solid plaster	0·60
3 in. thick, solid plaster	0·52
4 in. thick, solid plaster	0·48
4 in. hollow partition, plastered one side	0·43
4 in. hollow partition, plastered both sides	0·35

Windows—

Single window	1·10
Double window	0·60
Single skylight	1·20
Double skylight	0·70

Doors—

All wood, 1 in. thick	0·70
All wood, 2 in. thick	0·45
All wood, upper portion glass	0·75
All glass, wood framing	0·95
All steel	1·20
All steel, upper portion glass	1·15
All glass, steel framing	1·05
Inner vestibule door, all wood	0·30
Inner vestibule door, half glass	0·45
Inner vestibule door, all glass	0·60

For Air to Air in B.t.u./sq. ft. hr. °F.

Sketch.	Description.	Coefficient for Cold Air.	
		Below.	Above.
FLAT ROOFS:			
	Flat roof, reinforced concrete with asphalt, thickness of concrete 5″	—	0·30
	Ditto 6″	—	0·28
	Ditto 7″	—	0·27
	Ditto 9″	—	0·25
	Ditto 11″	—	0·23
	Ditto 13″	—	0·21
	Flat roof covered with metal with lath and plaster ceiling	—	0·17
CLOSED ROOF SPACE (Ceiling and Roofs)			
	Slates or tiles on battens and rafters, lath and plaster ceiling ...	—	0·35
	Ditto, with 1″ tongued and grooved boards under tiles	—	0·25
	Ditto, with roofing felt between tiles and boards	—	0·19
OPEN ROOF:			
	Slates or tiles on batten and rafters only	—	0·80
	Ditto, with 1″ tongued and grooved boards	—	0·35
	Ditto, with roofing felt between tiles and boards	—	0·25
	Slates or tiles on 1″ tongued and grooved boards, and lath and plaster ceiling...	—	0·30
	Corrugated iron, unlined...	—	1·80
	Corrugated asbestos, cement sheeting, unlined	—	1·45
	Protected sheet metal	—	0·90
	Single glass, skylights	—	1·20
	Asphalt ¼″ thick on cement screen and 6″ hollow tile fireproof roof with plaster under ...	—	0·22
Tile roof		—	1·00
Zinc or copper on 1″ boards		—	0·44
Flat asbestos sheets		—	1·00
Corrugated asbestos sheets, ¼″ asbestos boards ...		—	0·44
Corrugated asbestos sheets, ½″ asbestos boards ...		—	0·37
Corrugated steel with felt and 1″ boards		—	0·37

For Air to Air in B.t.u./sq. ft. hr. °F.

Sketch.	Description.	Coefficient for Cold Air.	
		Below.	Above.
FLOORS AND CEILINGS :			
	Concrete and steel, laid with $1\frac{1}{4}"$ wood blocks and plaster ceiling, concrete = 5" thick	0·20	—
	Ditto 7" ,,	0·19	—
	Ditto 9" ,,	0·18	—
	Ditto 11" ,,	0·17	—
	Ditto 13" ,,	0·16	—
	Board floor 1" thick on 7" joists with lath and plastered ceiling	0·08	0·18
	Board floor 1" thick on 7" joists ...	0·20	0·44
FLOORS :			
	4" concrete on earth	0·55	—
	6" ditto	0·49	—
	$1\frac{1}{4}"$ wood blocks, $\frac{1}{4}"$ screed and 5" concrete on earth	0·25	—
	Board floor 1" thick on joists, 9" air space and $4\frac{1}{2}"$ concrete	0·07	—

INSULATING PROPERTIES OF VARIOUS MATERIALS

Substance.	B.t.u. per sq. ft. per hr. per in. Thickness for 1°F. Temperature Difference between the Faces.
Slag Wool	0·38
Asbestos	1·10
Powdered Cork	0·29
Granulated Cork	0·35
Cork Slab	0·38
Hair Felt	0·26
Kieselguhr (loose)	0·46
Sawdust	0·49
Magnesia Asbestos Compo	0·44
Wool	0·32
Air (at rest)	0·15
Cotton Waste	0·41

HEAT TRANSMITTANCE COEFFICIENTS

HEAT LOSS COEFFICIENTS

B.t.u./hr. sq. ft.   For different temperature differences.

OVER-ALL COEF. "U"	TEMPERATURE DIFFERENCE °F.										OVER-ALL COEF. "U"
	18	20	23	25	28	30	33	35	38	40	
0·14	2·5	2·8	3·2	3·5	3·9	4·2	4·6	4·9	5·3	5·6	0·14
0·15	2·7	3·0	3·5	3·8	4·2	4·5	5·0	5·2	5·7	6·0	0·15
0·16	2·9	3·2	3·7	4·0	4·5	4·8	5·3	5·6	6·1	6·4	0·16
0·17	3·1	3·4	3·9	4·3	4·8	5·1	5·6	6·0	6·5	6·8	0·17
0·18	3·2	3·6	4·1	4·5	5·0	5·4	6·0	6·3	6·8	7·2	0·18
0·19	3·4	3·9	4·4	4·8	5·3	5·7	6·3	6·7	7·2	7·6	0·19
0·20	3·6	4·0	4·6	5·0	5·6	6·0	6·6	7·0	7·6	8·0	0·20
0·21	3·8	4·2	4·8	5·3	5·9	6·3	6·9	7·3	8·0	8·4	0·21
0·22	4·0	4·4	5·1	5·5	6·2	6·6	7·3	7·7	8·4	8·8	0·22
0·23	4·1	4·6	5·3	5·8	6·5	6·9	7·6	8·0	8·7	9·2	0·23
0·24	4·3	4·8	5·5	6·0	6·7	7·2	7·9	8·4	9·1	9·6	0·24
0·25	4·5	5·0	5·9	6·3	7·0	7·5	8·2	8·8	9·5	10·0	0·25
0·26	4·7	5·2	6·0	6·5	7·3	7·8	8·6	9·1	9·9	10·4	0·26
0·27	4·9	5·4	6·2	6·8	7·5	8·1	8·9	9·4	10·2	10·8	0·27
0·28	5·0	5·6	6·4	7·0	7·8	8·4	9·2	9·9	10·6	11·2	0·28
0·29	5·2	5·8	6·7	7·3	8·1	8·7	9·6	10·2	11·0	11·6	0·29
0·30	5·4	6·0	6·9	7·5	8·4	9·0	9·9	10·5	11·4	12·0	0·30
0·32	5·7	6·4	7·4	8·0	9·0	9·6	10·5	11·2	12·1	12·8	0·32
0·35	6·3	7·0	8·0	8·8	9·8	10·5	11·5	12·2	13·3	14·0	0·35
0·38	6·9	7·6	8·7	9·5	10·6	11·4	12·5	13·3	14·4	15·2	0·38
0·40	7·2	8·0	9·2	10·0	11·2	12·0	13·2	14·0	15·2	16·0	0·40
0·42	7·5	8·4	9·6	10·5	11·8	12·6	13·8	14·7	16·0	16·8	0·42
0·45	8·1	9·0	10·3	11·2	12·6	13·5	14·8	15·8	17·1	18·0	0·45
0·47	8·5	9·4	10·8	11·7	13·2	14·1	15·5	16·4	17·8	18·8	0·47
0·50	9·0	10·0	11·5	12·5	14·0	15·0	16·5	17·5	19·0	20·0	0·50
0·52	9·3	10·4	12·0	13·0	14·5	15·6	17·1	18·2	19·7	22·8	0·52
0·55	9·9	11·0	12·7	13·7	15·4	16·5	18·1	19·3	20·9	22·0	0·55
0·58	10·4	11·6	13·3	14·5	16·2	17·4	19·1	20·3	22·0	23·2	0·58
0·60	10·8	12·0	13·8	15·0	16·8	18·0	19·8	21·0	22·8	24·0	0·60
0·65	11·7	13·0	15·0	16·2	18·2	19·5	21·4	22·7	24·7	26·0	0·65
0·70	12·7	14·0	16·1	17·5	19·6	21·0	23·1	24·5	26·6	28·0	0·70
0·75	13·5	15·0	17·2	18·7	21·0	22·5	24·8	26·2	28·5	30·0	0·75
0·80	14·4	16·0	18·4	20·2	22·4	24·0	26·4	28·0	30·4	32·0	0·80
0·85	15·3	17·0	19·6	21·2	23·8	25·5	28·0	29·8	32·3	34·0	0·85
0·90	16·2	18·0	20·6	22·4	25·2	27·0	29·2	31·6	24·2	36·0	0·90

The Cooling Load for summer air conditions is made up from the following components:

1. Normal Heat Transfer through Walls, Windows, Ceilings, etc.
2. Transfer of Solar Radiation through Walls, etc.
3. Heat Emission of Occupants.
4. Heat introduced by Infiltration of Outside Air or Ventilation.
5. Heat Emission of Appliances (Mechanical, Electrical, Gas, etc.).

1. Normal Heat Transfer through Walls, etc. (B.t.u. per hr.)

$$H_1 = AU\,(t_1 - t_0)$$

A = Net area of wall, etc., in sq. ft.
U = Coefficient of transmission (B.t.u. per sq. ft. per hr. per °F.).
t_0 = Outside temperature °F.
t_i = Inside temperature (°F.).

2. Transfer of Solar Radiation: (B.t.u. per hr.)

$$H_2 = AFaJ$$

A = Net area of wall, etc., in sq. ft.
F = Radiation factor—percentage of absorbed solar radiation which is transmitted to the inside (for Glass : F=1 ; for walls, see Table).
a = Absorption coefficient—percentage of the incident solar radiation which is absorbed by the surface (see Table below).
J = Intensity of solar radiation striking the surface in B.t.u. per hr. (see Table below).

INTENSITY OF SOLAR RADIATION J
(B.t.u. per hr.) For Latitude 45°

Sun Time	North East	East	South East	South	South West	West	North West	Horizontal
5	25	24	9					2
6	89	99	52					26
7	149	194	125					90
8	140	219	171	22				156
9	92	194	183	65				210
10	33	144	171	98				251
11		75	139	121	32			274
12		91	128	91				282
1		32	121	139	75			274
2				98	171	144	33	251
3				65	183	194	92	210
4				22	171	219	140	156
5					125	194	144	90
6					52	99	89	26

SOLAR ABSORPTION COEFFICIENT a

Surface Material.	a
Very Light Coloured Surface White Stone Very Light Cement	0·4
Medium Dark Surface Unpainted Wood Brown Stone, Brick, Red Tile	0·7
Very Dark Surface Slate Roofing Very Dark Paints	0·9

RADIATION FACTOR F FOR DIFFERENT WALL TRANSMISSION COEFFICIENTS U

U =	0·1	0·2	0·3	0·4
F =	0·025	0·0475	0·07	0·095
U =	0·5	0·6	0·7	0·8
F =	0·115	0·14	0·16	0·18

ALTERNATIVE CALCULATION OF COOLING LOAD
(For England)

Skylights ... ... 200 B.t.u./sq. ft. hr.
Windows, west, east ... ... 125 ,,
Windows, south ... ... 75 ,,

Additional Temperature Difference for Walls and Flat Roofs:

Walls, west, east, black finish ... 25°F.
Walls, west, east, red finish ... 18°F.
Walls, west, east, white finish ... 10°F.
Walls, south, black finish ... 12·5°F.
Walls, south, red finish ... ... 9°F.
Walls, south, white finish ... ... 5°F.
Horizontal roofs, black finish ... 40°F.
Horizontal roofs, red finish ... 28°F.
Horizontal roofs, white finish ... 13°F.

The Latent Heat Load consists of the moisture given up by people, from infiltration of outside air, and from appliances.

The Total Refrigeration Load consists of the total heat gain of the room or building plus the sensible and latent heat removed from the outside air introduced into the room.

DESIRABLE INSIDE CONDITIONS FOR SUMMER AIR CONDITIONING WITH VARIOUS OUTSIDE TEMPERATURES

Outside Dry Bulb Temp. °F.	Inside Air Conditions.		
	Dry Bulb T. °F.	Rel. Humidity per cent	Effective Temp. °F.
100	83	40	75
95	80	51	74
90	78	56	73
85	77	56	72
80	75	61	71

TIME LAG IN TRANSMISSION OF SOLAR RADIATION THROUGH WALLS

Type of Wall	Time Lag in hours
6-in. Concrete	3
4-in. Gypsum	$2\frac{1}{2}$
22-in. Brick	10
3-in. Concrete + 1-in. Cork	2
2-in. Pine	$1\frac{1}{2}$

SOLAR RADIATION TRANSMITTED THROUGH SHADED WINDOWS

Type.	Per Cent Delivered
Canvas Awning, Plain ...	28
Canvas Awning, Aluminium	22
Inside Shade, Full Drawn ...	45
Inside Shade, Half Drawn, Buff	68
Inside Venetian Blind Slats at 45°, aluminium	58
Outside Venetian Blind, slats 45°, aluminium	22

3. Heat Emission by Occupants :

Number of Occupants in Halls, Restaurants, etc. : 1 person per 10–20 sq. ft.

Air velocity	Air temp. °F	50	54	57	61	65	68	72	75	79	82	86	90
Still Air	Sensible Heat	468	432	396	364	336	316	292	264	236	200	160	112
	Latent Heat grain/hr.	72	72	72	80	92	112	140	168	204	236	280
	grain/hr.	480	480	480	480	520	620	740	930	1120	1350	1570	1850
	Total	540	504	468	438	416	408	404	404	404	404	396	392
Air Velocity 3 ft. per sec.	Sensible Heat	520	484	448	416	384	356	332	300	276	236	188	128
	Latent Heat grain/hr.	64	64	64	64	64	68	84	108	132	168	208	264
	grain/hr.	430	430	430	430	430	450	560	720	880	1120	1380	1760
	Total	584	548	512	490	448	424	416	408	408	404	396	392

4. Heat introduced by Infiltration and Ventilation :

Total Heat Gain = Sensible Heat Gain + Latent Heat Gain.

$$H_4 = d.Q. (h_o - h_i)$$

H_4 = Total heat gain in B.t.u. per hr.
Q = Volume of outside air entering (cu. ft.).
d = Density of air (lb. of dry air per cu. ft.), at outside temperature.
h_o = Heat content of mixture of outside dry air and water vapour in B.t.u. per lb. of dry air at outside temperature.
h_i = Heat content of mixture of inside air at inside temperature.

5. Heat Emission of Appliances (in B.t.u. per hr.)

Lights and Electric Appliances	...	3,415 B.t.u. per kW.
Motors	...	2,546 B.t.u. per h.p.
	or	3,415 B.t.u. per kW.
Gas Lights	...	500–1,000 per cu. ft. of gas used.
Machinery driven from the outside	...	2,546 B.t.u. per b.h.p. supplied to the machine.

SOLAR RADIATION THROUGH HEAT ABSORBING GLASS

Solar Heat Gain can be reduced by using "Heat Absorbing Glass". This glass ("Antisun"—Pilkington Bros. Ltd.), is bluish-green with relative high light transmission but restricting the passage of Solar Radiant Heat.

Type and Thickness of Glass	*Transmission in per cent*	
	Visible Light	*Solar Radiation*
"Calorex"—Pilkington ⅛ in.	65	32
3/16 in.	55	25
¼ in.	48	20
"Antisun"—Pilkington 3/16 in.	78	53
¼ in.	74	46
Ordinary Window Glass	85	82

SOUND INSULATION OF SINGLE AND DOUBLE WINDOWS

Single or Double Window	*Type of Window*	*Type of Glass*	*Sound Reduction in Decibels*
Single	Opening Type (closed)	Any Glass	18–20
Single	Fixed or Opening Type with Air-tight Weather Strips	24/32 oz. Sheet Glass	23–25
		¼ in. Polished Plate Glass	27
		⅜ in. Polished Plate Glass	30
Double	Opening Type (closed)	Any Glass	22–24
Double	Opening Type (closed) Plus Absorbent Material on Sides of Airspace	24/32 oz. Sheet Glass, 4 in. space	28
		24/32 oz. Sheet Glass, 8 in. space	31
		¼ in. Polished Plate, 4 in. space	30
		¼ in. Polished Plate, 8 in. space	33
Double	Fixed or Opening Type with Air-tight Weather Strips	24/32 oz. Sheet Glass, 4 in. space	34
		24/32 oz. Sheet Glass, 8 in. space	40
		¼ in. Polished Plate, 4 in. space	38
		¼ in. Polished Plate, 8 in. space	44

VERTICAL GLAZING—THERMAL TRANSMITTANCE ("U"-value), B.T.U. per sq. ft. hour. °F

		Exposure to Wind																	
Orientation	S	Sheltered			Normal			Severe											
	W, SW, SE				Sheltered			Normal			Severe								
	NW							Sheltered			Normal			Severe					
	N, NE, E							Sheltered			Normal						Severe		
		A			B			C			D			E			F		
Single Glazing		·70			·79			·88			1·00			1·14			1·30		
Double Multiple Glazing No. of Air Spaces		1	2	3	1	2	3	1	2	3	1	2	3	1	2	3	1	2	3
Air Space	¾ in.	·41	·29	·22	·44	·31	·23	·47	·32	·24	·50	·33	·25	·53	·35	·26	·56	·36	·26
	½ in.	·42	·30	·24	·46	·32	·25	·48	·33	·25	·52	·35	·26	·55	·37	·27	·59	·38	·28
	⅜ in.	·44	·32	·25	·47	·34	·26	·51	·35	·27	·54	·37	·28	·58	·39	·29	·62	·41	·30
	¼ in.	·47	·35	·28	·51	·37	·29	·54	·39	·31	·58	·41	·32	·63	·43	·33	·67	·46	·34
	⅛ in.	·52	·41	·34	·57	·44	·37	·61	·47	·38	·68	·50	·40	·73	·54	·43	79	·57	·45

HORIZONTAL AND SLOPING GLAZING THERMAL TRANSMITTANCE ("U"-value), B.t.u. per sq. ft. per hour °F.

Exposure	Sheltered			Normal			Severe		
Single Glazing	0·97			1·13			1·36		
Double and Multiple Glazing No. of Air Spaces	1	2	3	1	2	3	1	2	3
Air Space $\frac{3}{4}$ in.	·52	·36	·27	·57	·38	·28	·62	·40	·30
$\frac{1}{2}$ in.	·53	·36	·28	·57	·38	·29	·63	·41	·30
$\frac{3}{8}$ in.	·53	·37	·28	·58	·39	·29	·64	·41	·31
$\frac{1}{4}$ in.	·56	·40	·30	·61	·42	·32	·67	·45	·33
$\frac{1}{8}$ in.	·65	·49	·39	·72	·52	·41	·80	·57	·44

MULTIPLYING FACTORS FOR "U"-VALUES OF WINDOWS TO ALLOW FOR HEAT TRANSFER OF WINDOW FRAME

Type of Frame	Ratio of Glass to Frame Area	Multiplying Factor for	
		Single Glass	Double Glass
All Glass	100	1·00	1·00
Wood Frame	80	0·90	0·95
Wood Frame	60	0·80	0·85
Steel Frame	80	1·00	1·20
Aluminium Frame ...	80	1·10	1·30

CONDENSATION ON GLASS WINDOWS

The chart indicates the maximum heat transmission coefficient of the glass required for avoiding condensation at various outside temperatures and inside temperatures and relative humidities.

Example:

Assumptions—

Inside temp.=70° F.
Outside temp.=20° F.
Relative humidity inside=50%

From the chart the maximum permissible "U"-value is 0·6 B.t.u. per hour per sq. ft. °F.

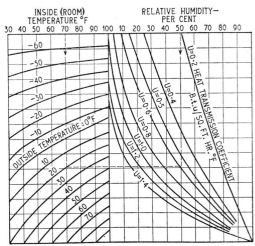

| | Town | Country | SUMMER. | | | | WINTER. | | |
			Average Max. Tem °F.	Mean Temp. °F.	Mean Humidity %	Corresp. Wet Bulb Temp. °F.	Mean Temp. to Feb. °F.		
EUROPE	Athens	Greece	100	78	49	64·4	50		
	Berlin	Germany	92	65	68	59	31		
	Budapest	Hungary	92	68	63	60	34		
	Bucarest	Rumania	96	71	56	61	29		
	Hamburg	Germany	91	—	—	—	30		
	Lisbon	Portugal	96	69	58	60	51		
	London	England	87	61	74	59	39		
	Oslo	Norway	87	61	69	57	24		
	Marseilles	France	93	70	64	60	44		
	Paris	France	93	64	73	62·5	37		
	Prague	Czechoslovakia	91	66	65	59	31		
	Rome	Italy	95	73	55	64	46		
	Seville	Spain	116	81	59	67	41		
	Sofia	Bulgaria	94	67	65	60	29		
	Vienna	Austria	91	66	70	55·5	30		
ASIA	Baghdad	Mesopotamia	117	93	36		—		
	Batavia	Java	93	79	78	74	—		
	Bombay	India	95	84	87	82	76		
	Hong-Kong	China	97	82	84	78	62		
	Calcutta	India	102	86	89	83	68		
	Manilla	Philippine	98	82	76	76	—		
	Singapore	Malaya	93	80	82	76	—		
	Tokyo	Japan	99	78	81	73·4	40		
AFRICA	Algiers	Algiers	106	78	72	71	57		
	Cairo	Egypt	109	84	70	76	55		
	Cape Town	South Africa	93	75	65	67	58		
	Katanga	Kongo	97	74	80	69	—		
	Tripoli	Tripoli	104	80	67	71	—		
AMERICA	Buenos Aires	Argentine	—	73	73	67	—		
	Caracas	Venezuela	87	69	78	64·5	—		
	Mexico	Mexico	86	65	71	60	—		
	Montevideo	Uruguay		71	66	64	—		
	New Orleans	U.S.A.	95	82	80	77	—		
	New York	U.S.A.	100	73	74	67	32		
	Rio de Janeiro	Brazil	—	78	79	73	—		
AUST-RALIA	Sydney	Australia	100	71	68	64	54		
	Melbourne	Australia	106	67	65	60	50		

NUMBER OF DEGREE-DAYS IN LONDON

	No.	%
September ...	177	4
October ...	473	10
November ...	561	12·5
December ...	618	14·5
January ...	821	18
February ...	652	14·5
March ...	536	12
April ...	420	9
May ...	245	5·5
Total ...	4,503	100

MEAN WINTER TEMPERATURE (AVERAGE) °F.

London	...	...	...	42·5
Scotland	...	..	...	40 to 41·0
England, N.E., E.	...	...	...	41·0
England, S.E.	...	...	...	43·5
England, N.W. and Wales	...	...	43·0
Ireland	...	...	...	43 to 44·5
England, S.W. and S. Wales	...	...	45·0

AVERAGE MINIMUM AND MEAN TEMPERATURES IN THE WINTER MONTHS IN THE UNITED KINGDOM

		Av. Min. Temp. °F.	Av. Mean Temp. °F
October ..	...	44	50
November	...	39	44
December	...	36	40
January ..	...	35	39
February	...	35	40
March ...	...	36	42
6 Months	...	37·3	42·6

NUMBER OF DEGREE-DAYS IN VARIOUS TOWNS IN ENGLAND, SCOTLAND AND WALES

From 1st October to 31st May. (Basis 60°F.)

Town.	Height in ft.	Degree-days.
Aberdeen	37	4,250
Appleby (Westmorland)	440	4,460
Banff	130	4,237
Bellingham (Northumberland)	849	4,845
Belper (Derby)	222	4,072
Berwick-on-Tweed	76	4,168
Birmingham	535	3,920
Blackpool	67	3,805
Brighton	32	3,415
Cambridge	41	3,810
Cardiff	202	3,650
Cranwell (Lincs.)	240	4,030
Crieff (Perth)	478	4,463
Deerness (Orkney)	160	4,366
Douglas (I.O.M.)	284	3,700
Dover	22	3,550
Dublin	54	3,380
Dundee	147	4,300
Durham	336	4,640
Edinburgh	441	4,210
Fort Augustus (Inverness)	68	4,343
Fortrose (Ross and Cromarty)	69	4,155
Glasgow	85	3,970
Hull	8	3,885
Kirkcaldy (Fife)	63	4,005
Lerwick (Shetland)	156	4,367
Liverpool	198	3,730
London, average	—	3,590
Manchester	125	3,720
Mayfield (Staffs.)	374	4,305
Nairn	20	4,267

NUMBER OF DEGREE DAYS IN VARIOUS TOWNS IN ENGLAND, SCOTLAND AND WALES—(contd.)

From 1st October to 31st May.   (Basis 60°F.)

Town.	Height in ft.	Degree-days.
Newport (I.O.W.)	48	3,525
Nottingham	192	3,905
Oxford	208	3,676
Plymouth	117	3,135
Portsmouth	15	3,245
Renfrew	19	4,154
St. Andrew's (Fifeshire) ...	13	4,200
Sheffield	428	3,865
Southampton	64	3,410
Stirling	151	4,275
Walton-on-Naze (Essex) ...	60	3,720
Wick (Caithness)	81	4,270
York	57	3,855

PRESSURE OF DRY AIR AT 60°F. AT VARIOUS VELOCITIES

Water Gauge.	Velocity ft./min.	Water Gauge.	Velocity ft./min.	Water Gauge.	Velocity ft./min.	Water Gauge.	Velocity ft./min.
0·1 in.	1250	0·6 in.	3070	1·1 in.	4170	1·6 in.	5020
0·2 in.	1760	0·7 in.	3320	1·2 in.	4350	1·7 in.	5170
0·3 in.	2170	0·8 in.	3550	1·3 in.	4590	1·8 in.	5330
0·4 in.	2520	0·9 in.	3770	1·4 in.	4700	1·9 in.	5470
0·5 in.	2800	1·0 in.	3950	1·5 in.	4860	2·0 in.	5620

The values quoted below are those authorized by the National Physical Laboratory.

Material	Moisture Content % of Dry Weight	Density in lb. per cu. ft. (Dry Weight)	Conductivity K B.t.u. per sq. ft. per hr. per degree F. per inch	Resistivity 1/K Degree F. per inch for one B.t.u. per sq. ft. per hour
Asbestos Cement Sheet	—	95	2·0	0·5
Asphalt	—	140	8·5	0·12
Bitumen	—	66	1·1	0·91
Brickwork	0	110	5·6	0·18
Brickwork	16	110	11·6	0·086
Firebrick	—	125	7·4	0·135
Concrete, No Fines 1:10	—	115	6·5	0·15
Concrete, Cellular ...	—	20	0·58	1·72
Foamed Slag Concrete	0	65	1·5	0·67
Pumice Concrete ...	0	45	1·1	0·91
Sawdust Concrete ...	0	66	2·1	0·48
Fibre Board	10–15	15	0·37	2·70
Hardboard	—	47	0·65	1·54
Flooring, Asphalt ...	—	105	5·2	0·19
Flooring, Rubber ...	—	80	2·2	0·45
Glass	—	157	7·3	0·14
Linoleum	—	77	1·3	0·77
Marble	—	170	17·4	0·06
Mortar	0	118	6·1	0·16
Paper	—	68	0·96	1·04
Plaster	—	90	3·3	0·30
Roofing, Asphalt ...	—	60	1·0	1·0
Roofing, Asphalt ...	—	120	4·0	0·25
Roofing, Felt	—	50	4·0	0·25
Slate	—	170	13·0	0·08
Granite	—	165	20·3	0·05
Sandstone	—	125	9·0	0·11
Terrazzo	—	152	11·0	0·09
Tiles, Clay	—	120	5·8	0·17
Tiles, Cork	—	33	0·58	1·72
Timber, Oak ...	—	48	1·11	0·90
Timber, Plywood ...	—	—	1·05	0·95
Plasterboard	—	60	1·1	0·91
Asbestos Felt	—	9	0·54	1·85
Cork Slab	—	10	0·34	2·94
Hair Felt	—	8·5	0·26	3·85
Fibre Glass	—	9	0·28	3·57

The total efficiency of a Central Heating Plant "E" can be divided into the following partial efficiencies:

1. Boiler Efficiency. $\qquad E_1 = 60\text{–}78\%$
2. Efficiency of Pipework (heat-loss of pipes). $\qquad E_2 = 75\text{–}90\%$
3. Efficiency of Heaters (according to type of heaters) $\qquad E_3 = 90\text{–}100\%$
4. Efficiency of Control (losses due to overheating) $\qquad E_4 = 80\text{–}95\%$

$$E = E_1 . E_2 . E_3 . E_4 = 30 \text{ to } 65\%$$

Fuel Consumption:

$$F = \frac{Hn\,(t_i - t_a)}{C.\,E\,(t_i - t_o)}\ \text{(lb.)}$$

F = Fuel consumption during considered period of n hours, in lb.
H = Heat loss for a temperature difference $(t_i - t_o)$ in B.t.u. per hr.
n = Number of heating hours.
E = Efficiency of utilization of fuel %.
t_i = Inside temperature, °F.
t_a = Average outside temperature during considered period, °F.
t_o = Outside design temperature, °F.
C = Calorific value of fuel (B.t.u. per lb.)

Degree-Day Method (for measuring Heat-Load):

Number of Degree-Days = Number days × (60°F. — average outside temp.
$\qquad D = N\,(t_i - t_a)$.

For one day the number of Degree-Days equals the temperature difference of inside and average outside temperature.

D = Number of degree-days.
N = Number of days.
t_a = Average outside temperature, in °F.
t_i = Mean inside temperature during 24 hours
$\qquad$ = 60°F. for practical use.

Heat Loss per Degree-Day:

$$h = \frac{24H}{(t - t_a)}\ \text{(B.t.u.)}$$

Fuel Consumption:

$$F = U \times D\ \text{(lb.)}$$

U = Unit fuel consumption per degree-day (to be found for the building concerned by test) in lb. per degree-day.
D = Number of degree-days.

Section VII

HOT WATER HEATING

THE HEATING MEDIUM IS WATER

carrying Heat through pipes from Boiler to Heaters.

Types of Hot Water Heating Schemes:

	Flow Temp.	Temp. Drop.
(a) Low Pressure H.W.H. { Forced circulation / Gravity	Up to 190°F.	20 to 30°F. / 40°F.
(b) Medium Pressure H.W.H.	190 to 250°F.	30 to 60°F.
(c) High Pressure H.W.H.	250 to 400°F.	50 to 150°F.

Classification according to Pipe Schemes:

One-pipe or Two-pipe System. }
Up-feed or Down-feed System. } Typical Schemes, see page VII. 4.

DESIGN OF HOT WATER HEATING SYSTEMS

1. Heat Losses of Heated Rooms.
2. Output and Heating Surface of Boiler.
3. Heating Surface of Radiators or Output of Unit Heaters.
4. Type and Size of Circulating Pump-Circulating Pressure.
5. Pipe Scheme and Pipe Sizing.
6. Expansion Tank, Type and Size.

1. Heat Losses (see chapter VI).

2. Boiler Heating Surface:

$$A = \frac{H_t (1 + X)}{K_B}$$

A = Heating surface of boiler, sq. ft.
H_t = Total heat-loss of plant, B.t.u. per hr.
X = Margin for heating up (per cent)
$\quad = 0.10$ to 0.15.
K_B = Heat transfer of boiler in B.t.u. per sq. ft. per hr.

K_B = Approximately. For cast-iron boilers.
$\quad$ 3,500 to 4,000.
$\quad$ Boiler to be chosen from Maker's Catalogue.

3. Heater, Heating Surface of Radiators and Pipe Coils:

$$A = \frac{H_r}{K_r \left(\frac{t_1 + t_2}{2} - t_r \right)}$$

A = Heating surface of radiator, sq. ft.
H_r = Heat loss of room, B.t.u. per hr.
t_1 = Flow temperature, °F.
t_2 = Return temperature, °F.
t_r = Room temperature, °F.

K_r = Heat transmission of heater, B.t.u. per sq. ft. per hr. °F.
$\quad$ (see Tables IV. 15–18).
Type and size of Unit Heaters to be chosen from Maker's Catalogue.

4. Circulating Pressure—Pump Size:

Circulating Pressure for Gravity Systems—

$$H = h (d_2 - d_1)$$

H = Pressure, in.

h = Height between middle of boiler and radiator, in.

$d_1 \, d_2$ = Density of water in flow and return, decimals.

Volume of Water Handled per minute—

Q = Volume of water handled (G.P.M. gal. per min.)

$$Q = \frac{H_t}{10 \times 60 \, (h_1 - h_2) \times d}$$

H_t = Total heat-loss of plant, B.t.u. per hr.

$h_1 \, h_2$ = Heat of water in flow and return respectively, B.t.u. per lb

d = Relative density of water in pump.

For Water Temperatures up to 212°F. :

$$Q = \frac{H_t}{10 \times 60 \times (t_1 - t_2)}$$

t_1 = Flow temperature, °F.

t_2 = Return temperature, °F.

Pump Head—

	Pump Head	Friction Resistances in milins. per ft.
For low pressure H.W.H. ...	3 to 10 ft.	100 to 150
For high pressure H.W.H. ...	20 to 72 ft.	120 to 400

5. Pipe Sizing (see Tables VII. 11 and Chart No. 1).

6. Expansion Tank:

Open Expansion Tanks (for Low Pressure H.W.H.):

Expansion of water from 45°F. to 212°F. = approximately 4 per cent.

Requisite volume of exp. tank = 0·08 × water volume of system.

For estimating:

Volume of exp. tank = 2 gal. for every 100 sq. ft. of radiator surface, or:

Output of Plant (B.t.u. per hr.)...	50,000	100,000	200,000	300,000	400,000	600,000	800,000
Water Content of System (gal. approx.)	45	110	240	375	570	750	1,200
Expansion Tank (gal.) ...	5	10	20	30	45	60	90

Closed Expansion Tanks (for Medium and High Pressure H.W.H.) :

$$V_1 = V (d_1 - d_2)$$

$$V_E p_1 = (V_E - V_1) p_2$$

$$V_E = \frac{V_1 \, P_2}{P_2 - P_1}$$

V_E = Volume of exp. tank, gal.

V_1 = Water volume expanded by warming, gal.

V = Water content of heating plant, gal.

d_1 = Density of water at 45°F.

d_2 = Density of water at max. flow temp.

P_1 = Pressure at tank connection at 45°F.

P_2 = Pressure at tank connection at max. flow temp., lb. per sq. in.

HEAT PUMPS

The Heat Pump is a common Refrigeration Unit arranged in such a way that it can be used for both cooling and heating, or for heating only. The initial cost of the installation is high, and savings and advantages are achieved mainly when heating and cooling are required in winter and summer respectively.

Operation of the Heat Pump:

Referring to the scheme drawing below, the Heat Pump consists of the following parts:

Compressor, with driving motor, for raising the pressure and temperature of the refrigerant vapour.

Condenser, for extracting heat from the refrigerant.

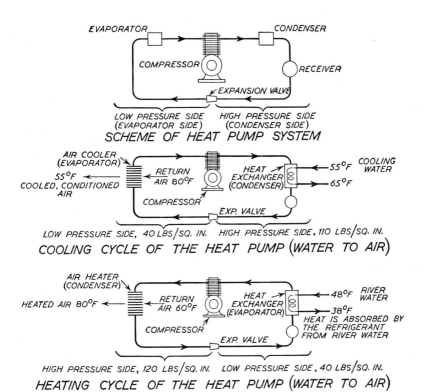

SCHEME OF HEAT PUMP SYSTEM

COOLING CYCLE OF THE HEAT PUMP (WATER TO AIR)

HEATING CYCLE OF THE HEAT PUMP (WATER TO AIR)

Receiver (Storage Tank) to hold the liquid refrigerant in the high pressure side before it passes the expansion valve.

Expansion Valve, for causing expansion of the refrigerant and for lowering the pressure from the high pressure to the low pressure side of the system.

Evaporator, in which heat is absorbed by the refrigerant from some source. Water, earth or air can be used as the source of heat.

A Commercial Refrigeration Unit and a Heat Pump consist of the same units and the same plant can be used either for cooling or heating.
The changing of the system from cooling to heating can be carried out by either of the following methods:

(a) Leave the flow of the refrigerant unchanged and change the circuit of the heat source and the medium to be heated.

(b) Leave the heat source and the medium to be heated unchanged and reverse the flow of the refrigerant by a suitable pipe and valve scheme.

Schemes for a Heat Pump indicating suitable temperatures when used for cooling and heating are shown, the data being chosen for the purpose of illustration only.

Section VIII

STEAM HEATING

THE HEATING MEDIUM IS STEAM
(Carrying Heat through Pipes from Boiler to Heaters)

Types of Steam Heating Schemes:
    (a) High Pressure Steam Heating System.
    (b) Low Pressure Steam Heating System.
    (c) Vacuum System.

Classification according to method of Returning of Condensate:
Gravity System.
Mechanical System.

Classification according to Pipe Scheme:
One-pipe or Two-pipe System.
Up-feed or Down-feed System.

Design of Steam Heating Systems:
    1. Heat-losses of Heated Rooms.
    2. Type and Capacity of Boiler.
    3. Heating Surface of Radiators or Output of Unit Heaters.
    4. Pipe Scheme and Sizing of Steam and Condense Pipes.

1. Heat-losses (see Section VI.)

2. Boiler, Heating Surface:

$$A_B = \frac{H_t (1 + X)}{K_B}$$

A_B = Heating surface of boiler (sq. ft.)
H_t = Total heat loss of plant (B.t.u. per hr.).
X = Margin for heating up (per cent).
    = 0·10 to 0·15.

Steam Consumption—

$$S = \frac{H_t}{H} = \frac{H_t}{1000}$$

S = Steam consumption (lb. per hr.).
H = Heat utilized from 1 lb. of steam.
    = Approximately 1,000 B.t.u. per lb.
K_B = Heat transfer of boiler (B.t.u. per sq. ft. per hr.).

K_B = Approximately 3,000 B.t.u. per sq. ft. per hr. for cast-iron boilers, hand-firing.
    = Approximately 4,000 B.t.u. per sq. ft. per hr. for cast-iron boilers, mechanically-fired.
    = Approximately 4,000 B.t.u. per sq. ft. per hr. for steel boilers.
Boiler Type and Capacity to be chosen from Maker's Catalogue.

3. Heater, Heating Surface of Radiators and Pipe Coils:

$$A_B = \frac{H_r}{K_r (t_s - t_r)}$$

A_R = Heating surface (sq. ft.).
H_r = Heat-loss of room (B.t.u. per hr.).
t_s = Temperature of steam (°F.).
t_r = Room temperature (°F.).
K_r = Heat transmission of heater in B.t.u. per sq. ft. per hr. (see IV. 15 to 18).

Type and Size of Unit Heaters to be chosen from Maker's Catalogue.

STEAM HEATING SYSTEMS

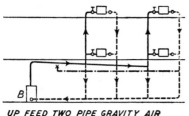

UP FEED TWO PIPE GRAVITY AIR
VENT SYSTEM WET RETURN.

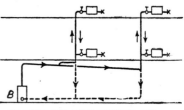

UP FEED ONE PIPE GRAVITY AIR
VENT SYSTEM WET RETURN.

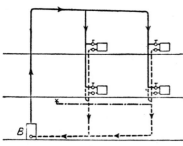

DOWN FEED TWO PIPE GRAVITY AIR
VENT SYSTEM WET RETURN.

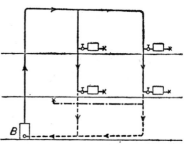

DOWN FEED ONE PIPE GRAVITY AIR
VENT SYSTEM WET RETURN.

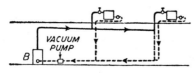

UP FEED VACUUM PUMP SYSTEM

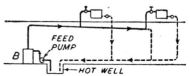

ATMOSTPHERIC SYSTEM HOT WELL OPEN
TO ATMOSTPHERE

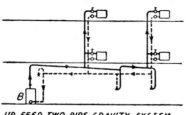

UP FEED TWO PIPE GRAVITY SYSTEM
DRY RETURN

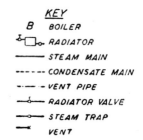

KEY

B   BOILER

RADIATOR

———— STEAM MAIN

- - - - - CONDENSATE MAIN

- · - · - VENT PIPE

RADIATOR VALVE

STEAM TRAP

VENT

CAPACITIES OF CONDENSATE PIPES (in B.t.u./hr.)

Pipe Size. Nom. Bore.	Wet Main.	Dry Main, with Gradient.			Vent Pipes.
		$\frac{3}{16}$ in. per yd.	$\frac{1}{16}$ in. per yd.	Vertical.	
$\frac{1}{2}$″	100,000	40,000	24,000	40,000	40,000
$\frac{3}{4}$	240,000	108,000	68,000	108,000	160,000
1	400,000	192,000	120,000	192,000	320,000
$1\frac{1}{4}$	1,000,000	440,000	280,000	440,000	720,000
$1\frac{1}{2}$	1,440,000	600,000	400,000	600,000	1,000,000
2	2,600,000	1,120,000	700,000	1,120,000	1,800,000
$2\frac{1}{2}$	6,400,000	2,800,000	1,760,000	2,800,000	4,000,000
3	9,600,000	4,000,000	2,520,000	4,000,000	6,400,000
$3\frac{1}{2}$	13,600,000	6,000,000	3,800,000	6,000,000	9,200,000

CAPACITIES OF STEAM TRAPS (in lb./hr.) ARMSTRONG

Pipe Size. Nom. Bore.	Working Pressure (lb./sq. in.)						
	5	10	15	30	50	70	100
$\frac{1}{2}$	800	950	1,300	950	800	900	800
$\frac{3}{4}$	1,500	1,800	2,000	2,000	1,800	2,000	1,800
1	2,800	3,400	4,000	3,500	3,700	3,700	3,300
$1\frac{1}{4}$	4,500	5,500	6,000	7,000	6,000	6,000	6,000
$1\frac{1}{2}$	7,500	8,500	9,000	10,000	9,000	9,000	9,000
2	14,000	16,000	19,000	18,000	18,000	18,000	18,000

SAFETY VALVES FOR STEAM HEATING (Working pres.=10lb.per sq.in.)

Output. (B.t.u. per hr.)	Radiation (sq. ft.)	Min. Clear Bore (in.)	Output. (B.t.u. per hr.)	Radiation (sq. ft.).	Min. Clear Bore (in.)
80,000	320	$\frac{3}{4}$	800,000	3,200	2
150,000	600	1	950,000	3,800	$2\frac{1}{2}$
250,000	1,000	$1\frac{1}{4}$	1,500,000	6,000	two 2
350,000	1,400	$1\frac{1}{2}$			

RECOMMENDED WORKING PRESSURE FOR LOW PRESSURE STEAM HEATING PLANTS

Length of Index Circuit in ft. ...	up to 600	900	1,500
Working Pressures in lb. per sq. in.	1–1·5	2	3

GENERAL FORMULAE FOR PIPE SIZING

$$H_T = H_1 + H_2$$

$$= pL + \Sigma F \frac{v^2 \rho}{2g}$$

$$H_T = P_1 - P_2$$

$$H_1 = pL, \quad p = \frac{H_1}{L}$$

$$H_2 = F \frac{v^2 \rho}{2g}$$

P_1 = Initial steam pressure at boiler.
P_2 = Final steam pressure at heater valve.
H_T = Total pressure drop.
H_1 = Pressure drop due to friction.
H_2 = Pressure drop due to fittings.
p = Pressure drop per unit length of pipe.
L = Length of pipe (ft.).
v = Velocity of steam (ft. per sec.).
ρ = Density of steam.
F = Coefficient of resistance.

or—

$$H_T = p (L + L_E) = pL_T$$

$$p = \frac{H_T}{L_T}$$

L_E = Equivalent length in ft. for the resistance of fittings (see Table VIII. 6).
$L_T = (L + L_E)$ = total length (ft.).
(Graph for Pipe Sizing, see Chart No. 2).

Ratio of the Resistance of Fittings (H_2) to the Total Resistance of the Circuit is about 33 per cent.

Resistance of Fittings at Low Pressure Steam Heating.

Values of "F" for various kind of Fittings:

Radiator ...	F =	1·5	Tee, Straightway ...		1·0
Abrupt Velocity Change		1·0	Branch	...	1·5
Cross-over ...	...	0·5	Counter Current		3·0
Long Sweep Elbow	...	1·5	Double Branch ...		1·5

Kind of Fitting.	½ in.	¾ in.	1 in.	1¼ in.	1½ in.	2 in.
Frictional Angle Valve	9	9	9	9		
Fractional Globe Valve ...	15	17	19	30		
Angle Cock	7	4	4	4		
Straight Cock	4	2	2	2		
Gate Valve, Screwed	1·5	0·5	0·5	0·5	0·5	0·5
Gate Valve, Flanged	0	0	0	0	0	0
Damper	3·5	2	2	1·5	1·5	1
Elbow Standard, G.F.	2	2	1·5	1·5	1	1
Long Sweep Elbow, G.F. ...	1·5	1·5	1	1	0·5	0·5
Bend, Short Radius	2	2	2	2	2	2
Bend, Long Radius	1	1	1	1	1	1
Standard Pipe Coupling, G.F.	0·5	0	0	0	0	0

PRESSURE DROP (H_2) DUE TO FITTINGS (in lb. per sq. in.)
(For various Velocities and Values of "F")

Velocity of Steam. ft. per sec.	Values of "F"						
	1	2	3	4	5	10	15
14	0·000874	0·00175	0·00262	0·00350	0·00437	0·00874	0·0131
20	0·00178	0·00357	0·00535	0·00714	0·00892	0·0178	0·0268
30	0·00401	0·00803	0·0120	0·0160	0·0201	0·0401	0·0602
40	0·00714	0·0143	0·0214	0·0286	0·0357	0·0714	0·107
50	0·0112	0·0223	0·0335	0·0446	0·0558	0·112	0·167
60	0·0161	0·0321	0·0482	0·0642	0·0803	0·161	0·241
70	0·0219	0·0437	0·0656	0·0874	0·109	0·219	0·328
80	0·0285	0·0571	0·0856	0·1142	0·143	0·285	0·428
90	0·0361	0·0723	0·108	0·1446	0·181	0·361	0·542
100	0·0446	0·0892	0·134	0·1784	0·223	0·446	0·669

DETERMINATION OF STEAM MAINS

The Available Pressure Drop is given by the initial pressure P_1 (Boiler pressure or pressure on header) and the required final pressure P_2.

The total pressure drop H is made up by:

1. Pressure drop due to friction H_1
2. Pressure drop due to fittings H_2

$$H = H_1 + H_2$$

The formula $p = \dfrac{P_1 - P_2}{L}$ expressing

the pressure drop due to friction for low pressure steam pipes is to be superseded for high pressure steam pipes by formula:

$$p = \frac{B_1 - B_2}{L}$$

L = length of pipe line
$B_1 = P_1^{1\cdot9375}$ ⎱ Auxiliary values
$B_2 = P_2^{1\cdot9375}$ ⎰   see Table VIII. 7

The pressure drop due to fittings is:

$$H = \Sigma F \frac{v^2 \rho}{2g}$$

F = coefficient of resistance

v = velocity of steam

ρ = density of steam

The pressure drop due to fittings (resistance), can also be expressed as an equivalent length of straight pipe (in ft.), see Table VIII. 6.

The pipe sizing is to be carried out by using the auxiliary value B_1 and B_2 and Chart No. 3.

Pressure Drop generally kept about 2 per cent of the initial pressure per 100 ft. of pipe.

Advisable Velocity of Steam:

For exhaust steam	...	70 to 100 ft. per sec.
For saturated steam...	...	... 100 to 130 ft. per sec.
For superheated steam	...	... 130 to 200 ft. per sec.

RESISTANCE OF VALVES AND FITTINGS TO FLOW OF STEAM
(Expressed as an equivalent length, in feet of Straight Pipe)

Nom. Bore. of Pipe.	Bends of Standard Rad.		Barrel of Tee.		Branch of Tee	Valves.			Lyre Expansion Bends.
in.	90°	45°	Plain	Reduced 25%		Through	Angle.	Globe.	
1	0·5	0·4	0·5	0·7	2·2	0·4	1·5	3·3	2·2
1¼	0·7	0·5	0·7	0·9	2·9	0·5	2·0	4·3	2·9
1½	0·9	0·7	0·9	1·1	3·6	0·7	2·4	5·4	3·6
2	1·3	1·0	1·3	1·6	5·1	1·3	3·4	7·6	5·1
2½	1·6	1·2	1·6	2·1	6·6	1·6	4·5	10·0	6·6
3	2·1	1·6	2·1	2·6	8·3	2·1	5·6	12·0	8·3
4	2·9	2·2	2·9	3·7	12·0	2·2	7·9	18·0	12·0
5	3·8	2·9	3·8	4·8	15·0	2·9	10·0	23·0	15·0
6	4·7	3·6	4·7	6·0	19·0	3·6	13·0	29·0	19·0
7	5·7	4·3	5·7	7·2	23·0	4·3	15·0	34·0	23·0
8	6·7	5·0	6·7	8·5	27·0	5·0	18·0	40·0	27·0
9	7·7	5·8	7·7	9·8	31·0	5·8	21·0	46·0	31·0
10	8·7	6·6	8·7	11·0	35·0	6·6	24·0	53·0	35·0

TABLES FOR PIPE SIZING (see Chart 3)

Table for: B = p.$^{1\cdot9375}$ p = Abs. Steam Pres. in lb. per sq. in.

p	B	p	B	p	B	p	B	p	B
14	167	29	680	44	1540	68	3550	98	7220
15	190	30	720	45	1610	70	3750	100	7500
16	215	31	775	46	1680	72	3960	105	8250
17	240	32	825	47	1750	74	4180	110	9020
18	270	33	875	48	1820	76	4400	115	9830
19	300	34	925	49	1890	78	4630	120	10680
20	330	35	980	50	1960	80	4870	125	11500
21	365	36	1035	52	2120	82	5110	130	12470
22	400	37	1090	54	2280	84	5350	135	13420
23	435	38	1150	56	2440	86	5590	140	14390
24	470	39	1210	58	2610	88	5850	145	15400
25	510	40	1270	60	2790	90	6110	150	16450
26	550	41	1330	62	2970	92	6380		
27	590	42	1400	64	3150	94	6660		
28	635	43	1470	66	3350	96	6940		

SUCTION LIFT OF BOILER FEED PUMPS
FOR VARIOUS WATER TEMPERATURES

Temperature of Feed Water °F.	Maximum Suction Lift Feet	Minimum Pressure Head Feet
130	10	—
150	7	—
170	2	—
175	0	0
190	—	5
200	—	10
210	—	15
212	—	17

QUANTITIES OF FLASH STEAM

Condensate		Percentage of Condensate Flashed off at reduction of Pressure to lb./sq. in. Gauge or ins. HG. Vac.					
Gauge Pressure lb./sq. in.	Temperature °F.	40	20	10	0	10"	20"
200	388	11·5	14·3	16·2	18·8	20·5	23·2
150	366	9·0	11·8	13·0	16·4	18·2	20·9
100	338	5·8	8·6	10·6	13·3	15·1	17·9
80	324	4·2	7·1	9·1	11·9	13·7	16·5
60	308	2·3	5·2	7·3	10·0	11·8	14·7
40	287	—	3·0	5·0	7·8	9·7	12·6
20	259	—	—	2·1	5·0	6·8	9·8
10	240	—	—	—	2·9	4·8	7·8
0	212	—	—	—	—	1·9	5·0

SCHEME OF FLASH STEAM RECOVERY

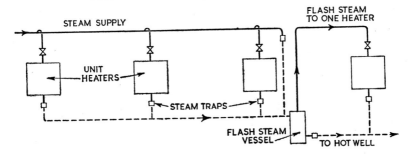

In vacuum steam heating systems, a partial vacuum is maintained in the return line by means of a vacuum pump. The vacuum maintained is approx. 3 to 10 in. mercury.

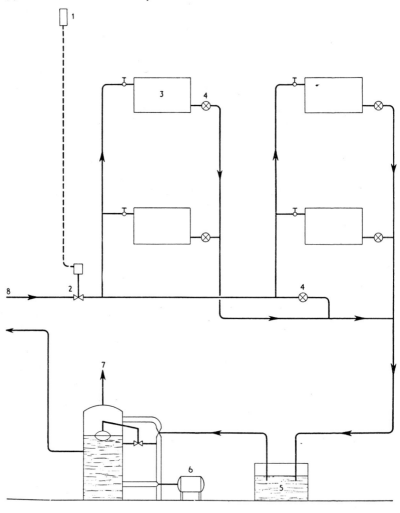

1 OUTSIDE THERMOSTAT
2 CONTROL VALVE
3 RADIATORS
4 STEAM TRAPS

5 CONDENSE RECEIVER
6 VACUUM PUMP
7 VENT
8 STEAM SUPPLY

VACUUM DIFFERENTIAL HEATING SYSTEM

Section IX

DOMESTIC HOT WATER SUPPLY AND GAS SUPPLY

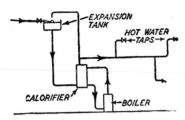

Direct Hot Water Service System

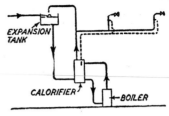

Direct Hot Water Service System
with Secondary Circulation.

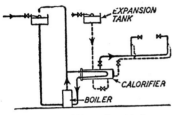

Indirect Hot Water Service System
with Secondary Circulation.

Classification of Hot Water Supply schemes:

$\left\{\begin{array}{l}\text{Direct system.}\\\text{Indirect system.}\end{array}\right.$

$\left\{\begin{array}{l}\text{Closed system.}\\\text{Open system.}\end{array}\right.$

Design of Hot Water Systems:

1. Determination of demand of hot water, quantity and temperature.
2. Design, type, capacity and output of hot water calorifier.
3. Design, type and size of boiler.
4. Design, arrangement of boiler, calorifier, automatic control and pipe scheme.
5. Determination of primary and secondary mains.

Requisite Output of Calorifier:

$$H = \frac{10Q\,(t_2 - t_1)}{n}.$$

H = Output of H.W. calorifier (B.t.u. per hr.).

Q = Required quantity of hot water (gal. per hr.)

n = Time for warming up in hours.

t_2 = Temperature of hot water (°F.).

t_1 = Temperature of cold water (°F.).

Heating Surface of Indirect Calorifier:

$$A_c = \frac{H}{k \left(t_m - \dfrac{t_e + t_1}{2}\right)}$$

A_c = Heating surface of coil (sq. ft.).
t_m = Mean temperature of heating medium °F.
Logarithmic mean temperature difference, see IV. 10, 14.
k = Coefficient of heat transmission for heating coil (B.t.u. per sq. ft. per hr.). per °F.
     See IV. 15 Heat Transmission Coefficients for Metals.

Heating Surface of Boiler:

$$A = \frac{1 \cdot 1 H}{k_b}$$

A = Heating surface of boiler (sq. ft.).
k_b = Rating of boiler in B.t.u. per sq. ft. per hr.
     = 3,800 to 4,400 B.t.u./sq. ft. hr. for cast-iron indirect boilers.
     = 10,000 B.t.u./sq. ft. hr. for cast-iron direct boilers.

TEMPERATURE DROP IN PIPES IN °F. PER FOOT OF BARE PIPE

Weight of water, lb. per hour	½ in.	¾ in.	1 in.	1¼ in.	1½ in.	2 in.	2½ in.	3 in.	4 in.
100	0·45	0·6	0·65	0·8	0·9	1·1	1·25	1·5	1·9
120	0·38	0·5	0·54	0·62	0·75	0·92	1·04	1·21	1·58
140	0·32	0·43	0·46	0·57	0·64	0·79	0·89	1·07	1·36
160	0·28	0·37	0·41	0·5	0·56	0·69	0·78	0·94	1·19
180	0·25	0·33	0·36	0·44	0·5	0·61	0·69	0·83	1·06
200	0·22	0·3	0·33	0·4	0·45	0·55	0·63	0·75	0·95
250	0·18	0·24	0·26	0·32	0·36	0·44	0·5	0·6	0·76
300	0·15	0·2	0·22	0·27	0·3	0·37	0·42	0·5	0·63
350	0·13	0·17	0·19	0·23	0·26	0·31	0·36	0·43	0·54
400	0·11	0·15	0·165	0·2	0·225	0·275	0·315	0·375	0·475
450	0·1	0·133	0·14	0·177	0·2	0·244	0·277	0·33	0·422
500	0·09	0·12	0·13	0·16	0·18	0·22	0·25	0·3	0·38
600	0·075	0·1	0·11	0·135	0·15	0·185	0·21	0·25	0·365
700	0·065	0·085	0·095	0·125	0·13	0·155	0·18	0·215	0·27
800	0·055	0·075	0·083	0·1	0·113	0·138	0·158	0·189	0·238
900	0·05	0·066	0·07	0·089	0·1	0·122	0·139	0·165	0·211
1000	0·045	0·060	0·065	0·08	0·09	0·11	0·125	0·15	0·19

HEAT PUMPS

The Heat Pump is a common Refrigeration Unit arranged in such a way that it can be used for both cooling and heating, or for heating only. The initial cost of the installation is high, and savings and advantages are achieved mainly when heating and cooling are required in winter and summer respectively.

Operation of the Heat Pump:

Referring to the scheme drawing below, the Heat Pump consists of the following parts:

Compressor, with driving motor, for raising the pressure and temperature of the refrigerant vapour.

Condenser, for extracting heat from the refrigerant.

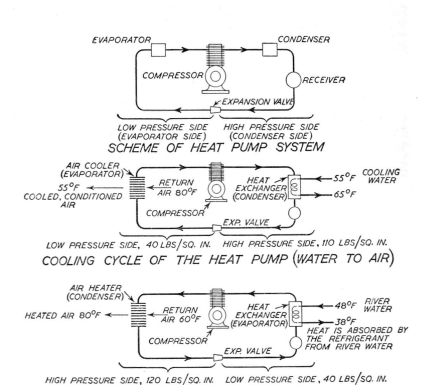

SCHEME OF HEAT PUMP SYSTEM

COOLING CYCLE OF THE HEAT PUMP (WATER TO AIR)

HEATING CYCLE OF THE HEAT PUMP (WATER TO AIR)

Receiver (Storage Tank) to hold the liquid refrigerant in the high pressure side before it passes the expansion valve.

Expansion Valve, for causing expansion of the refrigerant and for lowering the pressure from the high pressure to the low pressure side of the system.

Evaporator, in which heat is absorbed by the refrigerant from some source. Water, earth or air can be used as the source of heat.

A Commercial Refrigeration Unit and a Heat Pump consist of the same units and the same plant can be used either for cooling or heating.
The changing of the system from cooling to heating can be carried out by either of the following methods:

(*a*) Leave the flow of the refrigerant unchanged and change the circuit of the heat source and the medium to be heated.

(*b*) Leave the heat source and the medium to be heated unchanged and reverse the flow of the refrigerant by a suitable pipe and valve scheme.

Schemes for a Heat Pump indicating suitable temperatures when used for cooling and heating are shown, the data being chosen for the purpose of illustration only.

Section VIII

STEAM HEATING

THE HEATING MEDIUM IS STEAM

(Carrying Heat through Pipes from Boiler to Heaters)

Types of Steam Heating Schemes:

  (a) High Pressure Steam Heating System.
  (b) Low Pressure Steam Heating System.
  (c) Vacuum System.

Classification according to method of Returning of Condensate:
  Gravity System.
  Mechanical System.

Classification according to Pipe Scheme:
  One-pipe or Two-pipe System.
  Up-feed or Down-feed System.

Design of Steam Heating Systems:

  1. Heat-losses of Heated Rooms.
  2. Type and Capacity of Boiler.
  3. Heating Surface of Radiators or Output of Unit Heaters.
  4. Pipe Scheme and Sizing of Steam and Condense Pipes.

1. Heat-losses (see Section VI.)

2. Boiler, Heating Surface:

$$A_B = \frac{H_t\,(1 + X)}{K_B}$$

A_B = Heating surface of boiler (sq. ft.)
H_t = Total heat loss of plant (B.t.u. per hr.).
X = Margin for heating up (per cent).
    = 0·10 to 0·15.

Steam Consumption—

$$S = \frac{H_t}{H} = \frac{H_t}{1000}$$

S = Steam consumption (lb. per hr.).
H = Heat utilized from 1 lb. of steam.
    = Approximately 1,000 B.t.u. per lb.
K_B = Heat transfer of boiler (B.t.u. per sq. ft. per hr.).

K_B = Approximately 3,000 B.t.u. per sq. ft. per hr. for cast-iron boilers, hand-firing.
  = Approximately 4,000 B.t.u. per sq. ft. per hr. for cast-iron boilers, mechanically-fired.
  = Approximately 4,000 B.t.u. per sq. ft. per hr. for steel boilers.
Boiler Type and Capacity to be chosen from Maker's Catalogue.

3. Heater, Heating Surface of Radiators and Pipe Coils:

$$A_B = \frac{H_r}{K_r\,(t_s - t_r)}$$

A_R = Heating surface (sq. ft.).
H_r = Heat-loss of room (B.t.u. per hr.).
t_s = Temperature of steam (°F.).
t_r = Room temperature (°F.).
K_r = Heat transmission of heater in B.t.u. per sq. ft. per hr. (see IV. 15 to 18).

Type and Size of Unit Heaters to be chosen from Maker's Catalogue.

STEAM HEATING SYSTEMS

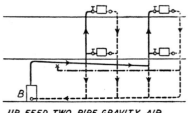

UP FEED TWO PIPE GRAVITY AIR
VENT SYSTEM WET RETURN.

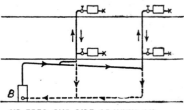

UP FEED ONE PIPE GRAVITY AIR
VENT SYSTEM WET RETURN.

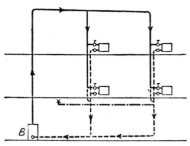

DOWN FEED TWO PIPE GRAVITY AIR
VENT SYSTEM. WET RETURN.

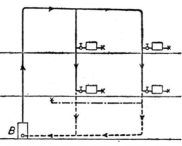

DOWN FEED ONE PIPE GRAVITY AIR
VENT SYSTEM. WET RETURN.

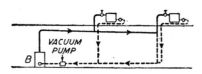

UP FEED VACUUM PUMP SYSTEM

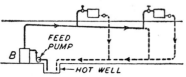

ATMOSTPHERIC SYSTEM HOT WELL OPEN
TO ATMOSTPHERE

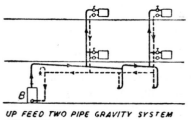

UP FEED TWO PIPE GRAVITY SYSTEM
DRY RETURN

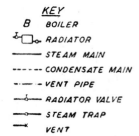

KEY

B	BOILER
	RADIATOR
	STEAM MAIN
	CONDENSATE MAIN
	VENT PIPE
	RADIATOR VALVE
	STEAM TRAP
	VENT

CAPACITIES OF CONDENSATE PIPES (in B.t.u./hr.)

Pipe Size. Nom. Bore.	Wet Main.	Dry Main, with Gradient.			Vent Pipes.
		$\frac{3}{16}$ in. per yd.	$\frac{1}{16}$ in. per yd.	Vertical.	
$\frac{1}{2}''$	100,000	40,000	24,000	40,000	40,000
$\frac{3}{4}$	240,000	108,000	68,000	108,000	160,000
1	400,000	192,000	120,000	192,000	320,000
$1\frac{1}{4}$	1,000,000	440,000	280,000	440,000	720,000
$1\frac{1}{2}$	1,440,000	600,000	400,000	600,000	1,000,000
2	2,600,000	1,120,000	700,000	1,120,000	1,800,000
$2\frac{1}{2}$	6,400,000	2,800,000	1,760,000	2,800,000	4,000,000
3	9,600,000	4,000,000	2,520,000	4,000,000	6,400,000
$3\frac{1}{2}$	13,600,000	6,000,000	3,800,000	6,000,000	9,200,000

CAPACITIES OF STEAM TRAPS (in lb./hr.) ARMSTRONG

Pipe Size. Nom. Bore.	Working Pressure (lb./sq. in.)						
	5	10	15	30	50	70	100
$\frac{1}{2}$	800	950	1,300	950	800	900	800
$\frac{3}{4}$	1,500	1,800	2,000	2,000	1,800	2,000	1,800
1	2,800	3,400	4,000	3,500	3,700	3,700	3,300
$1\frac{1}{4}$	4,500	5,500	6,000	7,000	6,000	6,000	6,000
$1\frac{1}{2}$	7,500	8,500	9,000	10,000	9,000	9,000	9,000
2	14,000	16,000	19,000	18,000	18,000	18,000	18,000

SAFETY VALVES FOR STEAM HEATING (Working pres. = 10 lb. per sq. in.)

Output. (B.t.u. per hr.)	Radiation (sq. ft.)	Min. Clear Bore (in.)	Output. (B.t.u. per hr.)	Radiation (sq. ft.).	Min. Clear Bore (in.)
80,000	320	$\frac{3}{4}$	800,000	3,200	2
150,000	600	1	950,000	3,800	$2\frac{1}{2}$
250,000	1,000	$1\frac{1}{4}$	1,500,000	6,000	two 2
350,000	1,400	$1\frac{1}{2}$			

RECOMMENDED WORKING PRESSURE FOR LOW PRESSURE STEAM HEATING PLANTS

Length of Index Circuit in ft. ...	up to 600	900	1,500
Working Pressures in lb. per sq. in.	1–1·5	2	3

GENERAL FORMULAE FOR PIPE SIZING

$H_T = H_1 + H_2$

$\quad = pL + \Sigma F \dfrac{v^2 \rho}{2g}$

$H_T = P_1 - P_2$

$H_1 = pL, \; p = \dfrac{H_1}{L}$

$H_2 = F \dfrac{v^2 \rho}{2g}$

$P_1 =$ Initial steam pressure at boiler.
$P_2 =$ Final steam pressure at heater valve.
$H_T =$ Total pressure drop.
$H_1 =$ Pressure drop due to friction.
$H_2 =$ Pressure drop due to fittings.
$p \;=$ Pressure drop per unit length of pipe.
$L \;=$ Length of pipe (ft.).
$v \;=$ Velocity of steam (ft. per sec.).
$\rho \;=$ Density of steam.
$F \;=$ Coefficient of resistance.

or—

$H_T = p (L + L_E) = pL_T$

$p = \dfrac{H_T}{L_T}$

$L_E =$ Equivalent length in ft. for the resistance of fittings (see Table VIII. 6).
$L_T = (L + L_E) =$ total length (ft.).
(Graph for Pipe Sizing, see Chart No. 2).

Ratio of the Resistance of Fittings (H_2) to the Total Resistance of the Circuit is about 33 per cent.

Resistance of Fittings at Low Pressure Steam Heating.

Values of "F" for various kind of Fittings :

Radiator	...	$F =$	1·5	Tee, Straightway ...	1·0
Abrupt Velocity Change			1·0	Branch ...	1·5
Cross-over	...	...	0·5	Counter Current	3·0
Long Sweep Elbow	...		1·5	Double Branch ...	1·5

Kind of Fitting.	½ In.	¾ In.	1 In.	1¼ In.	1½ In.	2 In.
Frictional Angle Valve	9	9	9	9		
Fractional Globe Valve ...	15	17	19	30		
Angle Cock	7	4	4	4		
Straight Cock	4	2	2	2		
Gate Valve, Screwed	1·5	0·5	0·5	0·5	0·5	0·5
Gate Valve, Flanged	0	0	0	0	0	0
Damper	3·5	2	2	1·5	1·5	1
Elbow Standard, G.F.	2	2	1·5	1·5	1	1
Long Sweep Elbow, G.F. ...	1·5	1·5	1	1	0·5	0·5
Bend, Short Radius	2	2	2	2	2	2
Bend, Long Radius	1	1	1	1	1	1
Standard Pipe Coupling, G.F.	0·5	0	0	0	0	0

PRESSURE DROP (H_2) DUE TO FITTINGS (in lb. per sq. in.)
(For various Velocities and Values of "F")

Velocity of Steam. ft. per sec.	Values of "F"						
	1	2	3	4	5	10	15
14	0·000874	0·00175	0·00262	0·00350	0·00437	0·00874	0·0131
20	0·00178	0·00357	0·00535	0·00714	0·00892	0·0178	0·0268
30	0·00401	0·00803	0·0120	0·0160	0·0201	0·0401	0·0602
40	0·00714	0·0143	0·0214	0·0286	0·0357	0·0714	0·107
50	0·0112	0·0223	0·0335	0·0446	0·0558	0·112	0·167
60	0·0161	0·0321	0·0482	0·0642	0·0803	0·161	0·241
70	0·0219	0·0437	0·0656	0·0874	0·109	0·219	0·328
80	0·0285	0·0571	0·0856	0·1142	0·143	0·285	0·428
90	0·0361	0·0723	0·108	0·1446	0·181	0·361	0·542
100	0·0446	0·0892	0·134	0·1784	0·223	0·446	0·669

DETERMINATION OF STEAM MAINS

The Available Pressure Drop is given by the initial pressure P_1 (Boiler pressure or pressure on header) and the required final pressure P_2.

The total pressure drop H is made up by:

    1. Pressure drop due to friction H_1

    2. Pressure drop due to fittings H_2

$$H = H_1 + H_2$$

The formula $p = \dfrac{P_1 - P_2}{L}$ expressing

the pressure drop due to friction for low pressure steam pipes is to be superseded for high pressure steam pipes by formula:

$$p = \frac{B_1 - B_2}{L}$$

L = length of pipe line

$\left. \begin{array}{l} B_1 = P_1^{1\cdot9375} \\ B_2 = P_2^{1\cdot9375} \end{array} \right\}$ Auxiliary values   see Table VIII. 7

The pressure drop due to fittings is:

$$H = \Sigma F \frac{v^2 \rho}{2g}$$

F = coefficient of resistance

v = velocity of steam

ρ = density of steam

The pressure drop due to fittings (resistance), can also be expressed as an equivalent length of straight pipe (in ft.), see Table VIII. 6.

The pipe sizing is to be carried out by using the auxiliary value B_1 and B_2 and Chart No. 3.

Pressure Drop generally kept about 2 per cent of the initial pressure per 100 ft. of pipe.

Advisable Velocity of Steam:

For exhaust steam ...	...	...	70 to 100 ft. per sec.
For saturated steam...	...	...	100 to 130 ft. per sec.
For superheated steam	...	...	130 to 200 ft. per sec.

RESISTANCE OF VALVES AND FITTINGS TO FLOW OF STEAM
(Expressed as an equivalent length, in feet of Straight Pipe)

Nom.Bore. of Pipe. in.	Bends of Standard Rad.		Barrel of Tee.		Branch of Tee	Valves.			Lyre Ex-pansion Bends.
	90°	45°	Plain	Reduced 25%		Through	Angle	Globe.	
1	0·5	0·4	0·5	0·7	2·2	0·4	1·5	3·3	2·2
1¼	0·7	0·5	0·7	0·9	2·9	0·5	2·0	4·3	2·9
1½	0·9	0·7	0·9	1·1	3·6	0·7	2·4	5·4	3·6
2	1·3	1·0	1·3	1·6	5·1	1·3	3·4	7·6	5·1
2½	1·6	1·2	1·6	2·1	6·6	1·6	4·5	10·0	6·6
3	2·1	1·6	2·1	2·6	8·3	2·1	5·6	12·0	8·3
4	2·9	2·2	2·9	3·7	12·0	2·2	7·9	18·0	12·0
5	3·8	2·9	3·8	4·8	15·0	2·9	10·0	23·0	15·0
6	4·7	3·6	4·7	6·0	19·0	3·6	13·0	29·0	19·0
7	5·7	4·3	5·7	7·2	23·0	4·3	15·0	34·0	23·0
8	6·7	5·0	6·7	8·5	27·0	5·0	18·0	40·0	27·0
9	7·7	5·8	7·7	9·8	31·0	5·8	21·0	46·0	31·0
10	8·7	6·6	8·7	11·0	35·0	6·6	24·0	53·0	35·0

TABLES FOR PIPE SIZING (see Chart 3)

Table for: B = p.$^{1·9375}$ p = Abs. Steam Pres. in lb. per sq. in.

p	B	p	B	p	B	p	B	p	B
14	167	29	680	44	1540	68	3550	98	7220
15	190	30	720	45	1610	70	3750	100	7500
16	215	31	775	46	1680	72	3960	105	8250
17	240	32	825	47	1750	74	4180	110	9020
18	270	33	875	48	1820	76	4400	115	9830
19	300	34	925	49	1890	78	4630	120	10680
20	330	35	980	50	1960	80	4870	125	11500
21	365	36	1035	52	2120	82	5110	130	12470
22	400	37	1090	54	2280	84	5350	135	13420
23	435	38	1150	56	2440	86	5590	140	14390
24	470	39	1210	58	2610	88	5850	145	15400
25	510	40	1270	60	2790	90	6110	150	16450
26	550	41	1330	62	2970	92	6380		
27	590	42	1400	64	3150	94	6660		
28	635	43	1470	66	3350	96	6940		

SUCTION LIFT OF BOILER FEED PUMPS
FOR VARIOUS WATER TEMPERATURES

Temperature of Feed Water °F.	Maximum Suction Lift Feet	Minimum Pressure Head Feet
130	10	—
150	7	—
170	2	—
175	0	0
190	—	5
200	—	10
210	—	15
212	—	17

QUANTITIES OF FLASH STEAM

Condensate		Percentage of Condensate Flashed off at reduction of Pressure to lb./sq. in. Gauge or ins. HG. Vac.					
Gauge Pressure lb./sq.in.	Temperature °F.	40	20	10	0	10″	20″
200	388	11·5	14·3	16·2	18·8	20·5	23·2
150	366	9·0	11·8	13·0	16·4	18·2	20·9
100	338	5·8	8·6	10·6	13·3	15·1	17·9
80	324	4·2	7·1	9·1	11·9	13·7	16·5
60	308	2·3	5·2	7·3	10·0	11·8	14·7
40	287	—	3·0	5·0	7·8	9·7	12·6
20	259	—	—	2·1	5·0	6·8	9·8
10	240	—	—	—	2·9	4·8	7·8
0	212	—	—	—	—	1·9	5·0

SCHEME OF FLASH STEAM RECOVERY

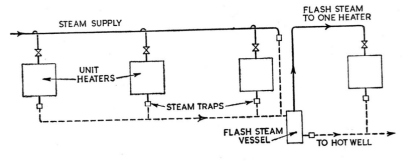

In vacuum steam heating systems, a partial vacuum is maintained in the return line by means of a vacuum pump. The vacuum maintained is approx. 3 to 10 in. mercury.

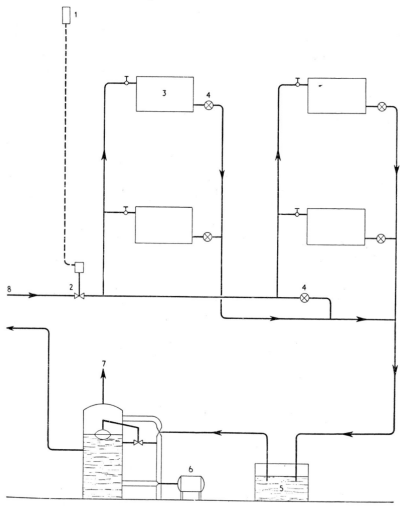

1 OUTSIDE THERMOSTAT	5 CONDENSE RECEIVER
2 CONTROL VALVE	6 VACUUM PUMP
3 RADIATORS	7 VENT
4 STEAM TRAPS	8 STEAM SUPPLY

VACUUM DIFFERENTIAL HEATING SYSTEM

Section IX

DOMESTIC HOT WATER SUPPLY AND GAS SUPPLY

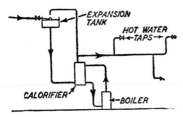

Direct Hot Water Service System

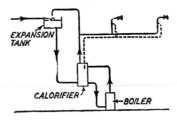

**Direct Hot Water Service System
with Secondary Circulation.**

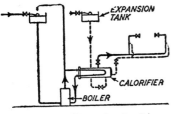

**Indirect Hot Water Service System
with Secondary Circulation.**

Classification of Hot Water Supply schemes :

$\begin{cases} \text{Direct system.} \\ \text{Indirect system.} \end{cases}$

$\begin{cases} \text{Closed system.} \\ \text{Open system.} \end{cases}$

Design of Hot Water Systems :

1. Determination of demand of hot water, quantity and temperature.

2. Design, type, capacity and output of hot water calorifier.

3. Design, type and size of boiler.

4. Design, arrangement of boiler, calorifier, automatic control and pipe scheme.

5. Determination of primary and secondary mains.

Requisite Output of Calorifier :

$$H = \frac{10Q \, (t_2 - t_1)}{n}.$$

H = Output of H.W. calorifier (B.t.u. per hr.).

Q = Required quantity of hot water (gal. per hr.)

n = Time for warming up in hours.

t_2 = Temperature of hot water (°F.).

t_1 = Temperature of cold water (°F.).

Heating Surface of Indirect Calorifier:

$$A_c = \frac{H}{k\left(t_m - \dfrac{t_e + t_1}{2}\right)}$$

A_c = Heating surface of coil (sq. ft.).
t_m = Mean temperature of heating medium °F.
Logarithmic mean temperature difference, see IV. 10, 14.
k = Coefficient of heat transmission for heating coil (B.t.u. per sq.
       ft. per hr.). per °F.
  See IV. 15 Heat Transmission Coefficients for Metals.

Heating Surface of Boiler:

$$A = \frac{1 \cdot 1 H}{k_b}$$

A = Heating surface of boiler (sq. ft.).
k_b = Rating of boiler in B.t.u. per sq. ft. per hr.
     = 3,800 to 4,400 B.t.u./sq. ft. hr. for cast-iron indirect boilers.
     = 10,000 B.t.u./sq. ft. hr. for cast-iron direct boilers.

TEMPERATURE DROP IN PIPES IN °F. PER FOOT OF BARE PIPE

Weight of water, lb. per hour	$\frac{1}{2}$ in.	$\frac{3}{4}$ in.	1 in.	$1\frac{1}{4}$ in.	$1\frac{1}{2}$ in.	2 in.	$2\frac{1}{2}$ in.	3 in.	4 in.
100	0·45	0·6	0·65	0·8	0·9	1·1	1·25	1·5	1·9
120	0·38	0·5	0·54	0·62	0·75	0·92	1·04	1·21	1·58
140	0·32	0·43	0·46	0·57	0·64	0·79	0·89	1·07	1·36
160	0·28	0·37	0·41	0·5	0·56	0·69	0·78	0·94	1·19
180	0·25	0·33	0·36	0·44	0·5	0·61	0·69	0·83	1·06
200	0·22	0·3	0·33	0·4	0·45	0·55	0·63	0·75	0·95
250	0·18	0·24	0·26	0·32	0·36	0·44	0·5	0·6	0·76
300	0·15	0·2	0·22	0·27	0·3	0·37	0·42	0·5	0·63
350	0·13	0·17	0·19	0·23	0·26	0·31	0·36	0·43	0·54
400	0·11	0·15	0·165	0·2	0·225	0·275	0·315	0·375	0·475
450	0·1	0·133	0·14	0·177	0·2	0·244	0·277	0·33	0·422
500	0·09	0·12	0·13	0·16	0·18	0·22	0·25	0·3	0·38
600	0·075	0·1	0·11	0·135	0·15	0·185	0·21	0·25	0·365
700	0·065	0·085	0·095	0·125	0·13	0·155	0·18	0·215	0·27
800	0·055	0·075	0·083	0·1	0·113	0·138	0·158	0·189	0·238
900	0·05	0·066	0·07	0·089	0·1	0·122	0·139	0·165	0·211
1000	0·045	0·060	0·065	0·08	0·09	0·11	0·125	0·15	0·19

HOT WATER CONSUMPTION PER FITTING (in gal. per hour at 150°F.)

Fitting: Basin (Private) 3   Basin (Public)   10   Bath   ...   20–40
           Shower   ...   40   Sink   ...   10–20

HOT WATER CONSUMPTION AND STORAGE PER OCCUPANT (at 150°F.)

Type of Building		Consumption in Gal/Day/ Occupant	Peak Consumption Gal/Hr/ Occupant	Storage Gal/Occupant
Schools (Boarding)	...	20	4	5
Blocks of Flats	... ...	20 to 35	10	7
Hotels	... ...	20 to 35	10	7
Factories, no process	...	5 to 10	2	1
Blocks of Offices ...	...	5	2	1
Hospitals, Infection	...	50	10	10
Hospitals, Sick	... ...	35	7	6
Hospitals, Mental ...	...	25	5	6
Hospitals, Maternity	...	40	8	7

METER PIT SIZES   Minimum 2 ft. 0 in. × 2 ft. 0 in. × 3 ft. 3 in. deep.
For 3 in. Main 3 ft. 0 in. × 2 ft. 0 in. × 3 ft. 3 in. deep.

CONTENTS OF DIFFERENT FITTINGS (in gallons)

Lavatory Basin, Normal   ...   1
Lavatory Basin, Full   2
Sink, Normal   5
Sink, Full   10
Bath   ...   ...   30 to 40 gal.

Shower Bath, "Winns"
        1 to 1½ g.p.m.
Shower Bath, 6–7 rose
        7 to 8 g.p.m.

PIPE DIAMETERS FOR DOMESTIC COLD AND HOT WATER SERVICE

Nom. Pipe dia. in.	Maximum Number of Taps.		
	Flow Pipes, Head up to 70 ft.	Flow Pipes, Head above 70 ft.	Re-circulating Pipes.
½	1	1 to 2	1 to 8
¾	2 to 4	3 to 9	9 to 29
1	5 to 8	10 to 19	30 to 66
1¼	9 to 24	20 to 49	67 to 169
1½	25 to 49	50 to 79	170 to 350
2	50 to 99	80 to 153	—
2½	100 to 200	154 to 300	—

When using the above Table one bath is to be taken into account as two taps. Sinks, Lavatory Basins, Showers, Slop Sinks = one tap.

HOT WATER SUPPLY BY ELECTRICITY.

(Immersion Heater with Thermostat.)

One electrical unit (kWh)=1,000 watts=3,412 B.t.u.

Electric Load.

$$E = \frac{10\,Q\,\triangle t}{3 \cdot 412 n}\ \text{kW.}$$

where E=Electric load in kW.

Q=Quantity of water heated.

$\triangle$t=Required temperature rise in °F.

n=Number of hours for warming up (approx. 3 to 4 hours).

Recommended loads

Capacity of Hot Water Supply Tank, in gals.	Load of Immersion Heater (kW.)
20	2
30	2½
40	3

CAPACITIES OF GAS TUBING

Gas flow in cu. ft. per hour for 0·3 in. pressure drop and for gas densities from 0·4 to 0·5.

Length of Tubing	Nominal Bore in Inches						
	½	¾	1	1¼	1½	2	3
10 feet	108	225	470	930	1,300	2,640	8,240
20 feet	76	160	330	655	920	1,865	5,830
30 feet	62	130	270	535	750	1,525	4,760
40 feet		110	235	465	650	1,320	4,120
50 feet		100	210	415	580	1,180	3,685
60 feet		92	190	380	530	1,075	3,365
70 feet		83	175	350	490	995	3,115
80 feet			165	330	460	930	2,915
90 feet			155	310	435	880	2,750
100 feet			145	295	415	835	2,605
125 feet				260	370	745	2,330
150 feet				240	340	680	2,130
175 feet				220	310	630	1,970
200 feet				205	290	590	1,840
250 feet				185	260	530	1,650
300 feet				170	240	480	1,505

MULTIPLYING FACTORS FOR DIFFERENT PRESSURE DROPS

Pres. drop in $\frac{1}{10}$ in.	1	2	3	4	5	6	7	8	9	10	15	20
Volume factor ...	2·0	1·3	1·0	0·9	0·8	0·75	0·68	0·65	0·60	0·55	0·45	0·40

Calorific Value of Town Gas=450 B.t.u./cu. ft.

Gas Board's Unit=one Therm=100,000 B.t.u.

Flow of Gas in Steel Tubes

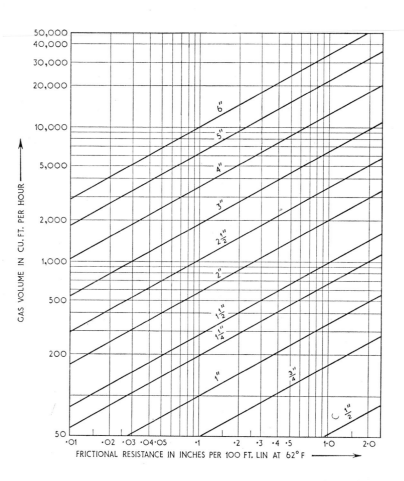

DIMENSIONS OF SUPER HIGH CAPACITY GAS METERS

Capacity	Dimensions in ft. and in.					Space Requirements, ft. and in.			
Cu. ft./hr.	A	B	C	D	E	L_1	L_2	W	H
700	2 $0\frac{1}{8}$	1 $10\frac{1}{4}$	1 $1\frac{1}{8}$	2	2 $3\frac{1}{2}$	—	2 0	2 3	2 6
1,200	2 4	2 3	1 4	3	1 8	—	4 6	1 9	3 8
1,800	2 $7\frac{1}{2}$	2 6	1 8	3	1 8	5 10	4 10	1 10	4 4
3,000	3 $2\frac{1}{2}$	2 $10\frac{1}{2}$	2 1	4	2 $2\frac{3}{4}$	6 11	5 8	2 $2\frac{1}{2}$	5 6
6,000	4 0	3 $6\frac{1}{2}$	2 $5\frac{1}{4}$	6	2 $10\frac{1}{2}$	8 3	6 3	2 7	6 0
9,000	4 9	4 $0\frac{1}{2}$	2 $8\frac{1}{4}$	6	3 5	—	—	—	—
15,000	5 5	4 $7\frac{1}{2}$	3 4	8	4 0	—	—	—	—
25,000	6 3	5 $1\frac{1}{2}$	4 1	10	4 1	—	—	—	—
30,000	6 10	5 4	4 5	10	4 $10\frac{1}{2}$	—	—	—	—
50,000	7 9	6 3	5 0	10	5 4	—	—	—	—

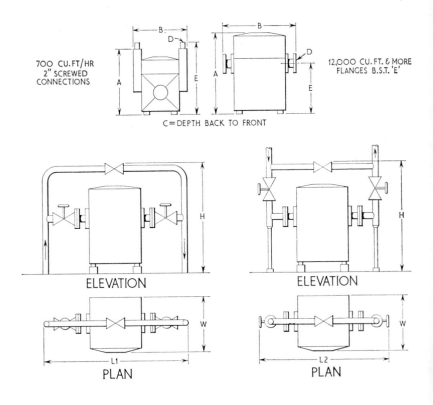

700 CU. FT/HR
2" SCREWED
CONNECTIONS

12,000 CU. FT. & MORE
FLANGES B.S.T. 'E'

C = DEPTH BACK TO FRONT

ELEVATION

ELEVATION

PLAN

PLAN

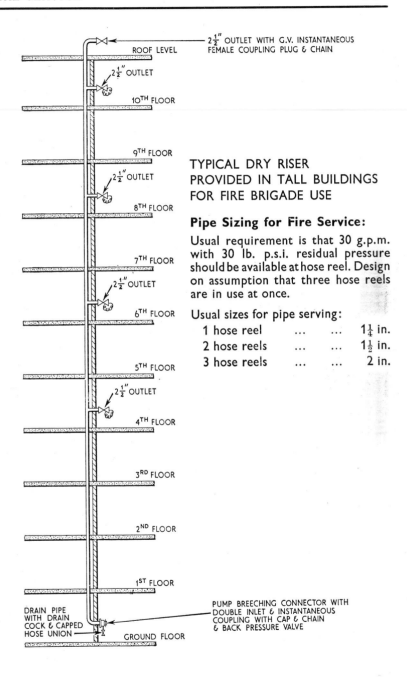

**TYPICAL DRY RISER
PROVIDED IN TALL BUILDINGS
FOR FIRE BRIGADE USE**

Pipe Sizing for Fire Service:

Usual requirement is that 30 g.p.m. with 30 lb. p.s.i. residual pressure should be available at hose reel. Design on assumption that three hose reels are in use at once.

Usual sizes for pipe serving:

1 hose reel	...	...	$1\frac{1}{4}$ in.
2 hose reels	...	...	$1\frac{1}{2}$ in.
3 hose reels	...	...	2 in.

(Diagram labels:)

$2\frac{1}{2}''$ OUTLET WITH G.V. INSTANTANEOUS FEMALE COUPLING PLUG & CHAIN

ROOF LEVEL

$2\frac{1}{2}''$ OUTLET

10TH FLOOR

9TH FLOOR

$2\frac{1}{2}''$ OUTLET

8TH FLOOR

7TH FLOOR

$2\frac{1}{2}''$ OUTLET

6TH FLOOR

5TH FLOOR

$2\frac{1}{2}''$ OUTLET

4TH FLOOR

3RD FLOOR

2ND FLOOR

1ST FLOOR

DRAIN PIPE WITH DRAIN COCK & CAPPED HOSE UNION

GROUND FLOOR

PUMP BREECHING CONNECTOR WITH DOUBLE INLET & INSTANTANEOUS COUPLING WITH CAP & CHAIN & BACK PRESSURE VALVE

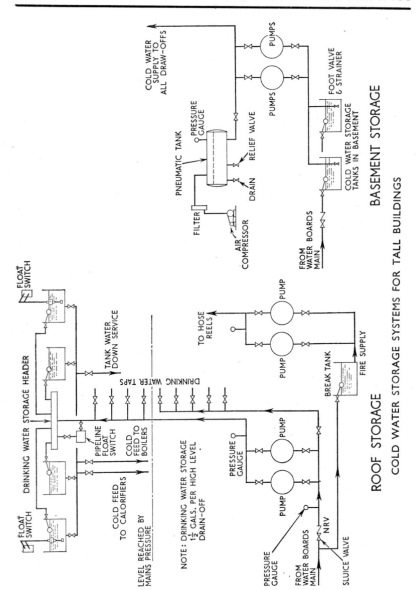

ROOF STORAGE   BASEMENT STORAGE

COLD WATER STORAGE SYSTEMS FOR TALL BUILDINGS

Section X

VENTILATION AND AIR CONDITIONING

SYSTEMS OF VENTILATION

General Types: (a) Central Conditioning System.
(b) Unit Conditioner.

(a) *Split System of Heating and Ventilating*—Heat-losses from building are supplied by direct radiators and ventilation or air conditioning delivers air at room temperature.

(b) *Combination System*—Entire operation of heating and ventilating is handled by central system.

Arrangement of Heating Unit and Fan:
(a) Draw-through, heating unit on suction side.
(b) Blow-through, heating unit on discharge.

Schemes of Air Distribution:
Fig. 1. Upward flow system.
" 2. Downward flow system.
" 3. High supply and return openings.
" 4. Low supply and return openings.
" 5. Ejector system.

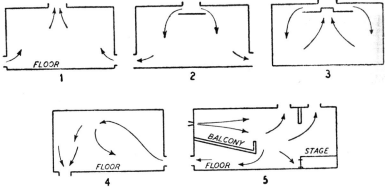

Diagrammatic Views (in Elevation) showing how various systems of Air Distribution are applied in buildings.

Dust Load for Air Filters:

Rural and suburban districts ...	0·2–0·4 gr. per 1,000 cu. ft.	
Metropolitan districts	0·4–0·8 "	"
Industrial districts	0·8–1·5 "	"

Classification of Air Filters:

(a) *Air Washers*

Overall length, approximately 6 to 7 ft.
Air velocity in washer, 500 ft. per minute.
Water quantity required, 3 to 5 gal. per 1,000 cu. ft. of air.
Water pressure for spray nozzles, 20–25 lb./ sq.in.
Water pressure for flooding nozzles, 5–10 lb./sq. in.

(b) *Viscous Air Filters*—Plates coated with a viscous fluid.

1. Unit Type:

Cartridges about 20 × 20 in.
Air volume 600 to 1,600 C.F.M. per cartridge.

2. Automatic Type:

Entrance velocity, 500 ft. per minute.
Resistance $\frac{3}{16}$ in. to $\frac{3}{8}$ in. W.G.

(c) *Dry Filters*

Felt, cloth, cellulose, glass, silk, etc., without adhesive liquid.
Air velocity 10 to 50 ft. per min.
Resistance of clean filter, 0·1 in. W.G. approximately.

Testing and Rating of Air Cleaning Devices:

(Standard Code, A.S.H.V.E.)

1. Air capacity cu. ft. per min.
2. Resistance in in. of water.
3. Dust precipitation, per cent.
4. Reconditioning power, energy necessary for automatic mechanism.
5. Dust-holding capacity, for non-automatic devices.

Design of Plenum Heating and Air Conditioning Systems:

1. Calculate heating load or cooling load:

(*a*) Sensible heat.
(*b*) Latent heat.

2. Calculate, or assume, temperature of air leaving grilles.
3. Calculate weight of air.
4. Estimate temperature loss in duct system.
5. Calculate output of heaters and washers and select type and size.
6. Calculate total heat required and select type and size of boiler.
7. Design duct system, calculate duct size.

Air Temperature at Supply Grills:

For heating, normally	80 to 90°F.	
For heating, when good mixing ...	100 to 120°F.	
For cooling, inlets near to occupied zone	10 to 15°F.	Below
For cooling, high velocity jets, diffusing	30°F.	room
nozzles		temp.

Quantity of Air required:

When temperature is limiting factor:

$$W = \frac{H_s}{0.24\,(t - t_i)} = 60\,V.d \quad \text{(lb. per hr.)}.$$

$$V = \frac{H_s}{60\,d.\,c.\,(t - t_i)} = \frac{55.2\,H_s}{60\,(t - t_i)} \quad \text{(C.F.M.)}.$$

W = Weight of air to be introduced (lb. per hr.).
V = Volume of air to be introduced (cu. ft. per min.—C.F.M.).
H_s = Sensible heat-loss or gain (B.t.u. per hr.).
t_i = Room temperature (°F.)
t = Outlet temperature at grills (°F.).
d = Density of air, lb. per cu. ft.
   = 0.075 at 70°F.
c = Specific heat of air at constant pressure.
   = 0.2415 B.t.u. per lb.
$d.c. = \frac{1}{55.2}$ (B.t.u. per cu. ft.).

When moisture content is limiting factor:

$$W = \frac{M}{(w_2 - w_1)} = 60\,V.d.$$
$$V = \frac{M}{60\,d\,(w_2 - w_1)}.$$

M = Moisture to be absorbed (grains per hr.).
w_2 = Desired specific humidity in room (grains per lb.).
w_1 = Specific humidity of air supply (gr. per lb.).

Heat required for Ventilation:

$$H = W.c.\,(t_2 - t_1) = 60.\,V.\,d.\,c.\,(t_2 - t_1)$$
$$= \frac{60.\,V\,(t_2 - t_1)}{55.2} \quad \text{(B.t.u. per hr.)}.$$

t_1 = Initial temperature, °F.
t_2 = Final temperature °F.

Requisite Temperature of Incoming Air:

$$t = t_i + \frac{55 \cdot 2\, H_s}{60\, V}$$

Temperature Drop in Ducts:

Let: W = Weight of air flowing (lb. per hr.).

     A = Area of duct walls (sq. ft.).

     s = Specific heat of air = 0·24 B.t.u. per lb.

     k = Heat-loss coefficient of duct walls.

     = 1·0 B.t.u. per sq. ft. per °F. per hr. for sheet metal ducts.

     = 0·4 for insulated ducts, 1 in. of cork board, asbestos or hair felt.

     t_2 = Initial temperature in duct (°F.).

     t_1 = Final air temperature in duct (°F.).

     t_r = Air temperature outside duct (°F.).

$$W \cdot s \cdot (t_2 - t_1) = A \cdot k \cdot \left(\frac{t_1 + t_2}{2} - t_r \right)$$

or

$$(t_2 - t_1) = A \cdot K \cdot \left(\frac{t_1 + t_2}{2} - t_r \right) \div W \cdot s$$

$$t_2 = \frac{(2\,W\,s + A\,k)\,t_1 - 2\,A\,k\,t_r}{2\,W\,s - A\,k}$$

For high temperature falls the logarithmic mean temperature is to be used.

$$W \cdot s \cdot (t_1 - t_2) = \frac{A \cdot k \cdot [(t_2 - tr) - (t_1 - tr)]}{\log_e \dfrac{t_2 - t_r}{t_1 - t_r}}$$

Allowance to be made for Altered Surface Conditions of Ducts:

(Th. Baumaister)

New brass seamless drawn tubing, clean, smooth ...	1·00
New galvanized iron pipe	1·15
High pressure steam lines, flanged	1·30
High pressure water lines, flanged	1·30
Sheet iron ducts	1·50
Concrete, very smooth	4·00
New asphalted cast-iron pipe	6·00
Concrete, ordinary	7·00
New black wrought iron pipe	1·80

Desirable Temperatures and Humidities for Industrial Processing (A.S.H.V.E. Guide)

Industry.	Process.	Temperature °F.	Relative Humidity %
Textile ...	Cotton—Carding	75–80	50
	Spinning	60–80	60–70
	Weaving	68–75	70–80
	Rayon—Spinning	70	85
	Twisting	70	65
	Silk—Spinning	75–80	65–70
	Weaving	75–80	60–70
	Wool—Carding	75–80	65–70
	Spinning	75–80	55–60
	Weaving	75–80	50–55
Tobacco ...	Cigar and Cigarette making...	70–75	55–65
	Softening	90	85
	Stemming and Strigging ...	75–85	70
Paint ...	Drying of Oil Paints	60–90	25–50
	Brush and Spray Painting ...	60–80	25–50
Paper ...	Binding, Cutting, Drying, Folding, Gluing	60–80	25–50
	Storage of Paper	60–80	35–45
Hospitals...	Operating Theatre	75–80	40–65
Libraries...	Book Storage...	65–70	38–50
Printing ...	Binding	70	45
	Folding	77	65
	Press Room/General ...	75	60–78
Photographic	Development of Film ...	70–75	60
	Drying	75–80	50
	Printing	70	70
	Cutting	72	65
Fur ...	Storage of Furs	28–40	25–40
	Drying of Furs	110	—

Air Change for Rooms, Occupancy known:

Type of Building	Air Changes per cu. ft. per person, per hour
Hospitals—Ordinary	2,500
Surgical Cases	3,000
Contagious Diseases	6,000
Schools, Theatres, Prisons, Assembly Halls	1,800
Factories, Shops	2,000
Factories, Unhealthy Trades	3,500
London County Council Regulations	1,000 min.
Code, A.S.H.V.E.	600 min.

Air Change for Rooms, Occupancy unknown:

Type of Building	Air Changes per hour
Cinemas, Theatres	5–10
Assembly Rooms	5–10
Kitchens, large	10–20
Kitchens, small	20–40
Lavatories	5–10
Restaurants	5–10
Offices	3–8
Baths	5–8
Garages	5–6
Boiler Houses, Engine Rooms	4

Garage Ventilation:

Allow 6 air changes per hour.
Two-thirds total extracted at high level; one-third total extracted at low level.
Two fans should be provided one serving as a stand by.

Bathroom and W.C. Ventilation:

Allow 40 C.F.M. per room, or 6 air changes per hour.
P.V.C. ducting is often employed for quietness and durability. To provide a standby service two fans with an automatic change-over switch are installed.

Typical Schemes:

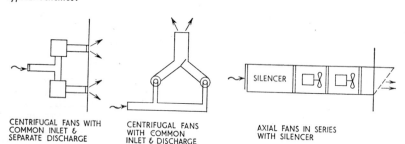

CENTRIFUGAL FANS WITH
COMMON INLET &
SEPARATE DISCHARGE

CENTRIFUGAL FANS
WITH COMMON
INLET & DISCHARGE

AXIAL FANS IN SERIES
WITH SILENCER

THEORETICAL VELOCITY OF AIR   (Due to Natural Draught).

$$V = 8.02 \sqrt{\frac{h (t_c - t_o)}{460 + t_o}}$$

V = Theoretical velocity (no friction) in ft.
h = Height of flue in ft.
t_c = Temperature of warm air column (°F.).
t_o = Temperature of outside air (°F.).

Height of	Excess of Temperature in Flue above External Air °F. (t_o=35°F.).								
Flue ft.	5	10	15	20	25	30	50	100	150
1	0·8	1·1	1·4	1·6	1·8	2·0	2·5	3·6	4·4
5	1·8	2·5	3·1	3·6	4·0	4·5	5·6	8·1	9·9
10	2·6	3·6	4·4	5·1	5·7	6·6	8·1	11·4	14·0
15	3·1	4·4	5·4	6·3	7·0	7·7	9·9	14·0	17·1
20	3·6	5·1	6·3	7·2	8·1	8·8	11·4	16·1	19·8
30	4·4	6·3	7·8	8·8	9·9	10·8	14·0	19·8	24·2
40	5·1	7·3	8·9	10·2	11·4	12·5	16·1	22·8	27·9
50	5·7	8·1	9·9	11·4	12·8	14·0	18·0	25·5	31·1
60	6·3	8·8	10·8	12·6	14·0	15·3	19·8	27·8	33·3
70	6·8	9·5	11·7	13·6	15·2	16·5	21·4	30·0	36·1
80	7·3	10·2	12·5	14·4	16·2	18·7	22·9	32·2	38·9
90	7·7	10·8	13·3	15·3	17·2	18·8	24·3	34·2	41·6
100	8·1	11·4	14·0	16·2	17·8	19·8	25·6	36·0	45·2
125	9·1	12·8	15·6	18·1	20·1	22·1	28·7	40·3	49·3
150	9·9	14·0	17·2	19·8	22·2	24·3	31·4	44·3	54·3

AIR VELOCITIES AND EQUIVALENT PRESSURES FOR STANDARD AIR

$$V = 1,096.2 \sqrt{\frac{h}{w}} = 4,000\sqrt{h}.$$

V = Velocity of air in ft. per min.
h = Velocity head in in. water gauge.
w = Density of air = 0·075 lb. per cu. ft. for Standard Air.

v	h	v	h	v	h
60	0·00023	1200	0·0915	3430	0·750
120	0·00092	1250	0·1000	3600	0·824
180	0·00206	1500	0·1430	4000	1·000
240	0·00366	1770	0·2000	4200	1·121
360	0·00824	1800	0·2059	4800	1·464
480	0·01464	2000	0·2500	4850	1·500
600	0·0229	2100	0·2803	5400	1·853
720	0·0329	2400	0·366	5600	2·000
840	0·0448	2700	0·463	6000	2·288
960	0·0586	2800	0·500	6260	2·500
1080	0·0741	3000	0·572	6870	3·000

GENERAL FORMULA FOR AIR FLOW

$$Q = AV; \quad A = \frac{Q}{V}; \quad V = \frac{Q}{A}$$

Q = Air volume (cu. ft. per min.).
A = Area of duct (sq. ft.).
V = Air velocity (ft. per min.).

Total Loss of Head (H_r) = Loss of head due to friction in duct (H_1).
+ Loss of head due to fittings (H_2).
+ Loss of head in apparatus (Filters, Heaters) (H_3).

$$H_t = H_1 + H_2 + H_3.$$

1. Loss of Head due to Friction:

for Circular Ducts—

$$H_1 = f\frac{2V^2}{gD} \times L = h_1 L$$

$$h_1 = \frac{H_1}{L}$$

H_1 = Loss of head due to friction (ins. W.G.).
h_1 = Ditto, per unit of length (ins. per ft.)
L = Length of duct (ft.).
V = Velocity of air (ft. per sec.).
D = Diameter of circular duct (ft.).
g = Gravity of earth (ft./sec.²)(=32).
f = Friction factor, which is a function of Reynold's number.

for Rectangular Ducts—

The diameter of the above formula is to be replaced by the equivalent diameter (see Table X. 10).

$$D_E = 1.265 \sqrt[5]{\frac{(ab)^3}{(a + b)}}$$

D_E = Equivalent diameter.
= Diameter of equivalent circular duct.
a, b = Sides of rectangular duct.

(For Sizing of Air Ducts, use Graph No. 4).

Addition to Friction Factor—

For smooth ducts of brickwork or plaster ... 100 per cent.
For rough ducts ... ... 200 per cent.

2. Loss of Head due to Fittings:

$$H_2 = \Sigma F \frac{V^2\rho}{2g}$$

For Standard Air:

$$H_2 = F \left(\frac{V}{4,000}\right)^2$$

H_2 = Total loss of head due to fittings (ins. W.G.).
v = Air velocity (ft. per sec.).
V = Air velocity (ft. per min.).
F = Coefficient of resistance.
ρ = Density of air.
(Values for F, see Table X. 9).

RATIO OF THE RESISTANCE OF FITTINGS TO THE TOTAL RESISTANCE OF THE CIRCUIT IN PER CENT.

Inside Dimensions of Duct...	2–4	4–12	8–24	16–45	Over 40
Sheet Metal Ducts	40	60	80	90	95
Brick Ducts	30	50	70	80	85

3. Loss of Head in Apparatus (generally given by the Manufacturers):
Average Values in inches W.G.

Filters ... ... $\frac{3}{16}$ to $\frac{3}{8}$
Air Washers ... ... $\frac{3}{16}$ to $\frac{3}{8}$
Heating Batteries ... ... $\frac{1}{8}$ to $\frac{3}{8}$

COEFFICIENTS OF RESISTANCE. For Fittings of Ventilating Systems

ITEM	RESISTANCE		F	ITEM	RESISTANCE		F
1	ELL 90°		1·5	8	ABRUPT ENLARGEMENT OF AREA $\rightarrow A_1 \; A_2$	$\left[1-\left(\frac{A_1}{A_2}\right)\right]^2$	
2	ELL 90°, ROUNDED		0·5	9	FLOW FROM DUCT INTO ROOM		1·0
3	LONG SWEEP ELL 90°, R=2D		0·1	10	GRADUAL REDUCING		0
4	ELL 45°		0·5	11	ABRUPT REDUCING		0 TO 0·35
5	ELL 45°, ROUNDED		0·2	12	FLOW FROM ROOM INTO DUCT		0 TO 0·35
6	LONG SWEEP ELL 45°, R=2D		0·05	13	BRANCH $A_1 + A_2 = A_0$ SEE N°6. SEE N°10.		—

ITEM	RESISTANCE		F				
7	GRADUALLY INCREASED AREA α FOR $\alpha \leqq 8°$ FOR $\alpha > 8°$ A_1, A_2 = SECTIONAL AREA	$0·15\left[1-\left(\frac{A_1}{A_2}\right)\right]^2$ $\left[1-\left(\frac{A_1}{A_2}\right)\right]^2$					
14	GRILLS						
	FREE AREA DIVIDED BY TOTAL SURFACE	0·6	0·5	0·4	0·3	0·2	
	WIRE GAUZE	2	3	5	8	17	
	SHEET METAL	4	6	10	20	50	

RESISTANCE H_2. For various Velocities and Values of $H_2 = \dfrac{V^2 F}{2g}$,

Velocity of Air. ft. per min	Resistance H in in. W.G. for °F.								
	1	2	3	4	5	6	7	8	9
400	0·0099	0·0198	0·0297	0·0396	0·0496	0·0595	0·0694	0·0793	0·0892
500	0·0155	0·0310	0·0465	0·0620	0·0775	0·0929	0·108	0·124	0·139
600	0·0223	0·0446	0·0669	0·0892	0·112	0·134	0·156	0·178	0·201
700	0·0304	0·0607	0·0911	0·121	0·152	0·182	0·213	0·243	0·273
800	0·0396	0·0793	0·119	0·159	0·198	0·238	0·277	0·317	0·357
900	0·0502	0·100	0·151	0·201	0·251	0·301	0·351	0·401	0·452
1,000	0·0619	0·124	0·186	0·248	0·310	0·372	0·434	0·496	0·557
1,200	0·0892	0·178	0·268	0·357	0·446	0·535	0·624	0·714	0·803
1,400	0·121	0·243	0·364	0·486	0·607	0·728	0·850	0·974	1·09
1,600	0·159	0·317	0·476	0·634	0·793	0·952	1·11	1·27	1·43
1,800	0·201	0·401	0·602	0·803	1·00	1·20	1·41	1·61	1·81
2,000	0·248	0·496	0·743	0·991	1·24	1·49	1·73	1·98	2·23
2,400	0·357	0·714	1·07	1·43	1·78	2·14	2·50	2·85	3·21
2,800	0·486	0·971	1·46	1·94	2·43	2·91	3·40	3·88	4·37
3,200	0·634	1·27	1·90	2·54	3·17	3·81	4·44	5·07	5·71
3,600	0·803	1·61	2·41	3·21	4·01	4·82	5·62	6·42	7·22
4,000	0·991	1·98	2·97	3·96	4·96	5·95	6·94	7·93	8·92

CIRCULAR EQUIVALENTS OF RECTANGULAR DUCTS FOR EQUAL FRICTION

$$d = 1.265 \sqrt[5]{\frac{(ab)^3}{a+b}}$$

Side Rect. Duct.	36	34	32	30	28	26	24	22	20	18	16	15	14	13	12	11	10	9	8	7	6	5
5																						5·5
6																					6·6	6·0
7																				7·7	7·0	6·5
8																			8·8	8·2	7·6	6·9
9																		9·9	9·3	8·7	8·0	7·3
10																	11·0	10·4	9·8	9·2	8·4	7·7
11																12·1	11·5	10·9	10·2	9·6	8·8	8·1
12															13·2	12·6	12·0	11·4	10·7	10·0	9·2	8·4
13														14·3	13·7	13·3	12·5	11·9	11·1	10·4	9·6	8·8
14													15·4	14·9	14·3	13·6	12·9	12·3	11·5	10·8	9·9	9·0
15												16·5	16·0	15·3	14·7	14·1	13·4	12·7	11·9	11·1	10·2	9·2
16											17·6	17·1	16·5	15·8	15·2	14·5	13·8	13·1	12·3	11·5	10·5	9·6
17											18·2	17·5	17·0	16·3	15·7	14·9	14·2	13·3	12·6	11·9	10·8	9·8
18										19·8	18·7	18·1	17·4	16·8	16·1	15·4	14·6	13·9	12·9	12·1	11·1	10·1
19										20·4	19·2	18·7	18·0	17·2	16·5	15·8	15·0	14·2	13·3	12·4	11·4	10·3
20									22·0	20·9	19·7	19·1	18·4	17·6	17·0	16·2	15·4	14·5	13·6	12·7	11·6	10·5
22								24·2	23·1	21·9	20·6	20·0	19·2	18·5	17·8	16·9	16·1	15·1	14·2	13·2	12·1	11·0
24							26·4	25·2	24·0	22·8	21·5	20·8	20·0	19·3	18·5	17·8	16·8	15·8	14·8	13·7	12·6	11·4
26						28·6	27·5	26·3	25·1	23·8	22·3	21·6	20·8	20·0	19·2	18·2	17·3	16·4	15·4	14·2	13·1	11·8
28					30·8	29·7	28·5	27·3	26·0	24·6	23·1	22·4	21·5	20·7	19·8	18·9	18·0	16·9	15·9	14·7	13·5	12·2
30				33·0	32·4	30·7	29·5	28·2	26·8	25·4	23·9	23·1	22·2	21·4	20·5	19·5	18·7	17·4	16·4	15·2	13·9	12·6
32			35·2	34·1	33·0	31·7	30·5	29·1	27·7	26·2	24·6	23·8	22·9	22·0	21·1	20·1	19·1	18·0	16·9	15·6	14·3	12·9
34		37·4	36·3	35·1	34·0	32·7	31·3	30·0	28·5	26·9	25·3	24·4	23·5	22·6	21·6	20·7	19·6	18·5	17·3	16·1	14·7	13·2
36	39·6	38·5	37·3	36·1	34·8	33·6	32·2	30·8	29·3	27·7	26·0	25·2	24·2	23·2	22·2	21·2	20·1	19·1	17·7	16·5	15·1	13·6
38	40·7	39·5	38·4	37·1	35·9	34·5	33·1	31·5	30·0	28·4	26·7	25·8	24·8	23·8	22·9	21·7	20·6	19·4	18·2	16·8	15·4	13·9
40	41·7	40·5	39·3	38·0	36·7	35·3	33·9	32·4	30·8	29·1	27·3	26·4	25·4	24·4	23·3	22·2	21·1	19·9	18·6	17·2	15·7	14·3
42	42·7	41·5	40·3	39·0	37·6	36·0	34·5	33·0	31·4	29·8	27·9	26·9	25·9	24·9	23·8	22·7	21·6	20·3	19·0	17·6	16·1	14·5
44	43·7	42·5	41·2	39·9	38·5	36·9	35·2	33·7	32·1	30·3	28·5	27·5	26·5	25·4	24·2	23·2	22·0	20·7	19·4	18·0	16·4	14·8
46	44·8	43·5	42·2	40·8	39·3	37·8	36·2	34·6	32·8	31·0	29·1	28·1	27·0	25·9	24·8	23·6	22·4	21·1	19·8	18·3	16·7	15·1
48	45·6	44·4	43·0	41·5	40·0	38·5	37·0	35·2	33·4	31·6	29·6	28·6	27·5	26·4	25·2	24·1	22·8	21·5	20·1	18·6	17·0	15·4
50	46·5	45·2	43·8	42·3	40·8	39·2	37·6	35·9	34·1	32·2	30·3	29·1	28·0	26·9	25·7	24·5	23·2	21·9	20·4	19·0	17·3	15·7
54	48·2	47·0	45·5	44·0	42·4	40·7	38·9	37·2	35·3	33·4	31·2	30·1	29·0	27·8	26·6	25·3	24·0	22·6	21·1	19·6	17·9	16·1
60	50·9	49·3	47·8	46·1	44·5	42·7	40·9	39·1	37·1	34·9	32·7	31·6	30·5	29·1	27·8	26·5	25·1	23·6	22·1	20·4	18·7	16·8
64	52·4	50·9	49·2	47·5	45·8	44·0	42·2	40·2	38·2	35·9	33·7	32·6	31·3	29·9	28·6	27·3	25·9	24·3	22·7	21·0	19·2	17·3
70	54·5	52·9	51·3	49·5	47·8	46·0																

RECOMMENDED VELOCITIES FOR VENTILATING SYSTEMS
(in ft. per min.)

Service.	Public Buildings.	Industrial Plants.
Air Intake from the outside	500–900	1,000–1,200
Air Washers	500	500–600
Heater Connection to Fan	700–900	1,000–1,400
Main Ducts	1,000–1,500	1,200–2,400
Branch Ducts and Risers	500–600	900–1,800
Supply Registers and Grilles	250–450	—
Supply Openings	—	350–500
Supply Grilles near the Floor	150–250	—

RECOMMENDED VELOCITIES FOR EXHAUST VENTILATING SYSTEMS
(in ft. per min.)

Service.	Public Buildings	Industrial Plants
Risers	500–600	900–1,800
Main Ducts	900–1,500	1,200–2,400

Air velocities in gravity exhaust Systems are 200 to 600 ft. per min.

SIZE OF DUCTS

	Air Ministry Specification.			Specification "A"		Specification "B"	
	Longest Side or dia. in in.	Gauge. I.S.W.G.	Angle Iron. Flanged Points.	Longest Side or dia. in in.	Gauge I.S.W.G.	Longest Side or dia in in.	Gauge I.S.W.G.
Rectangular	Up to 15	22	1–1– $\frac{1}{8}$	Up to 6	24	Up to 12	24
	16–24	20	$1\frac{1}{2}$–$1\frac{1}{2}$– $\frac{3}{16}$	6–12	22	12–18	22
	25–30	18	2 –2 – $\frac{1}{4}$	12–18	20	18–30	20
	Above 30	16	2 –2 – $\frac{1}{4}$	18–36	18	30–48	18
				36–54	16	Above 48	16
				Above 54	14		
Circular	Up to 15	22	1 –1 – $\frac{1}{8}$	Up to 12	22	Up to 18	24
	16–24	20	$1\frac{1}{2}$–$1\frac{1}{2}$– $\frac{3}{16}$	12–20	20	18–30	22
	25–30	18	$1\frac{1}{2}$–$1\frac{1}{2}$– $\frac{3}{16}$	20–42	18	30–42	20
	Above 30	16	2 –2 – $\frac{1}{4}$	Above 42	16	42–72	18
						Above 72	16

WEIGHTS OF SHEET METAL (in lb. per sq. ft.)

Gauge.	14	16	18	20	22	24
Galvanized (lb. per sq. ft.)	3·25	2·6	2·1	1·67	1·35	1·1
Black (lb. per sq. ft.) ...	3·15	2·5	2·0	1·57	1·25	1·0

Ducts outside Buildings exposed to atmosphere are one gauge heavier.
Ducts over 30 in. longest side to have Flanged Joints.
Minimum radius of Duct Bends R min. = 1·5D.

Weight of Air to be circulated :

$$W = \frac{X}{w_2 - w_1}$$

W = Weight of air to be circulated (lb. per hr.).
X = Weight of water to be evaporated (lb. per hr.)
w_1 = Absolute humidity of entering air (lb. per lb.)
w_2 = Absolute humidity of leaving air (lb. per lb.)

The relative humidity of the air leaving the dryer is usually kept below 75 per cent.

Heat Amount :

Total Heat Amount = 1. Heat for evaporating moisture.
2. Heat for heating of stock.
3. Heat-loss due to air change.
4. Heat transmission loss of drying chamber.

WATER CONTENT OF VARIOUS MATERIALS

Material	Original per cent	Final per cent	Material	Original per cent	Final per cent
Bituminous Coal ...	40–60	8–12	Hides	45	0
Earth	45–50	0	Glue	80–90	0
Earth, Sandy ...	20–25	0	Glue, Air Dried ...	15	0
Grain	17–23	10–12	Macaroni	35	0
Rubber Goods ...	30–50	0	Soap	27–35	25–26
Green Hardwood ...	50	} 10–15	Starch	38–45	12–14
Green Softwood ...	30–50		Starch, Air Dried ...	16–20	12–14
Air Dried Hardwood	17–20		Peat	85–90	30–35
Air Dried Softwood	10–15	} 10–15	Yarn, Washing ...	40–50	0
Cork	40–45				

DRYING TEMPERATURES AND TIME FOR VARIOUS MATERIALS

Material.	Temp. °F.	Time Hours	Material.	Temp. °F.	Time Hours
Bedding	150–190		Hides, Thin	90	2–4
Cereals	110–150		Ink, Printing	70–300	
Coconut	145–155	4–6	Knitted Fabrics ...	140–180	
Coffee	160–180	24	Leather, Thick Sole ...	90	4–6
Cores, Oil Sand ...	300	0·5	Lumber :		
Films, Photo	90		Green Hardwood ...	100–180	3–180
Fruits, Vegetable ...	140	2–6	Green Softwood ...	160–220	24–350
Furs	110		Macaroni	90–110	
Glue	70–90	2–4	Matches	140–180	
Glue Size on Furniture	130	4	Milk	250–300	
Gut	150		Paper Glued	130–300	
Gypsum Wall Board...			Paper Treated ...	140–200	
Start Wet	350		Rubber	80–90	6–12
Finish	190		Soap	125	12
Gypsum Blocks ...	350–190	8–16	Sugar	150–200	0·3–0·5
Hair Goods	150–190		Tannin...	250–300	
Hats, Felt	140–180		Terra Cotta	150–200	12–96
Hops	120–180				

The defogging of rooms is carried out by blowing in dry, hot air and exhausting humidified air.

Weight of Water Evaporated from Open Vats:

$$W = \frac{9.4 \, Ac \, (p_s - p_a)}{P}$$

W = Weight of water evaporated (lb. per hr.).
A = Surface of vats (sq. ft.).
P_s = Partial pressure of water vapour of saturated air at the temperature of the water in vats (in. of mercury).
P_a = Partial pressure of water vapour of the surrounding air (in. of mercury).
P = Atm. pres. (in. of mercury).
c = 0·55 for still air.
  = 0·71 for slight air movement.
  = 0·86 for fast air movement.

Weight of Air to be circulated:

$$G = \frac{W}{(w_2 - w_1)}$$

G = Weight of air (lb. per hr.).
W = Weight of water vapour to be removed (lb. per hr.).
w_1 = Original absolute humidity of air (lb. per lb.).
w_2 = Final absolute humidity of air (lb. per lb.).

Amount of Heat:

$$H = Gc \, (t_i - t_o)$$

H = Amount of heat, without fabric loss of room or other losses (B.t.u. per hr.).
G = Weight of air, see above (lb. per hr.).
t_i = Inside air temperature (°F.).
t_o = Outside air temperature (°F.).
c = 0·24 = specific heat of air (B.t.u./lb. °F.).

Air Change for Good Conditions:

Laundries	10–15 air changes per hour
Large Kitchens	10–20 ,,
Dyeing Shops	10–20 ,,
Swimming Baths	5–10 ,,

Principle of Air Conditioning: Air conditioning is the control of atmospheric conditions within an enclosure with reference to temperature, humidity, air motion, and cleanliness. Often combined with removing of bacteria, odours, toxic gases, and with ionization of air.

Requirements:

1. *For Human Comfort.*—Human comfort depends on cooling of the body surface and takes place partially by evaporation, so that both temperature and humidity, as well as air velocity of surrounding air affect comfort and health.

   Thermo-Equivalent Conditions are combinations of temperature, humidity and air movement which produce the same feeling of warmth. (See page V. 12, et seq.)

2. *Industrial Purposes.*—Hygroscopic materials such as textile fibres, paper, timber, leather, etc., take up or give off moisture to the atmosphere to an extent governed by the temperature and humidity of the surrounding air. Eventually the water content of the material approaches an ultimate value termed the Equilibrium Water Content. Therefore many process works have to be carried out in air-conditioned rooms. (See X. 5.)

Air Conditioning Equipment consists of all apparatus and installations used for ventilation and plenum heating plants (such as Fans, Heater Batteries, Mixing Chambers with Dampers, Distribution Ducting, etc.) with the addition of an Air Washer for humidification or dehumidification, and a Refrigeration Plant for cooling in summer, if required, and an Automatic Control System.

HUMIDITY (see V. 8 to V. 14)

Dry-Bulb Thermometer, i.e., an ordinary thermometer, indicates the air temperature without being affected by the moisture in the air.

Wet-Bulb Thermometer has its bulb covered with cloth dipped into water, and it is exposed to a current of air. It indicates the temperature of adiabatic saturation.

The Wet-Bulb Depression is the difference in the readings of Dry-Bulb and Wet-Bulb Temperatures, and is a measure of the relative humidity of the air. (See V. 8 to V. 14.)

DETERMINATION OF HUMIDITY

1. Dew Point Method.—A mirror surface is cooled by evaporation of ether, or any other low-boiling solvent, and the temperature at which moisture begins to form is measured.

2. Wet-Bulb Method.—Dry Bulb and Wet Bulb Temperatures are measured by a Sling Psychrometer or an Aspiration Psychrometer. Table V. 14 to be used for determination of the relative humidity.

3. Hair Hygrometer.—The sensitive hygroscopic element is a human hair.

4. Electric Hygrometer is an instrument, the electrical resistance of which varies with the relative humidity of the surrounding air.

APPARATUS

Wet and Dry Bulb Thermometer: On a wet bulb thermometer the water evaporates from the surface of the cloth dipped into water. The latent heat of evaporation is taken from the surrounding air, and, therefore, the wet bulb thermometer gives a lower reading than the dry bulb thermometer.

The Wet Bulb Depression is the difference in reading on Dry and Wet bulb thermometer and is the measurement for the humidity in the air.

Sling Psychrometer consists of a Dry bulb and a Wet bulb thermometer mounted on a board with a handle for slinging through the air. The peripheral velocity should be not less than 15 ft. per sec.

Aspiration Psychrometer (Assman) consists of a Dry bulb and Wet bulb thermometer the bulbs of which are enclosed in a casing. Air is drawn through the casing by means of a spring operated propeller fan.

Humidity in Heated Rooms: The humidity in heated rooms should be maintained within 35% to 50%, for good practice 40% relative humidity at 68°F. Dry bulb temperature.

DESIGN OF AIR CONDITIONING SYSTEMS (see X. 2 to X. 4)

Air Conditioning Cooling Load:

The Air Conditioning Cooling Load is made up from the Sensible Heat Load and the Latent Heat Load.

(*a*) *The Sensible Heat Load* consists of:
  1. Heat transfer through walls, windows, ceilings, etc.
  2. Heat gained by solar radiation.
  3. Heat emission of occupants.
  4. Heat introduced by infiltration of outside air, or ventilation.
  5. Heat emission of appliances (mechanical, electrical, gas, etc.).

(*b*) *The Latent Heat Load* consists of:
  1. Moisture given off by people.
  2. Infiltration of outside air, or ventilation.
  3. Latent heat from appliances.
       (See pages V. 11, VI. 11 to VI. 13.)

Methods of Cooling:
  1. Spray-type air conditioners, air washers.
  2. Surface type coolers.
  3. Adsorption type.
  4. Absorption type.

Compression Refrigeration System: The plant consists of a compressor, condenser, receiver, reducing valve and evaporator.
The function is as follows : Hot compressed vapour, called refrigerant, leaving the compressor is liquefied in the condenser by cooling with air or water. The liquid refrigerant then passes from the high pressure side through the expansion valve to the low pressure side and evaporates in the evaporator, extracting the required latent heat of evaporation from the surroundings thus reducing the temperature of the medium to be cooled.

Direct System : The evaporator in which the expansion of the liquid refrigerant takes place is fixed directly in the room to be cooled, e.g. a direct expansion coil in an air washer.

Indirect, or Brine System : Indirect cooling coils are supplied with cold brine which has been previously cooled by a refrigerant.

Absorption System of Refrigeration: The compressor used in the compression system is replaced by a generator where the refrigerant, ammonia, is absorbed and then driven off by applying heat.

AIR WASHER

Air Washers are sheet metal, or sometimes bricked or concrete chambers, where air is drawn through a mist caused by spray nozzles and then through eliminators. The water for the spray nozzles is recirculated by a pump and can be heated or cooled. A tempering heater is installed before, and a reheating battery after, the air washer.

General Data on Air Washers:

Cleaning efficiency : 70 per cent with fine dust.

Cleaning efficiency : 98 per cent with coarse dirt.

Air velocity through washer : 450 to 550 f.p.m.

Resistance : 0·2 to 0·5 ins. W.G.

Water pressure for sprays : 15 to 25 lb. per sq. in.

Water quantity for spray nozzles : 3 to 3·5 gal. per 1000 cu. ft. air.

Humidifying efficiency :

$$E = \frac{t_1 - t_2}{t_1 - t_w} \, 100 \text{ per cent.}$$

$t_1 =$ initial dry bulb temperature ° F.

$t_2 =$ final dry bulb temperature °F.

$t_w =$ initial wet bulb temperature °F.

$E =$ Efficiency of humidification or saturation.

$E =$ 60 to 70 per cent with one bank of nozzles, downstream.

65 to 75 per cent with one bank of nozzles, upstream.

85 to 100 per cent with two banks of nozzles.

Refrigeration Units:

The Standard Term for measuring the capacity of refrigeration equipment is the Ton of Refrigeration. One Ton of Refrigeration is equal to the quantity of Heat in B.t.u. required to melt 1 American ton of pure ice of 32°F. to water 32°F. in 24 hours.

Therefore, one Ton of Refrigeration equals:

2,000 lb. per 24 hrs. × 144 B.t.u./lb. = 288,000 B.t.u. per 24 hrs.

= 12,000 B.t.u. per hour.

= 200 B.t.u. per min.

SURFACE TYPE AIR CONDITIONERS

Surface Type Air Conditioners consist of plain or gilled tubes containing a heating medium (steam, hot water, etc.) or a cooling medium (cold water, brine, refrigerant). Dehumidification is achieved by cooling the air below dew point causing part of the moisture content to be condensed out.

Required Surface of a Cooler:

$$A = \frac{H}{C\,(t_a - t_m)}$$

A = Area of cooler, or heater in sq. ft.

H = Sensible heat loss to be removed in B.t.u. per hr.

$(t_a - t_m)$ = log. mean temperature difference between air and cooling, or heating medium, °F. (see IV. 11).

C = Heat transfer coefficient, in B.t.u. per sq. ft. per hr. per °F.

Heat Transfer Coefficient for finned tubes, $\frac{3}{4}$ in. tube dia., $1\frac{1}{2}$ in. O.D. of fins, 7 fins per in. run, 50 per cent free area, one to five rows of tubes, air velocity over tubes 500 ft. per min.

For heating by steam, up to 150 lb./sq. in S.W.P.:

$$C = 10 \text{ B.t.u. per sq. ft. per hr. per °F.}$$

For cooling, by water (water velocity 2 ft./sec.): $C = 9$

For cooling, by direct expansion $C = 6$

(Coefficients for other Air Velocities, see IV. 15)

ADSORPTION SYSTEMS

In Adsorption Systems humidity of the air is reduced by adsorbent materials, such as silica-gel or activated alumina. The adsorbent material can be reactivated by heating, the water adsorbed being evaporated, and used repeatedly. The adsorption system is especially suitable for dehydration at room temperature, and where gas or high pressure steam is available for reactivation.

Temperature for Reactivation: 325 to 350°F.

Heat required for Reactivation: 2100 to 2500 B.t.u./lb. of water removed.

The action is physical—no chemical change.

Silica-gel, SiO_2 is a hard, hygroscopic crystalline substance; size of a pea; very porous.

Voids are about 50% by volume.

Adsorbs water up to 40% of own weight.

Bulk density: 30 to 45 lbs. per cu. ft.

Specific heat: 0·27 B.t.u./lb.

Activated Alumina, about 90% aluminium oxide, Al_2O_3; very porous.

Voids about 50 to 70% by volume.

Adsorbs water up to 60% of own weight.

Bulk density: 50 to 54 lb. per cu. ft.

Specific heat: 0·24 B.t.u./lb.

ABSORPTION SYSTEMS

Humidity from the air is absorbed by a hygroscopic solution such as calcium chloride solution.

SUMMARY OF AIR CONDITIONING PROCESSES

Air Conditioning Processes are either heating, cooling, humidifying or dehumidifying of the air, and the air temperature and humidity alter by any of these processes. Computations can be carried out by using either algebraic equations or a psychrometric chart. (See V. 7 to V. 18.) Computations are to be based upon the weight of 1 lb. of dry air since the weight remains constant during the process.

SUMMARY OF PROCESSES

Process	Indication in chart Fig.	Final Air Conditions	Equipment used
Heating	A-B	S.H. and D.P. unchanged. R.H. reduced. W.B.T. increased.	Air passes over surface air heater.
Cooling above Dew Point.	A-C	S.H. and D.P. unchanged. R.H. increased. W.B.T. reduced ; no condensation of vapour.	Air passes an air washer using refri-gerated water for spray nozzles or air passes a surface cooler.
Cooling to Dew Point Temperature.	A-D	S.H. and D.P. unchanged. R.H. becomes 100 per cent. D.B.T. and W.B.T. coincide; the air is satura-ted but there is no condensation of vapour.	
Cooling below Dew Point Temperature Dehumidification	A-D-E	S.H. and D.P. reduced. The final air is saturated and part of the humidity has condensed.	
Humidification i.e. adiabatic saturation.	A-F	The process is adiabatic, no heat is added or abstracted. W.B.T. un-changed. R.H. increased. D.P. and S.H. increased.	Air passes air washer using recir-culated water for spray nozzles.
Mixing two airs	A-G-H	Points A and G representing the initial conditions of the atmospheres to be mixed are to be connected by a straight line. This line is to be divided inversely proportional to the weights of both airs. The point "H" thus found indicates the conditions of the air mixture.	Mixing cham-ber or two ducts with dampers.

See Chart and Key on page X. 21.

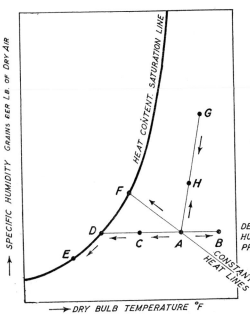

KEY

R.H. = RELATIVE HUMIDITY
S.H. = SPECIFIC HUMIDITY
D.B.T. = DRY BULB TEMPERATURE
W.B.T. = WET BULB TEMPERATURE
D.P. = DEW POINT TEMPERATURE

DEW POINT LINES ·CONSTANT SPECIFIC HUMIDITY AND CONSTANT VAPOUR PRESSURE

PSYCHROMETRIC CHART

The Psychrometric Chart is plotted with Dry Bulb Temperature as abscissa and Specific Humidity as ordinate. Any point on the chart represents conditions of air-vapour mixture, such as Dry Bulb Temperature, Wet Bulb Temperature, Dew Point, Relative Humidity, Specific Humidity, Specific Volume, and Vapour Pressure. Any two values locate the point representing the state of air, and the remaining values can be read from the Chart.

Example of the use of the Psychrometric Chart:

All conditions to be found for air at 100°F. Dry Bulb Temperature and 60% Relative Humidity.

The Wet Bulb Temperature is found on the intersection of the constant heat line with saturation line : it is 87°F.

The Dew Point is found on the intersection of the horizontal Dew Point line with the saturation line : it is 84°F.

The Specific Humidity is found by following the same horizontal dew point line to the scale on the left ; it is 176 grains per lb.

The Vapour Pressure is found by following the same horizontal dew point line to the scale on the right : it is 38 millibars.

The Specific Volume may be read from the red lines : it is by interpolation 14·8 cu. ft. per lb.

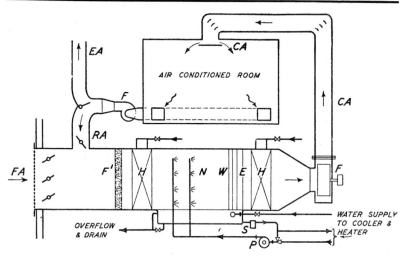

AIR-CONDITIONING LAYOUT WITHOUT BYPASS

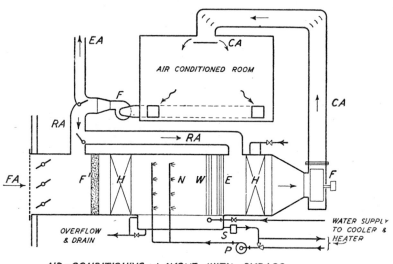

AIR-CONDITIONING LAYOUT WITH BYPASS

REFERENCE

FA = FRESH AIR	*F* = FAN	*P* = PUMP
CA = CONDITIONED AIR	*F'* = FILTER	*S* = STRAINER
RA = RECIRCULATED AIR	*H* = HEATER	*W* = WET SCRUBBER
EA = EXHAUST AIR	*N* = SPRAY NOZZLES	*E* = ELIMINATOR PLATES

PROPERTIES OF REFRIGERANTS

Refrigerant	Symbol	Boiling Temp. °F.	Critical Temp. °F.	Properties	Inflammability	Use
Ammonia.	NH_3	−28	271	Penetrating odour soluble in water, harmless in concentration up to 1/30 per cent.	Non-inflammable explosive.	Large plants.
Sulphur dioxide.	SO_2	14	311	Colourless vapour, unpleasant to breathe but not poisonous.	Not combustible or corrosive if not in contact with water.	Small plants.
Carbon dioxide.	CO_2	−108·4	87·8	Heavy, colourless odourless gas, harmless to breathe.	Not inflammable	Large plants.
Ethyl chloride	C_2H_5Cl	55	—	Colourless, very volatile, sweet taste.	Inflammable; non-corrosive with steel iron, copper.	—
Methyl chloride.	CH_3Cl	−10·7	289·6	Colourless, sweet smelling vapour.	Inflammable, explosive, non-corrosive with steel,iron,copper	Small plants.
Dichloro-difluoro-methane, F-12 "Freon".	CCl_2F_2	−21·7	222·7	Odourless, non-toxic.	Not inflammable not explosive; non-corrosive.	Small plants.
Carrene, methylene chloride.	$CHCl$	103·6	473	Colourless liquid at atm. conditions, sweet pleasant odour, similar to chloroform.	Not explosive.	—
Dieline dichloro-ethylene.	$C_2H_2Cl_2$	122	470	Colourless liquid odourless, non-toxic.	Inflammable non-corrosive with steel, iron, nickel, copper, aluminium.	Small plants.
Trieline. Trichlor-ethylene	C_2HCl_3	−126	188	Heavy, colourless liquid, pleasant odour.	Non-inflammable; non-explosive; non-corrosive.	—
Water.	H_2O	212	706	See data, p. IV. 24.	—	Steam jet and centrifugal plants.

PROPERTIES OF REFRIGERANT

Refrigerant	Symbol	Saturation Pressure in lbs. per sq. in. Abs.		Ratio of Compression	Heat Content			Per ton of Refrigeration Theoretical	
		Evaporator 5°F.	Condenser 86°F.		Vapour Leaving Evaporator B.t.u./lb.	Liquid Leaving Condenser B.t.u./lb.	Refrigerant Effect B.t.u./lb.	H.P.	Displacement-cu.ft.
Ammonia	NH_3	34·27	169·2	4·93	613·3	138·9	474·4	0·99	3·44
Sulphur Dioxide ...	SO_2	11·82	65·9	5·57	162·3	18·2	144·1	0·99	9·26
Carbon Dioxide ...	CO_2	331·8	1,039·6	3·14	101	46·8	54·2	1·87	0·99
Ethyl Chloride ...	C_2H_5Cl	4·65	20·89	5·83	165	23	142	0·92	23·95
Methyl Chloride ...	CH_3Cl	20·89	95·53	4·57	154	25·1	138·9	1·06	6·83
Dichloro-difluoro-methane "F-12" Freon ...	CCl_2F_2	26·51	107·9	4·07	78·79	27·72	51·07	1·00	5·82
Methylene Chloride, Carrene	$CHCl$	1·2	10·25	8·56	163·80	29·24	134·56	0·965	71·5
Dieline Dichlorethylene	$C_2H_2Cl_2$	0·9	7·4	8·23	137·35	23·22	114·13	0·918	110
Trieline Trichlorethylene	C_2HCl_3	0·16	1·72	10·84	113·67	20·1	93·57	0·928	513
Water	H_2O	0·0886 (32° F.)	0·946 (100° F.)	10·68	—	—	—	0·78	655

EQUIPMENT FOR INDUSTRIAL EXHAUST SYSTEMS

A. Suction hoods, booths, or canopies for fume and dust collection, or suction nozzles, or feed hoppers for pneumatic conveying.

B. Conveying, ducting or tubing.

C. Fan or exhauster to create the necessary pressure or vacuum for pneumatic conveying.

D. Dust separator, for separating the conveyed material from the conveying air.

CLASSIFICATION OF SCHEMES

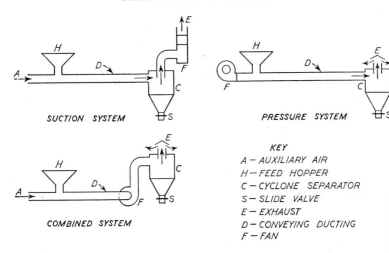

SUCTION SYSTEM   PRESSURE SYSTEM

COMBINED SYSTEM

KEY
A – AUXILIARY AIR
H – FEED HOPPER
C – CYCLONE SEPARATOR
S – SLIDE VALVE
E – EXHAUST
D – CONVEYING DUCTING
F – FAN

Pneumatic Conveying Plants are suitable for conveyance of material in powdered form or in solids up to 2 in. size, dry: not more than 20 per cent moisture, not sticking.

Efficiency of pneumatic conveying plants is low but compensated by easy handling, free of dust.

Suction Type—Distance of conveying up to 1,000 ft. difference in heights up to 140 ft. Required vacuum 8 to 16 in. mercury.

Pressure Type—Distance of conveying above 1,000 ft. working pressure up to 6 lb per sq. in. Advantage: possibility of conveying material over long distances by connecting more systems in series.

Working pressure above 6 lb. per sq. in. not suitable, because of high running cost.

FUME AND DUST REMOVAL

TYPES OF HOODS

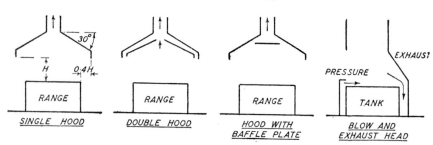

| SINGLE HOOD | DOUBLE HOOD | HOOD WITH BAFFLE PLATE | BLOW AND EXHAUST HEAD |

Single Hoods—For removing fumes which rise naturally, for ranges, forge fires, vats, kettles, etc. Projection beyond the range approx. $4\frac{3}{4}$ in. for each foot of height above range. 50 to 300 f.p.m. entrance velocity. Duct area about one-fifth to one-tenth of hood area.

Double Hoods with gap around the perimeter for fume extraction in rooms with cross currents, high velocity of entering air, approximately 1,000 f.p.m.

Velocity in Ducts—Approximately 2,000 f.p.m.

Recommended Velocities through Top Hoods and Booth, subject to cross draughts
Velocities in f.p.m.

Canopy Hood, open 200–250	Canopy Hood, double 1000
Canopy Hood, closed 1 side ... 175–200	Booths, through 1 side ... 100–150
Canopy Hood, closed 2 sides ... 150–175	Laboratory Hoods, through
Canopy Hood, closed 3 sides ... 100–150	doors 50–75

Coefficients of Entry and Velocity. Pressure Loss of Dust Extraction Hoods:

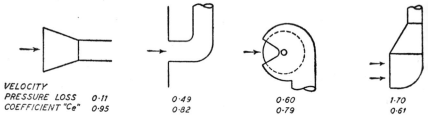

VELOCITY			
PRESSURE LOSS	0·11	0·49	0·60	1·70
COEFFICIENT "Ce"	0·95	0·82	0·79	0·61

Flow of Air into a Hood:

$$Q = 4000 C_e A_t \sqrt{h_t}$$

Q = Air volume   c.f.m.
C_e = Entrance coefficient.
A_t = Area of throat   sq. ft.
h_t = Static suction in throat, inches W.G.
h_v = Velocity pressure.

Coefficient of Entry: $C_e = \dfrac{\sqrt{h_v}}{h_t}$

Entrance Loss into Hood:

$$h_e = \frac{(1 - C^2_e)}{C_e^{\,2}} h_v \text{ inches of water.}$$

The Transporting Velocity for material varies with the size, specific
gravity and shape of the material.   (Dalla Valle).

Vertical Lifting Velocity

$$V = 13,300 \quad \frac{s}{s+1} \times d^{0.57}$$

Horizontal Transport Velocity

$$V = 6,000 \frac{s}{s+1} \times d^{0.40}$$

V = Velocity, f.p.m.

s = Specific gravity of material.

d = Average dia. of largest particle in inches.

For practical use, see Table below.

Friction Loss of Mixtures

$$\frac{F_m}{F_a} = 1 + 0.32 \frac{W_s}{W_a}$$

where:

F_m = Friction loss of mixture.

F_a = Friction loss of air.

W_s = Weight of solid.

W_a = Weight of air.

$W_s \div W_a$	0	1	2	3	4
$F_m \div F_a$	1	1·32	1·64	1·96	2·28
$W_s \div W_a$	5	6	7	8	10
$F_m \div F_a$	2·60	2·92	3·24	3·56	4·20

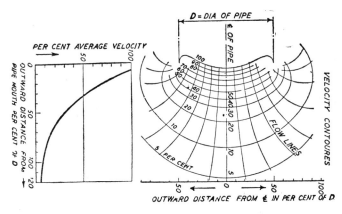

Velocity contours and flow directional lines in radial plane of circular
suction pipe.

Velocities for Dust Extraction:

Material	Velocity		f.p.m.
Sawdust and Shavings, light	2000	to	3000
Sawdust and Shavings, heavy	3500	–	4500
Grinding and Foundry Dust	3500	–	4500
Sandblast	3500	–	4500
Lead Dust	4000	–	5000
Cotton Lint Flyings	1500	–	2000
Grain Dust, Rubber Dust	2000	–	3000
Bakelite Moulding Powder	3000	–	3500
Bakelite Dust	2000	–	2500

Velocities for Pneumatic Conveying:

Material	Velocity		f.p.m.
Coal, Powdered	4000	to	5500
Sawdust	4000	–	6000
Cork	3500	–	5500
Pulp Chips	4500	–	7000
Wool, Jute, Cotton	4500	–	6000
Coffee Beans	3000	–	4000
Ashes, Powdered Clinker	6000	–	8500
Sand, Cement	6000	–	9000
Lime	5000	–	7000
Flour	3500	–	6000
Rags	4500	–	6500
Corn, Wheat, Rye	5000	–	7000
Oats	4500	–	6000

USUAL DIMENSIONS OF CYCLONE
SEPARATORS FOR DUST COLLECTING.
SEPARATION FACTOR OF CYCLONES:

$$S = \frac{V^2}{gr}$$ V = tangential velocity (ft. per sec.)

r = radius of cyclone = $\frac{A}{2}$ ft.

g = gravity of earth (ft. per sec.).

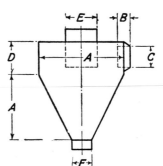

Fan Outlet		Dimensions in inches					
Dia., in.	Area, sq. in.	A	B	C	D	E	F
5	20	30	3	9	14	9	5
7–8	35–50	42	4	12	19	13	8
10	78	54	5	18	23	18	8
11–12	95–113	60	$5\frac{1}{2}$	21	26	20	12
13–14	133–154	66	$6\frac{1}{2}$	24	30	24	12
16–17	201–227	78	8	30	36	28	12
18	254	84	$8\frac{1}{2}$	32	39	32	13
19–20	283–314	90	9	34	42	34	13
22	380	98	10	40	48	39	14
23–24	415–452	102	11	43	50	41	14
30	707	126	12	60	66	58	15
34	908	138	13	66	72	68	15

Air Outlet = 4 × inlet area.   Leaving Air Velocity = 350 to 450 f.p.m.

ONE MICRON = 0.001 m.m. is the usual unit for measuring the dimensions of fine
particles.

TYLER STANDARD SCREEN SCALE:

Meshes per inch	10	20	35	48	65	100	150	200	325
Micron Scale ...	1650	830	420	300	220	150	110	74	44

Dust = over 10 microns.   *Clouds* = 0·1 to 10·0 microns.   *Smoke* = below 0·001 microns.

MINIMUM PARTICLE SIZE FOR WHICH VARIOUS SEPARATOR
TYPES ARE SUITABLE :

Gravity	200 microns
Inertial	50 to 150
Centrifugal, large dia. cyclone	40 to 60
Centrifugal, small dia. cyclone	20 to 30
Fan Type	15 to 30
Filter	0·5
Scrubber	0·5 to 2·0
Electrical	0·001 to 1·0

Size of Particles:

Outdoor Dust	0·5 microns
Sand Blasting	1·4
Foundry Dust	1·0 to 200
Granite Cutting	1·4
Coal Mining	1·0
Raindrops	500 to 5000
Mist	40 to 500
Fog	1 to 40
Fly Ash	3 to 70
Pulverized Coal	10 to 400

Automatic Control Apparatus or Regulators:

These operate to maintain measured conditions subject to changes within certain limits. They consist of the two following parts:

The *Controller or Measuring Device*, indicating the change of the required conditions, and the magnitude of the change; for instance, thermostats, humidistats, pressure controls, etc.

The *Operating Device*, carrying out the corrective action based on the indications of the controller; for instance, magnetic valves, motorized valves, etc.

Classification of Controls according to operation:

(a) Two positions, or "off" and "on", or positive acting control.
The operating device is either fully open or fully shut; no intermediate positions.

(b) Gradual, intermediate, modulating, or graduated acting control. The motion of the operating mechanism is proportional to the change in required conditions.

Classification of Controls according to operating medium:

(a) Self-contained, or direct operated apparatus. Controller and operating mechanism in self-contained unit.

(b) Electric control systems.
Electricity is used for operating the controlling devices, either line voltage or low voltage circuits are switched on and off by the controller.

(c) Pneumatic control systems.
Compressed air is used for operating the controlling devices. Controller and operating mechanism are connected to a compressed air piping, the air pressure being varied by the measuring devices, according to the change in the required conditions.

EQUIPMENT

Controllers:

Thermostats are sensitive to changes of temperature and cause the regulation of the flow of heating or cooling medium (steam, hot water, cold water, brine, etc.)
Room thermostat for installation in rooms.
Immersion thermostat for tubings.
Duct thermostats for air ducts.

Pressure and Vacuum Controls are sensitive to changes of pressure.

Humidistats or Psychrostats are sensitive to the difference between dry bulb and wet bulb temperature.

Clocks and Time Switches are used for maintaining different conditions by day and by night, for starting up and switching off plants, etc.

Operating Mechanisms:

Electric Motors fitted to valves, dampers, i.e., motorized valves, motorized dampers, etc.

Magnetic or Solenoid Valves, dampers, etc.

Diaphragm Valves, operated by fluid pressure on diaphragm.

CONTROL OF AIR CONDITIONING SYSTEMS

(Reproduced by courtesy of The Drayton Regulator and Instrument Co. Ltd.)

The following diagrams show typical applications of controllers applied to central fan heating and conditioning systems. As the design of air conditioning plant embodies almost endless variations, it should be realized that these diagrams show only a few of the possible combinations; they should serve as a basis to assist the reader to select suitable controllers for any particular plant he may have under consideration.

Simple Plenum Used for Ventilation (Fig. 1)

These generally supply tempered air, the main heating being done by other means. A modulating duct thermostat is suggested. Care must be taken in positioning the bulb to measure the average temperature, as stratification can occur.

To prevent the risk of freezing occurring in the bottom of large heater batteries during very cold weather a low limit thermostat may be inserted in this heater to come into operation should the temperature drop to, say, 40°F.

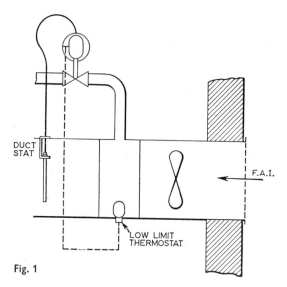

DUCT STAT

F.A.I.

LOW LIMIT THERMOSTAT

Fig. 1

Partial Air Conditioning

Without Recirculation

The most common type in Britain consists of a preheater, a washer and a reheater, as shown in Fig. 2. For maintaining comfort conditions, dew point control of humidity is usual and a duct thermostat controlling the

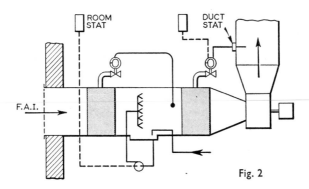

Fig. 2

preheater is satisfactory. For plants which are shut down at night, a room stat in the conditioned space will ensure that the washer pump does not start up until the space temperature is high enough to prevent condensation on cool surfaces.

The final heater may be controlled by a room stat with a duct stat at the fan outlet as low limit control. When the batteries are steam heated, it is undesirable that the steam trap should "lift", but where this is absolutely unavoidable a low limit stat is preferable. This type applied to a normally proportioning control results in floating control when the low limit temperature is reached. The relatively rapid opening of the valve assists the condensate removal from the heater battery.

Another type replaces the preheater by a heater for the spray water, as shown in Fig. 3. It is preferable to control the dew point by a three-way

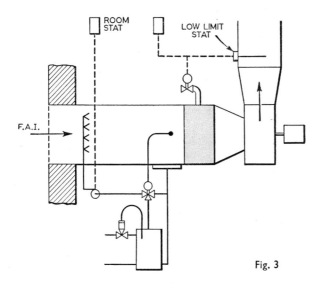

Fig. 3

mixing valve in the spray water circuit rather than by controlling the calorifier or heat exchanger direct. The diagram shows a direct-acting valve controlling the calorifier temperature. As before, a low limit room stat in the space prevents the spray pump starting until a minimum temperature has been reached in the room.

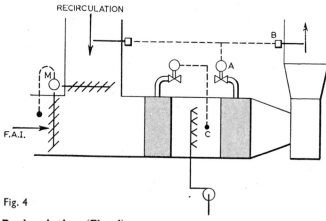

Fig. 4

With Recirculation (Fig. 4)

It is convenient and usually preferable to control the space temperature from the recirculation duct. A thermostat controls the valve A with B as low limit. A dew point thermostat C controls the preheater.

Recirculation dampers may be controlled by a motorized controller and an operating motor M. The bulb of the motorized controller should be located in the fresh air. The throttling range should be set wide—usually 30°F. so that with outside air at 30°F., recirculation is the maximum permitted by the minimum ventilation requirements. This is usually arranged by a mechanical stop on the dampers. With outside air at 60°F. there will be no recirculation of air. Because of difficulties in mixing the air streams, attempts to control the damper from the temperature of the mixed air are not usually successful.

The system shown in Fig. 4 does not conserve all the heat from the space which may be permitted with adequate ventilation. Fig. 5 shows a system by which the discharge air temperature is controlled by a thermostat operating a motor which actuates a damper by-passing the plant. The recirculation and fresh air dampers are usually hand-set so that resistances are such that air will by-pass the plant if allowed to do so by the damper controlled by the operating motor M. Recirculating air will go through the plant in preference to fresh air, but a predetermined minimum of fresh air always enters.

Valve B is set at a temperature low enough to preclude overheating. The space temperature is controlled by thermostat A in the recirculation duct operating valve B on the final heater, while the thermostat C controls the dew point by operating valve D.

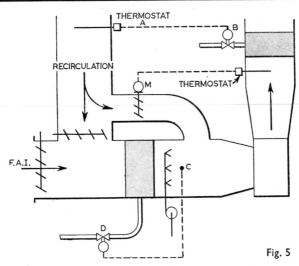

Fig. 5

It should be noted that, should the space have a high humidity gain, all control of humidity will be lost and different methods, referred to later, must be adopted.

Complete Air Conditioning

Spray Cooling

Fig. 6 shows a scheme of control where precise humidity control is not necessary and where hand changeover between summer and winter control is used. A thermostat A in the recirculation duct and a low limit duct stat B are connected through changeover switch C so that, under winter

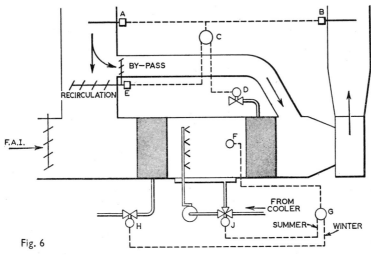

Fig. 6

conditions, they control valve D on the final heater; when switched to summer, B is cut out and A controls on the damper motor E. In winter, when A controls D, the changeover switch maintains E closed to by-pass and open to recirculation. In summer D is maintained shut by the switch. The dew point thermostat F operates through changeover switch G on to preheater valve H in winter, J being maintained closed to cooler and open to recirculation.

The operation will be clear from the above. The fresh air damper is set to the fixed minimum for ventilation in winter, when the space is losing heat, and economy is effected by recirculation. The dew point thermostat maintains humidity sufficiently accurately for comfort conditions. Water make-up is brought in through a hand-operated valve or ball-valve, which is not shown. The space temperature is maintained by control of the reheater, subject to the low limit thermostat B. Switch G can also be used to stop the refrigerator compressor in winter. In summer valve J mixes recirculated and refrigerated water to give a fixed dew point, the reheat being obtained by by-passing the plant with a controlled amount of hot air. In practice switches C and G would be combined into one multiple cell rotary switch.

Limitations. This system of control will not maintain the humidity in the conditioned space accurately if the ratio of sensible heat load to latent heat load of the space varies. The scheme is used for comfort conditioning or other applications where variations in humidity are permissible.

Where it is essential that humidity is precisely maintained, a humidity controller in the space or, better still, in the recirculation duct is used. When applied directly to the preheater or refrigeration the time delays cause wide fluctuation. Fig. 7 shows a humidistat which, through a summer-winter changeover switch, resets dew point controller A on the preheater in winter or a dew point controller B on the three-way mixing valve supplying the sprays in summer. The switch C locks the controller A shut in summer and controller B open to by-pass in winter. The thermostat F controls the recirculation temperature through changeover switch G by operating valve H in winter, with thermostat J as low limit stat, and by operating the recirculation and by-pass dampers through K in summer. H is locked shut in summer and K shut to by-pass in winter.

Limitation. This system will not maintain both humidity and dry bulb temperatures correctly in the space if the ratio of sensible heat gains to latent heat gains under summer conditions falls beyond the critical value where reheat becomes necessary.

Automatic Changeover Between Summer and Winter Control

The obvious way is to duplicate the controls, setting the summer controls sufficiently high so that it is not possible for both to operate together. This requires a total width of control band which may not be permissible in some cases. With this method the total width of control band can be narrowed by using a two-step thermostat or humidistat, together with a relay as a change-over switch. In a simple comfort conditioner as in Fig. 8, for instance, A and B control dry bulb temperature and dew point

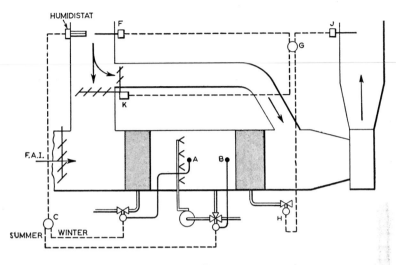

Fig. 7

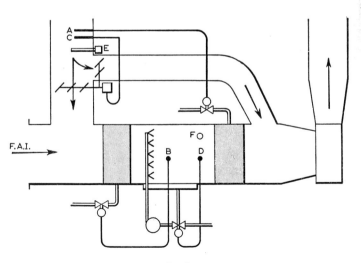

Fig. 8

respectively in winter, while C and D do likewise in summer. It might be found that A and C have to be set each with 7° throttling range for steady control, while the minimum permissible "dead zone" is found to be 2°. Suppose a thermostat E with two switches operating a relay fitted with maintaining contact be put in the recirculation duct. The relay, when de-energized, keeps C closed to by-pass and, when energized, keeps A closed. On rising temperature from cold the thermostat breaks the relay coil circuit but the relay remains energized by the maintaining contact. Further rise closes A and then the second switch in thermostat E breaks, de-energizing the relay which maintains A shut and allows C to move the dampers into the partially-open to by-pass position. The diagram Fig. 9 shows how the total throttling range is narrowed. Similarly the dew point thermostat can be interlocked by a two-switch thermostat, F.

Another way of automatically changing from summer to winter control

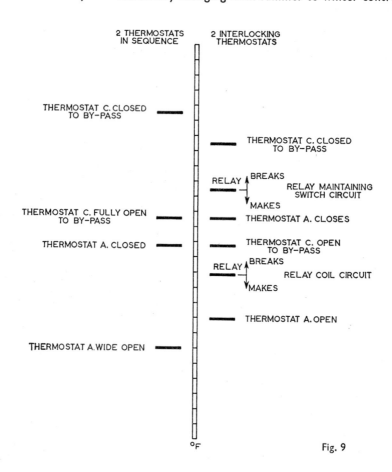

Fig. 9

is to have one dry bulb thermostat operating both the final heater valve and the by-pass damper motor in sequence through a two-step relay. Similarly one dew point thermostat controls both preheater and spray water valve in sequence through a two-step relay. It should be noted that using a relay introduces a response lag which may or may not have material significance in the final accuracy obtained.

Control of Direct Expansion Cooling Systems

In this system the compressed refrigerant is allowed to expand direct into a cooling coil located in the conditioner. The expansion is controlled by an expansion valve supplied by the refrigerator manufacturers, who also supply a pressure switch to stop the compressor on reaching a preset high side pressure. By the operation of a magnetic unloader valve or by operating a two-speed compressor motor, two-step control of the coil surface temperature can be obtained, and where the heat load is large, several compressors may be used so the steps can be multiplied. One system of control is to use a face and by-pass damper as Fig. 10 operated by

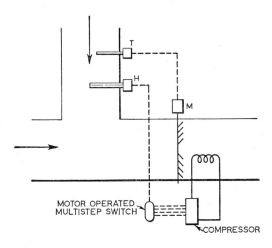

Fig. 10

MOTOR OPERATED
MULTISTEP SWITCH

COMPRESSOR

proportioning damper motor M controlled by thermostat T, while a humidistat H operates a motorized multistep sequential switch which varies the load of the compressor.

Pneumatically-operated Regulators

The following diagrams show air operated regulators applied to similar central fan systems.

For simple plenums Fig. 11 shows a proportioning duct thermostat operating a diaphragm valve on the heater battery. Frost protection of the heater is effected by a low limit thermostat in the bottom header of the heater, which in the event of the temperature falling near freezing point would vent the diaphragm to atmosphere and so open the valve.

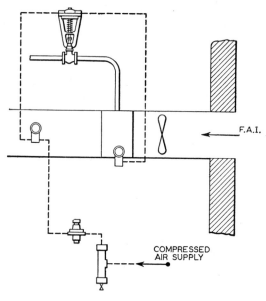

Fig. 11

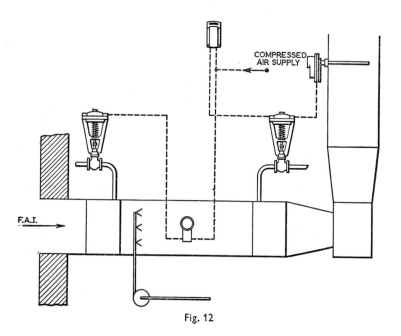

Fig. 12

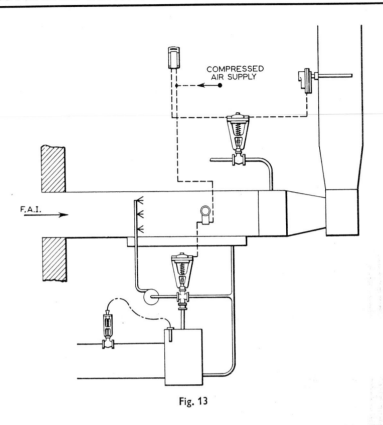

COMPRESSED
AIR SUPPLY

F.A.I.

Fig. 13

Fig. 12 shows dew point and space temperature control of a plant without recirculation. A dew point thermostat controls a diaphragm valve on the preheater. Space temperature is controlled by room thermostat with a low limit duct thermostat controlling a valve on the reheater.

On plants where the preheater is replaced by heating of the spray water the dew point thermostat would be applied to a three-way diaphragm valve mixing heated and recirculated spray water as in Fig. 13.

Fig. 14 shows three transmitting type pneumatic regulators applied to a partial air conditioning system with recirculation. Regulator A—with its bulb in the fresh air intake—operates a diaphragm motor which proportions the fresh air and recirculated air according to outside temperature. The adjustable throttling range is usually set at about 30°F. so that with outside air at 60°F. no air is recirculated. With fresh air at 30°F. the dampers move to minimum fresh air, maximum recirculated air position. Regulator B controls the dew point by operation of the preheater valve. Regulator C, with its bulb in the recirculation duct, regulates, in conjunction with a low limit duct thermostat, the final heater valve.

A plant with spray water refrigeration is shown in Fig. 15. Control is by pneumatic regulators with automatic changeover from winter to summer conditions.

In winter when the fresh air is below the required temperature, duct thermostat A applies no pressure to the three-way pilot valves B and C, so that diaphragm motor M is vented to atmosphere and maintains the by-pass damper closed and recirculation damper open.

Thermostat D in the recirculation duct operates diaphragm valve E on the final heater, subject to the limitations of low limit thermostat F.

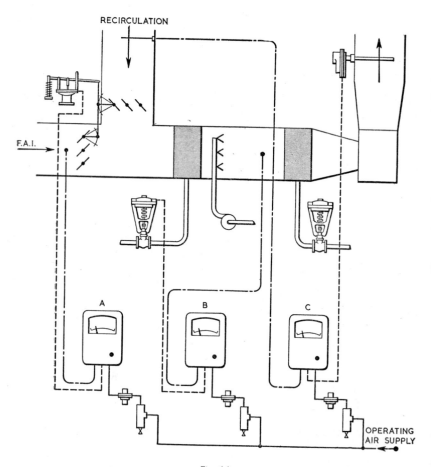

Fig. 14

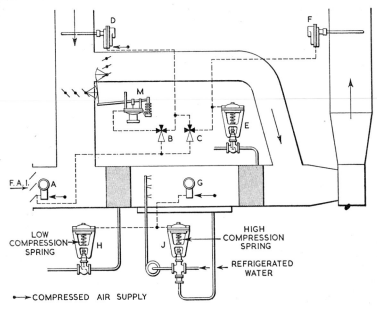

Fig. 15

Dew point thermostat G operates valve H on the preheater and the three-way valve J on the spray water in sequence. On rising dew point temperature valve H is moved towards the closed position and when fully closed, on further temperature rise, valve J is proportioned to pass refrigerated spray water and less recirculated water.

When the fresh air temperature reaches the preset changeover temperature, thermostat A applies a pressure to pilot valves B and C, which vents E to atmosphere and holds it shut. Low limit thermostat F is made inoperative. Thermostat D now controls damper motor M so that on falling recirculation air temperature M opens the by-pass damper and closes the recirculation damper.

D in the diagram is shown as a reverse acting regulator but could, if desired, be a transmitting type regulator or recorder regulator.

F is a low limit type regulator.

A and G are direct-acting regulators but could equally well be transmitting types if desired.

Valve E is reverse acting, while valves H and J are direct acting with springs adjusted to give sequential operation.

HUMIDITY CHART FOR DRY AIR FOR HIGH TEMPERATURES
Barometric pressure 29·92 inches. See also Chart 5 and page V. 10.

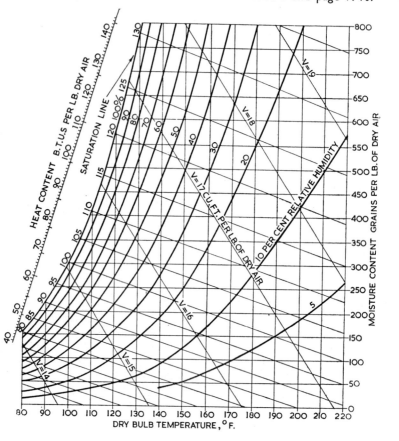

Performance of a Cold-Air Machine (per 1,000 cu. ft. of cold air delivered per hour). (*Molesworth*)

Compression, including atmosphere, lb. per sq. in.	65
Temperature of air (admission, Fahr.)	52°
,, ,, (compression, Fahr.)	267°
,, ,, after cooling	70°
,, ,, ,, expansion	—82°
Temperature of cooling water (initial)	57°
,, ,, ,, (final)	145°
H.P. consumed in compression	2·87
I.H.P. exerted in expansion	1·87
I.H.P. difference	1·00
I.H.P. of steam cylinder	1·64
Lbs. cooling water used per minute	0·62

Basic systems: 1. Single duct system.
              2. Dual duct system.
              3. Induction system.

SINGLE DUCT SYSTEM

A central plant delivers conditioned air through high velocity ducting to attenuator boxes throughout the building. The distribution boxes have sound attenuators.

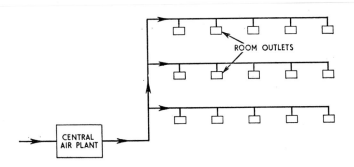

Advantages:
    Space saving through use of high velocity small diameter ducts.
    Low initial cost.
    Zone control can be used.

Disadvantages:
    Large volume of air to be treated in central plant.
    Individual room control not possible.
    Recirculating system necessary.

DUAL DUCT SYSTEM

A central plant delivers two streams of air through two sets of high velocity ducting to attenuator mixing boxes in the various rooms. The two streams are at different temperatures and humidities, and the ratio in which they are mixed can be set at each mixing box independently of all others in the building.

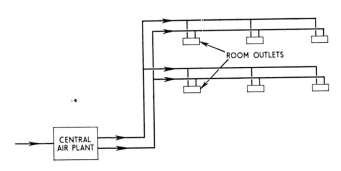

Advantages:

Space saving through use of high velocity small diameter ducts.
Individual room control—zoning not necessary.
Flexible in operation.
Units are available for mounting under window-sills or in ceilings.
Suitable for use where large air volumes are required.

Disadvantages:

Two sets of air ducting are needed, using more space.
More air has to be treated in central plant.
Recirulating system is necessary.

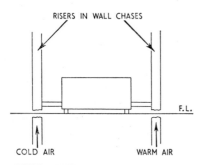

DUAL DUCT SYSTEM—TYPICAL
CONNECTIONS TO ROOM UNIT

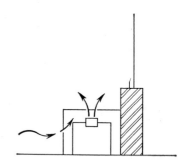

TYPICAL ARRANGEMENT OF
UNIT UNDER WINDOW SILL

Control

An individual pneumatic or electric room thermostat adjusts the ratio in which air streams are mixed.

Each stream is kept at constant temperature and humidity by automatic controls in plant room.

INDUCTION SYSTEM

A central air plant delivers conditioned air through high velocity ducting to induction units in the rooms. Water from a central plant is also supplied to the induction units. The conditioned, or primary, air supplied to the units induces room, or secondary, air through the unit. This induced secondary air passes over the water coil and is thus heated or cooled.

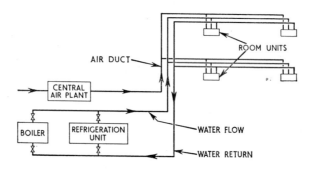

Advantages:

Space saving through use of high velocity small diameter ducts.
Low running costs.
Individual room control.
Very suitable for modular building layouts.
Central air plant need handle only part of the air treated.
Particularly applicable to perimeter zones of large buildings—hotels, hospitals, schools and flats, etc.
Suitable for large heat loads with small air volumes.

Disadvantages:

Higher capital cost.

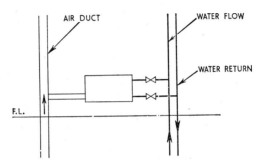

INDUCTION SYSTEM — TYPICAL CONNECTIONS TO ROOM UNIT

PRIMARY AIR PLANT

Central air handling plant consists of:

      1. Intake louvres.
      2. Air filter.
      3. Preheater.
      4. Humidifier or dehumidifier.
      5. Reheater.
      6. Fan.
      7. Silencer or sound absorber.

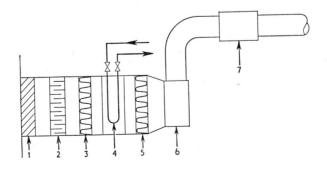

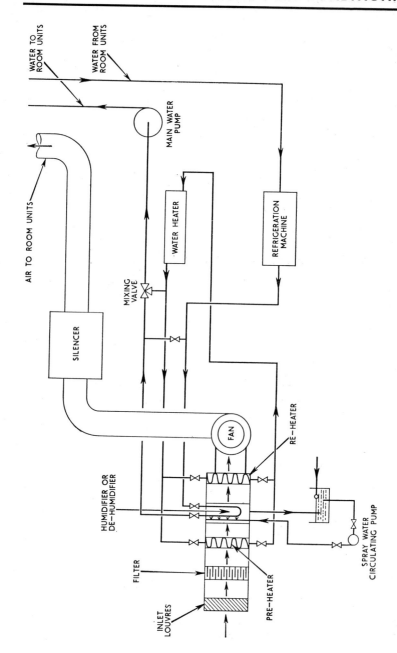

SCHEME OF CENTRAL PLANT FOR INDUCTION SYSTEM

Air-handling plant can be installed either in the basement or on the roof.

To provide heated water and chilled water for the air plant a boiler and a refrigerator unit are provided. For reasons of weight these are usually installed in the basement; they need not necessarily be near the air-handling plant.

AIR DISTRIBUTION FOR HIGH VELOCITY SYSTEMS

High pressures are used to obtain the advantages of high velocities and small ducts.

Pressure at inlet to farthest unit	$\frac{1}{2}$ to 1 in. w.g.
Typical pressure at fan	5 to 6 in. w.g.
Air velocities in ducts	3,000 to 4,000 f.p.m.

Ducts for these systems are always circular. Welded construction is used to avoid leaks at the higher air pressures. Spirally wound ducting is also available.

Alternatively special fittings are obtainable.

Ducts must be insulated.

ROOM DISTRIBUTION UNITS

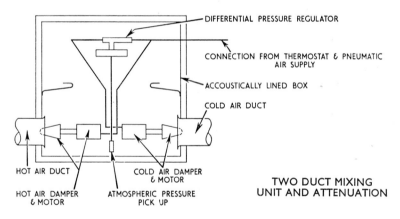

DIFFERENTIAL PRESSURE REGULATOR

CONNECTION FROM THERMOSTAT & PNEUMATIC AIR SUPPLY

ACCOUSTICALLY LINED BOX

COLD AIR DUCT

HOT AIR DUCT

COLD AIR DAMPER & MOTOR

HOT AIR DAMPER & MOTOR

ATMOSPHERIC PRESSURE PICK UP

TWO DUCT MIXING UNIT AND ATTENUATION

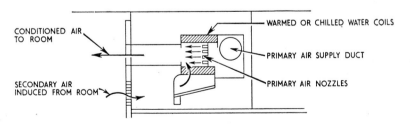

CONDITIONED AIR TO ROOM

SECONDARY AIR INDUCED FROM ROOM

WARMED OR CHILLED WATER COILS

PRIMARY AIR SUPPLY DUCT

PRIMARY AIR NOZZLES

CEILING MOUNTED INDUCTION UNIT

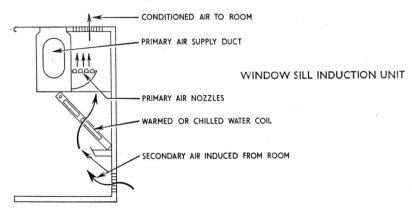

CONDITIONED AIR TO ROOM

PRIMARY AIR SUPPLY DUCT

WINDOW SILL INDUCTION UNIT

PRIMARY AIR NOZZLES

WARMED OR CHILLED WATER COIL

SECONDARY AIR INDUCED FROM ROOM

DESIGN DATA

Air Heater: 800–1,200 ft./min. over free area.
      500–600 ft./min. over total area.

Supply of primary fresh air per person:
      1,400 cu. ft./hr.
      1,800 cu. ft./hr. where heavy smokers are present.

Air velocities in primary ducts:
      3,000–4,000 ft./min.

Induction units: Secondary air/primary air—3/1.
      Pressure of primary air—$\frac{3}{4}$ in. w.g.

Design sequence for induction units:
1. Calculate heat gain.
2. Select suitable room unit from manufacturer's data.
3. Temperature of chilled water is settled by dew-point of room air.
4. Allow primary air quantity from data above.
5. Design ducting, using "equivalent length" method. Table on page X. 51 takes into account static regain.
6. Water pipes are designed and sized exactly as for a conventional radiator system.

FRICTION LOSS THROUGH FITTINGS

	FITTING	LE 4"	6"	8"	10"	12"	14"	16"	18"	20"
	(tee, branch down)	−9	−15							
	(tee, straight)	12	21							
	90°	3	4	7	10	12	15	18	21	24
	45°	1	2	4	5	6	8	9	10	12
	30°	1	1	2	3	4	5	6	7	8
	(tee branch)	−5	−9	−13	−17	−22	−26	−31	−36	−42
	(tee)	12	21	30	40	52	63	75	87	100
	(cross)	−13	−22	−32	−42	−54	−66	−78	−91	−105
	(cross)	13	22	32	42	54	66	78	91	105
	$\frac{d}{D} > 0.4$	−8	−10	−11	−13	−17	−20	−24	−28	−32
	$\frac{d}{D} \leqslant 0.4$					−9	−9	−10	−10	−10
		13	22	32	42	54	66	78	91	105
	(reducer)		−21	−30	−40	−52	−63	−75	−87	−100
	(reducer)	13	22	32	42	54	66	78	91	105
		14	23	37	49	62	76	90	106	121

LE = EQUIVALENT LENGTH OF PIPE IN FEET

CALCULATION OF PRESSURE LOSS

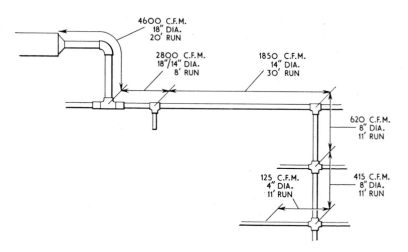

4600 C.F.M.
18" DIA.
20' RUN

2800 C.F.M.
18"/14" DIA.
8' RUN

1850 C.F.M.
14" DIA.
30' RUN

620 C.F.M.
8" DIA.
11' RUN

125 C.F.M.
4" DIA.
11' RUN

415 C.F.M.
8" DIA.
11' RUN

QUANTITY	SYMBOL	DIA. IN.	PRESS DROP IN. W.G./100 FT.	DUCT FT.	LENGTH FT.	PRESS DROP IN. S.W.G.	AIR VELOCITY F.P.M.
4600	⋗	18	0·53	106	} 111		
				20			
	⌐			21		·59	
	...L			−36			
2800	...L		0·21	87	} 0		
	⋗			−87			
	⋗	14	0·72	66	} 8		
				8		·06	
	⫶			−66			
1850	⫶		0·34	66	} 76		
				30		·26	
	⊤···			−20			
620	⊤···	8	0·73	32	} 11		
				11		·08	
	|···			−32			
415	|···		0·34	32	} 32		
				11		·11	
	⊣			−11			
125	⊣	4	1·1	13	} 23	·25	
				10			
						1·35	

Section XI

HYDRAULICS

Pressure due to Head of Water:

$$p = wh.$$

h = Head of water (ft.).
W = Specific weight (lb. per cu. ft.).
P = Pressure (lb. per sq. ft.).

Bernoulli's Theorem: The total energy of unit weight of a perfect fluid (or total head) flowing through any section of a stream is the sum of its kinetic head, pressure head and elevation head and is constant along any stream tube.

$$\frac{v_1^2}{2g} + \frac{P_1}{w} + Z_1 = \frac{v_2^2}{2g} + \frac{P_2}{w} + Z_2 = H.$$

where: $Z_1 \ Z_2$ = Heights.
$v_1 \ v_2$ = Velocities.
$P_1 \ P_2$ = Pressures.
W = Specific weight.
$a_1 \ a_2$ = Areas.

Venturimeter: Instrument for measuring the quantity of water flowing through a pipe.

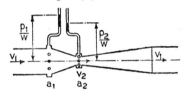

$$Q = \frac{C_v a_2}{\sqrt{1 - \left(\frac{a_2}{a_1}\right)^2}} \times \sqrt{2g \frac{P_1 - P_2}{w}}$$

Q = Quantity of water in cu. ft. per sec.
$a_1 \ a_2$ = Areas in sq. ft.
$P_1 \ P_2$ = Pressures lb. per sq. ft.
C^v = 0.96 to 0.99 coefficient of velocity.

Discharge of Water through Small Orifices:

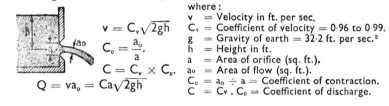

$$v = C_v \sqrt{2gh}$$
$$C_c = \frac{a_0}{a}.$$
$$C = C_v \times C_c.$$
$$Q = va_0 = Ca\sqrt{2gh}$$

where:
v = Velocity in ft. per sec.
C_v = Coefficient of velocity = 0.96 to 0.99.
g = Gravity of earth = 32.2 ft. per sec.²
h = Height in ft.
a = Area of orifice (sq. ft.).
a_0 = Area of flow (sq. ft.).
$C_c = a_0 \div a$ = Coefficient of contraction.
C = $C_v . C_c$ = Coefficient of discharge.

COEFFICIENT OF DISCHARGE "C", FOR SHARP EDGED, CIRCULAR ORIFICES

Head in ft.	Diameter of Orifice in in.				
	0·75	1·00	1·50	2·0	2·50
0·2	0·684	0·645	0·617	0·611	0·609
0·8	0·666	0·636	0·613	0·607	0·606
2·0	0·651	0·630	0·611	0·607	0·606
60·0	S·634	0·624	0·611	0·607	0·606
100·0	0·634	0·624	0·611	·0·607	0·606

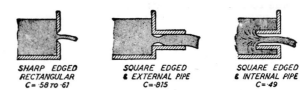

SHARP EDGED
RECTANGULAR
C = ·58 TO ·61

SQUARE EDGED
& EXTERNAL PIPE
C = ·815

SQUARE EDGED
& INTERNAL PIPE
C = ·49

DISCHARGE THROUGH NOTCHES

Rectangular Notch:

$$\text{Discharge—}Q = \tfrac{2}{3}\,C_d\sqrt{2g}\,LH^{\frac{3}{2}}$$

Triangular or "V" Notch:

Most satisfactory type for measuring of quantity of flowing water.

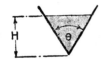

Discharge—

angle of notch $Q = 2\cdot56 \tan \tfrac{\theta}{2} H^{\frac{5}{2}}$

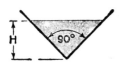

90° notch $Q = 2\cdot56\,H^{\frac{5}{2}}$

Q = Discharge through notch (cu. ft. per sec.).
H = Height of water surface above sill (ft.).
L = Breadth of notch (ft.).
C_d = Coefficient of discharge
    = 0·62 average.

The Pitot Tube is an instrument for measuring the velocity head of a flowing fluid.

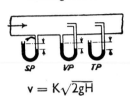

SP = Static pressure.
VP = Velocity pressure.
TP = Total pressure.
(Velocity Head) = (Total Head) — (Static Head)
v = Velocity
H = Head.

$v = K\sqrt{2gH}$

K = Coefficient for the instrument.
   = 1·0 for British Standard pitot-static-tube.

FLUID FLOW THROUGH PIPES

Total Loss of Head (H) = Loss of head due to friction (H_1).
    + Loss of head due to obstructions (H_2).
     (Fittings, Valves, Bends, etc.).
$$H = H_1 + H_2.$$

Loss of Head due to Friction:

$H_1 = li; \quad i = \dfrac{H_1}{l}.$

$i = \dfrac{4f}{d} \cdot \dfrac{v^2}{2g}$

i = Slope of hydraulic gradient.
   = Head lost in resistance per unit length of pipe.
l = Length of pipe (ft.).
d = Inside diameter of pipe (ft.).
v = Velocity of fluid (ft. per sec.).
f = Friction factor.

Friction factor (f) is a function of the "Reynold's Number"

$f = \phi\left(\dfrac{dv\rho}{\mu}\right)$

$\left(\dfrac{dv\rho}{\mu}\right) = R_e.$

ρ = Density of fluid.
μ = Absolute viscosity of fluid.
R_e = Reynolds' number.

Viscous, or streamline flow—motion solely in axial direction—low velocities and highly viscous fluids.
$$R_e < 2,000.$$

Turbulent or eddying flow—radial velocity components, eddies.
$$R_e > 3,000$$

Region of Discontinuity (Critical Region) R_e = From 2,000 to 3,000.
    (Lower and higher critical velocity).

Loss of Head due to Obstructions (Fittings):

$H_2 = F\dfrac{v_1^2}{2g}\rho$

H_2 = Loss of head in ft.
v_1 = Actual velocity of water at the point where the resistance is encountered in ft. per sec.
F = Coefficient of resistance (always applied to smaller velocity).
ρ = Density of Fluid.

VELOCITY HEADS AND THEORETICAL VELOCITIES OF WATER

$$h = \frac{v^2}{2g}$$

h = Head in ft.
v = Velocity in ft. per sec.
g = Gravitation of earth = 32·2 ft. per sec.²

v	h	v	h	v	h	v	h
0·1	0·0002	2·1	0·068	4·1	0·261	6·1	0·578
0·2	0·0006	2·2	0·075	4·2	0·274	6·2	0·597
0·3	0·0014	2·3	0·082	4·3	0·289	6·3	0·616
0·4	0·0025	2·4	0·089	4·4	0·301	6·4	0·636
0·5	0·0039	2·5	0·097	4·5	0·314	6·5	0·656
0·6	0·0056	2·6	0·105	4·6	0·329	6·6	0·676
0·7	0·0076	2·7	0·113	4·7	0·343	6·7	0·697
0·8	0·0099	2·8	0·122	4·8	0·358	6·8	0·718
0·9	0·0126	2·9	0·131	4·9	0·373	6·9	0·739
1·0	0·0155	3·0	0·140	5·0	0·388	7·0	0·761
1·1	0·019	3·1	0·149	5·1	0·404	7·1	0·783
1·2	0·022	3·2	0·159	5·2	0·420	7·2	0·805
1·3	0·026	3·3	0·169	5·3	0·436	7·3	0·827
1·4	0·030	3·4	0·179	5·4	0·453	7·4	0·850
1·5	0·035	3·5	0·190	5·5	0·470	7·5	0·874
1·6	0·040	3·6	0·201	5·6	0·487	7·6	0·897
1·7	0·045	3·7	0·212	5·7	0·505	7·7	0·921
1·8	0·050	3·8	0·224	5·8	0·522	7·8	0·945
1·9	0·056	3·9	0·236	5·9	0·541	7·9	0·969
2·0	0·062	4·0	0·248	6·0	0·559	8·0	0·994

RESISTANCE OF VALVES AND FITTINGS TO FLOW OF FLUIDS IN TERMS OF EQUIVALENT LENGTH OF STRAIGHT PIPE (Crane Co.)

Description of Fitting		Nominal Diameter										
		½	¾	1	1¼	1½	2	2½	3	4	5	6
Globe Valve		13	16	26	35	40	55	65	80			
Angle Valve		8	11	15	18	20	27	32	40			
Gate Valve		0·3	0·5	0·5	0·5	1	1	1·5	2	2·5	3	3
Elbow		1	2	2	3	4	5	6	8	11	13	17
Long Sweep Elbow		1	1·5	2	2·5	3	3	4	5	6	8	10
Run of Tee ...		1	1·5	2·5	2·5	3	3	4	5	6	8	10
Run of Tee, reduced ½		1	2	2	3	4	5	6	8	11	13	17
Branch Tee... ...		3·5	5	6	8	10	13	15	18	24	30	35
Sudden d = ¼ ...		1	2	2	3	4	5	6	8	11	13	17
Enlargement D = ½ ...		1	1·5	2	2·5	3	3·5	4	5	7	9	11
= ¾ ...		0·3	0·5	0·5	1	1	1	1·5	2	2·5	3	3
Sudden ... d = ¼ ...		0·8	1·0	1·2	1·5	2	2·5	3	4	5	6	8
Contraction D = ½ ...		0·5	0·8	1·0	1·2	1·5	2	2	3	4	5	6
= ¾ ...		0·4	0·5	0·6	1·0	1	1·5	1·5	2	2·5	3	3·5
Ordinary Entrance		1	1	1·5	2	2·5	3	3·5	4·5	6	8	10
Boiler Radiator, Tank ...		3	4·5	6	7·5	9	12	15	18	21	24	40

Notation:

$V_1 V_2$ = Absolute velocity of entering and leaving water, respectively.

$W_1 W_2$ = Velocity of water relative to wheel at inlet and outlet, respectively.

$U_1 U_2$ = Tangential velocity of wheel at inlet and outlet, respectively.

$V_{w1} V_{w2}$ = Velocity of whirl at inlet and outlet, respectively, parallel to direction of motion.

$V_{F1} V_{F2}$ = Velocity of flow at inlet and outlet, respectively, perpendicular to direction of motion.

θ = Angle between relative velocity & direction of motion at inlet.

ϕ = Angle between relative velocity & direction of motion at outlet.

VELOCITY TRIANGLES
(For Inlet and Outlet)

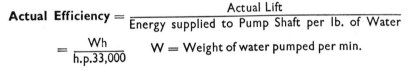

Theoretical Gross Lift $= H + \dfrac{V_d^2}{2g} = \dfrac{V_{w2} U_2}{g}$

Gross Lift $= h + h_t + \dfrac{V_d^2}{2g}$, $h = \dfrac{V_2^2}{2g} - \dfrac{V_1^2}{2g}$.

H = Total theoretical lift (ft.).

v_d = Discharge velocity (ft./sec.).

h = Actual height (ft.) water is lifted.

h_f = Head lost in friction in delivery and suction pipe (ft.).

Actual Efficiency $= \dfrac{\text{Actual Lift}}{\text{Energy supplied to Pump Shaft per lb. of Water}}$

$= \dfrac{Wh}{\text{h.p.}33,000}$ W = Weight of water pumped per min.

Manometric Efficiency $= \dfrac{\text{Gross Lift}}{\text{Theoretical Gross Lift}}$.

Hydraulic Efficiency $= \dfrac{\text{Gross Lift}}{\text{Energy supplied to Impeller per lb. of Water}}$.

The Specific Speed of a centrifugal pump is the speed at which the pump would deliver 1 gallon of water per minute under a head of 1 ft. The value varies between 500 and 8,000 for a single impeller.

$$n_s = \frac{n\sqrt{Q}}{h^{\frac{5}{4}}}$$

n_s = Specific speed in revolutions per minute.

n = Speed in revolutions per minute.

Q = Discharge in gallons per minute.

h = Total head or lift in feet.

Diameter of Impeller:

$$D_2 = 2D_1$$

$$D_2 = \frac{1,840\sqrt{H}}{n}$$

For a manometric efficiency $E = 0.75$.

D_1 = Inner diameter of impeller (in.).
D_2 = External diameter of impeller (in.).
H = Theoretical lift (ft.).
h = Actual lift (ft.).
E = Actual efficiency.
hp = Horse-power.
W = Weight of water (lb. per min.).
Q = Volume of water (gal. per min.).
d = Density of water.
n = Speed in revolutions per minute.

The Horse Power:

$$h.p. = \frac{W \times h}{33,000 \times E} = \frac{10 \times Q \times h \times d}{33,000 \times E}.$$

Data for Centrifugal Pumps:

Actual lift not more than 140 ft. for 1 impeller.
Speed between 1,000 and 2,000 revolutions per minute.
Velocities in suction and delivery pipes 5 to 15 ft. per sec.
Blade angles θ and ϕ between 12° and 30°.

Characteristic Curves of Pumps for one speed, showing relation between head, discharge, efficiency and brake horse power.

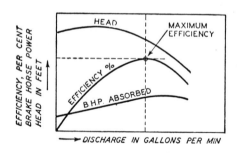

Pump Laws:

1. Water quantity delivered varies directly as speed

$$\frac{Q_2}{Q_1} = \frac{N_2}{N_1}$$

2. Head developed varies as the square of speed.

$$\frac{H_2}{H_1} = \left(\frac{N_2}{N_1}\right)^2$$

3. Horse-power required varies as the cube of speed.

$$\frac{hp_2}{hp_1} = \left(\frac{N_2}{N_1}\right)^3$$

TYPES OF FANS

1. Axial Flow Fans or Propeller Fans:

Static head (or resistance head) up to 1 in. W.G.

2. Radial Flow or Centrifugal Fans:

TYPES OF FAN BLADES *VELOCITY TRIANGLES*

   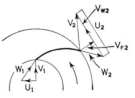

STRAIGHT	FORWARD	BACKWARD
STEEL PLATE	MULTIVANE	FORCED DRAFT
PADDLE WHEEL	MULTIBLADE	TURBOVANE
		HIGH SPEED

$V_1 \ V_2$ = Absolute velocity of entering & leaving air, respectively.
$W_1 \ W_2$ = Velocity of air relative to wheel at inlet & outlet, respectively.
$U_1 \ U_2$ = Tangential velocity of wheel at inlet & outlet, respectively.
V_{F2} = Velocity of flow at outlet.
V_{w2} = Velocity of whirl at outlet.

Theoretical Head:

$$Hth = \frac{U_2^2 - U_1^2}{2g} + \frac{W_1^2 - W_2^2}{2g} + \frac{V_2^2 - V_1^2}{2g} = \frac{V_2 V_{w2}}{g}.$$

Actual Head: E = Efficiency = 0·40 for small fans.
$$H_A = H_{th} \times E.$$ 0·60 for medium fans.
                                      0·80 for large fans.

The Horse Power:

$$hp = \frac{WH}{33,000 \times E}$$

h.p. = Horse-power.
W = Weight of air handled (lb. per min.).
Q = Air volume C.F.M. at 60°F. and 29·92. in. Hg.

$$= \frac{Q.T.P.}{6,356 \times E}$$

H = Total head in ft. of air.
T.P. = Total pressure in in. W.G.

Static Pressure = Pressure of Air to Casing.

Dynamic Pressure = Pressure Head of Velocity = $\frac{v^2}{2g} \rho$ ft. of air.

Static Efficiency = $\dfrac{\text{C.F.M.} \times \text{Static Pressure in in. W.G.}}{6,356 \times \text{hp Input}}$.

Total or Mechanical Efficiency = $\dfrac{\text{C.F.M.} \times \text{Total Pressure in in. W.G.}}{6,356 \times \text{h.p. Input}}$

LAWS APPLYING TO CENTRIFUGAL FANS

1. Air capacity varies directly as speed. $\dfrac{Q_2}{Q_1} = \dfrac{N_2}{N_1}$

2. Static pressure varies as square of speed. $\dfrac{H_2}{H_1} = \left(\dfrac{N_2}{N_1}\right)^2$

3. Horse-power varies as cube of speed. $\dfrac{HP_2}{HP_1} = \left(\dfrac{N_2}{N_1}\right)^3$

Horse-power and static pressure vary directly as barometric pressure (at constant capacity and speed).

Horse-power and static pressure vary inversely as the absolute temperature.

Characteristic Curves for Centrifugal Fans:

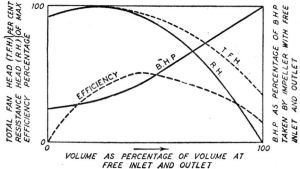

Characteristic Curves for Axial Flow Fans:

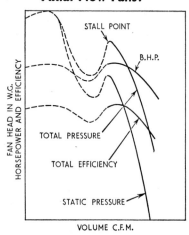

TYPICAL DUTIES OF AXIAL FLOW FANS

Fan Dia. in.	Approximate Volume Range C.F.M.		Maximum Static Pressure. High speed fan, in. of water	
	Minimum Low speed fan	Maximum High speed fan	Single Stage	Two Stage
12	200	2,500	0·86	2·6
15	400	5,000	1·5	4·1
19	600	11,000	2·5	6·8
24	1,000	20,000	3·8	12·5
30	2,000	35,000	6·0	19·5
38	3,000	45,000	2·6	7·0
48	6,000	60,000	4·2	11·4
60	10,000	100,000	2·8	7·8
75	20,000	130,000	2·0	—
95	50,000	150,000	1·0	—

(Woods of Colchester Ltd.)

Data for the Selection of Fans:

1. Air volume to be moved.
2. Static pressure or resistance.
3. Degree of noise permissible.
4. Motive power available.

Fans should be selected as near as possible to the point of maximum efficiency.

Resistance Heads commonly used for typical Vent-Installations:

For Public Buildings, ventilating only ... ... $\frac{3}{8}''$ to $\frac{1}{2}''$ w.g.
For Public Buildings, heating and ventilating ... $\frac{1}{2}''$ to 1''
For Public Buildings, heating and ventilating, including air washer ... ... $\frac{3}{4}''$ to $1\frac{1}{4}''$
For Factories, heating ... ... $\frac{3}{4}''$ to $1\frac{1}{2}''$
For Factories, heating and ventilating, including air washer ... ... $1\frac{1}{4}''$ to 2''

FAN OUTLET VELOCITIES FOR SILENT RUNNING (in ft. per min.)

	Inlet.	Extract.
Sound Studios, Churches, Libraries ...	800 to 1,000	1,000 to 1,400
Cinemas, Theatres, Ballrooms	1,000 to 1,500	1,200 to 1,600
Restaurants, Hotels, Offices, Stores ...	1,200 to 1,600	1,400 to 1,800

A Decibel (db) is the standard unit for noise or sound.

One decibel is equal to ten times the logarithm to the base "e" of the ratio of the sound intensities.

$$L_1 - L_2 = 10 \log \frac{I_1}{I_2}$$

L = Loudness in db.
I = Intensity.

Scale of Loudness in Decibels:

0 db	Threshold of audibility.	70 db	In express train (windows open).
10 ,,	Rustling of leaves.	80 ,,	In tube train (windows open).
20 ,,	Whispering.	90 ,,	Pneumatic drill at 4 ft.
30 ,,	Very quiet house.	100 ,,	Near express train.
40 ,,	Suburban house.	110 ,,	Near aeroplane engine.
50 ,,	Average conversation.	120 ,,	Heavy gun-fire.
60 ,,	Loud conversation.	130 ,,	Threshold of feeling.

Acceptable Noise Levels:

Radio Broadcast Studios ... ... 10 db.
Hospitals ... ... 15 ,,
Theatres, Cinemas, Churches, Libraries, Auditoriums ... 20 ,,
Offices, Classrooms ... ... 30 ,,
Large Public Offices, Banking Rooms ... ... 35 ,,
Restaurants, Stores, Shops ... ... 40 ,,
Typewriting Offices ... ... 45 ,,
Factories ... ... 50 ,,

SOUND ABSORPTION OF VARIOUS MATERIALS

(in per cent) for various cycles.

Material.	Thickness inches.	Frequency in cycles per sec.		
		128	512	2048
Brickwork	18	2·4	3·1	4·9
Glass	—	3·5	2·7	2·0
Plaster...	$\frac{3}{4}$	4·8	6·0	4·3
Poured concrete	—	1·0	1·6	2·3
Hairfelt	6	55·0	69·0	86·0
Plywood	$\frac{3}{4}$	9·8	10·0	8·2
Wood, fibre	$\frac{3}{8}$	39·0	52·0	59·0
Wood, varnished		5·0	3·0	3·0
Glass silk	1–1·5	12·0	71·0	72·0

Sound Insulation of Walls:

The test results of the N.P.L., The Bureau of Standards, Knudsen & Meyer, all show that the insulation of homogeneous partitions is proportional to the log. of the weight per square foot.

From the average of the results the following relation is found :

Insulation in d b. = 14·3 $\log_{10}$ wt. per sq. ft. + 22·7 db., and the following values are of interest:

Mass per sq. ft. of wall area, Weight in lb.		Equivalent Insulation Values in decibels at a frequency of 512 cycles per sec.
1	...	22·7
5	...	32
10	...	37
20	...	41
40	...	45
60	...	48
100	...	51·3
400	...	60

ATTENUATION OF NOISE BY BUILDING MATERIALS

9 in. brick wall	will attenuate by 50 db.		
6 in. concrete wall	,,	,,	,, 42 db.
Average wood joist floor and ceiling	,,	,,	,, 40 db.
Average lath and plaster partition	,,	,,	,, 38 db.
Double glazed window, 2 in. spacing	,,	,,	,, 30 db.
$\frac{1}{2}$ in. T. and G. boarded partition	,,	,,	,, 26 db.
$\frac{3}{32}$ in. glass windows	,,	,,	,, 23 db.

ATTENUATION ALONG STRAIGHT DUCTS:

$$\text{attenuation (db.)} = K \times \frac{\text{perimeter in ft.}}{\text{area in sq. ft.}} \times \text{length in ft.}$$

where $K = $ a constant $\times$ (absorption coefficient)$^{1\cdot4}$

APPROXIMATE ATTENUATION OF SHEET METAL DUCTS:

12 in. size	...	...	0·08 db. per ft. length
24 in. size	...	...	0·05 db. per ft. length
48 in. size	...	...	0·02 db. per ft. length

Splitters. The introduction of splitters into a duct may increase the attenuation quite considerably in the ratio:

$$R_s = R \left(1 + \frac{BN}{A + B}\right)$$

where $R_s = $ attenuation of duct with splitters

$R \ \ = $ attenuation of duct without splitters

$A \ \ = $ length of longer side

$B \ \ = $ length of shorter side

$N \ \ = $ number of splitters parallel to side B.

Splitters increase attenuation by increasing ratio perimeter : area.

Lining. An idea of the order of attenuation possible from ducts lined with sound-absorbent material is given below.

12 in. size	...	...	0·8 to 1·5 db. attenuation per ft. length
24 in. size	...	...	0·5 to 1·0 db. attenuation per ft. length
48 in. size	...	...	0·3 to 0·6 db. attenuation per ft. length

LIKELY ATTENUATION FROM SHEET METAL DUCTS

Size of duct	Unlined db. per ft.	Lined db. per ft.
12	0·08	0·8–1·5
24	0·05	0·5–1·0
48	0·02	0·3–0·6

ATTENUATION OF DUCTS LINED WITH ABSORPTIVE MATERIAL

attenuation db. $= K\dfrac{LP}{A}$ where a $=$ coefficient of absorption.

L $=$ length of duct in feet.

A $=$ cross section of duct in sq. ft.

P $=$ perimeter of duct in ft.

$$\frac{P}{A} = \frac{2\,(W + D)}{WD}.$$

N $=$ number of splitters.

$$\frac{P}{A} = \frac{2\,[(N + 1)\,W + D]}{WD}.$$

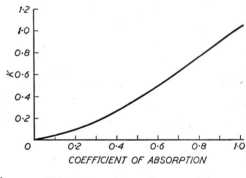

COEFFICIENT OF ABSORPTION

GRAPH TO OBTAIN K FROM A

ATTENUATION AT ENTRY TO ROOM

Type of room— A: reverberant—concrete floor, plastered walls—empty.

B: average.

C: absorbent—carpeted, curtained, occupied.

Volume of room—cu. ft.

Area of outlet—sq. ft.

	A	B	C
2,000	7 db.	13 db.	17 db.
5,000	11 db.	17 db.	21 db.
10,000	14 db.	20 db.	24 db.
20,000	18 db.	24 db.	28 db.

Attenuation from bends

For right angled elbows:

12 in. size 2 db.

24 in. size 1·5 db.

48 in. size 1 db.

Attenuation by building structure

9 in. brick wall	50 db.
6 in. concrete wall	42 db.
Wood joist floor and ceiling ...	40 db.
Lath and plaster partition ...	38 db.
Double window, 2 in. spacing ...	30 db.
½ in. T. and G. boarded partition	26 db.
3/32 in. glass window	23 db.

Coefficient of Absorption 'a'

Note.—This is for range of frequencies usual in fan work.

Plaster walls ... ... ∴.	0·01–0·03
Unpainted brickwork ...	0·02–0·05
Painted brick	0·01–0·02
3-plywood panel	0·01–0·02
¼ in. cork sheet	0·1 –0·2
¼ in. porous rubber sheet ...	0·1 –0·2
½ in. fibreboard on battens ...	0·3–0·4
1 in. wood-wool cement board on battens ...	0·6 –0·7
2 in. slag wool or glass silk ...	0·8 –0·9
½ in. acoustic felt	0·5 –0·6
Hardboard (Masonite) ...	0·3
1 in. sprayed asbestos ...	0·6 –0·7
Persons each	2·0 –5·0
Acoustic tiles...	0·4 –0·8

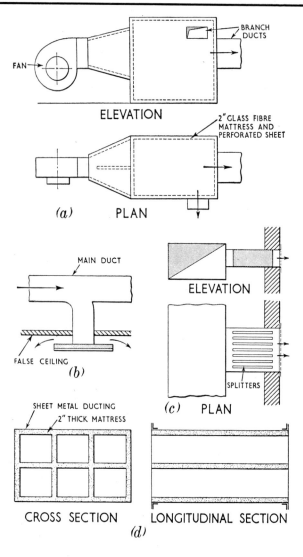

BRANCH DUCTS

FAN

ELEVATION

2" GLASS FIBRE MATTRESS AND PERFORATED SHEET

(a)   PLAN

MAIN DUCT

FALSE CEILING

(b)

ELEVATION

PLAN

SPLITTERS

(c)

SHEET METAL DUCTING

2" THICK MATTRESS

CROSS SECTION   LONGITUDINAL SECTION

(d)

(a)   Sound absorption by increase of duct area.

(b)   Ceiling air outlet with sound-absorbing plate.

(c)   Sound absorption in branch duct with splitter.

(d)   Arrangement of splitters in main duct.

Section XII

LABOUR RATES FOR INSTALLATION

In the following Tables the times for the erection of pipe lines and heating plants on site are given in hours.

Included: Hauling of all parts into position, erection on site, surveying of builders' work, testing of the plant.

Not included: Delivery to site, travelling time, removing and refixing of radiators for painting, addition for overtime work.

Additions to Total Basic Time:

For jobs up to 1 week...	40%
For jobs up to 2 weeks	20%
For jobs up to 3 weeks	8%
For installations in existing buildings, unoccupied...	5%
For installations in existing buildings, occupied ...	15%
For installations in existing buildings, with visible pipes	15–20%

ESTIMATING ERECTION TIME

The working time is stated in normal working hours of one fitter and mate.

Description of Work	Time in hours
Cast-iron Sectional Boilers for Hot Water Heating, including Boiler Mountings.	
Without Insulating Jacket for a duty of:	
Up to 125,000 B.t.u./hr. ...	15
From 125,000 to 250,000 B.t.u./hr. ...	20
From 251,000 to 500,000 B.t.u./hr. ...	30
From 501,000 to 750,000 B.t.u./hr. ...	40
From 751,000 to 1,000,000 B.t.u./hr. ...	50
From 1,001,000 to 1,500,000 B.t.u./hr. ...	60
From 1,501,000 to 2,000,000 B.t.u./hr. ...	65
From 2,001,000 to 2,500,000 B.t.u./hr. ...	70
Cast-iron Sectional Boilers for Low-pressure Steam	
With Mountings—No Jacket:	
Up to 125,000 B.t.u./hr. ...	28
From 126,000 to 250,000 B.t.u./hr. ...	30
From 251,000 to 500,000 B.t.u./hr. ...	40
From 501,000 to 750,000 B.t.u./hr. ...	50
From 751,000 to 1,000,000 B.t.u./hr. ...	65
From 1,001,000 to 1,500,000 B.t.u./hr. ...	75
From 1,501,000 to 2,000,000 B.t.u./hr. ...	80
From 2,001,000 to 2,500,000 B.t.u./hr. ...	90

BOILERS

Description of Work	Time in hours
Insulating Jackets for Cast-iron Sectional Boilers:	
Up to 500,000 B.t.u./hr. ...	6
From 501,000 to 1,000,000 B.t.u./hr. ...	8
From 1,001,000 to 2,000,000 B.t.u./hr. ...	10
From 2,001,000 to 2,500,000 B.t.u./hr. ...	12
Domestic H.W.S. Boilers Non-sectional Duty	
Up to 50,000 B.t.u./hr. ...	8
From 51,000 to 100,000 B.t.u./hr. ...	10
From 101,000 to 150,000 B.t.u./hr. ...	12
Boiler Smoke Pipes:	
Straight Pipes, 6 in. diameter, per ft. ...	0·3
Elbows, 6 in. diameter, each	0·3
Straight Pipes, 12 in. diameter, per ft. ...	0·6
Elbows, 7–12 in. diameter, each	0·6
Straight Pipes, above 12 in. per ft. ...	1
Elbows, above 12 in., each	1
Expansion Tanks, including Ball Valve and Overflow:	
Up to 20 gallons capacity	6
From 21 to 50 gallons capacity	9
From 51 to 100 gallons capacity	12
From 101 to 200 gallons capacity	15
Above 200 gallons capacity...	20
Centrifugal Pumps with Motors, Direct Coupled or Belt Drive with Base Plate or Slide Rails:	
Duty up to 50 g.p.m. Size: 1½ in. ...	10
From 51 to 100 g.p.m. Size: 1½ to 2 in. ...	14
From 101 to 300 g.p.m. Size: 3 to 4 in. ...	18
Above 300 g.p.m. Above 4 in. ...	24

BOILERS

BOILER HOUSE EQUIPMENT

Description of Work	Time in hours
Heating Accelerators: Pipe Line Model:	
Size up to 1½ in.	6
Size 2 to 3 in.	10
Size 4 in. and above	14
Starters	2
Hot Water Service Storage Cylinders	
Direct or Indirect, or Calorifiers:	
Contents up to 60 gallons	9
From 61 to 120 gallons	12
From 121 to 200 gallons	20
From 201 to 300 gallons	30
From 301 to 500 gallons	35
From 501 to 750 gallons	40
From 750 to 1,000 gallons	45
Centrifugal Fans with Motors:	
Impeller diameter up to 12 in.	15
From 13 to 24 in.	20
From 25 to 36 in.	28
From 37 to 48 in.	40
From 49 to 60 in.	50
Electric Motors only, with Slide Rails:	
Up to 2½ h.p.	7½
From 2½ to 5 h.p.	12
From 5 to 7½ h.p.	15
From 7½ to 10 h.p.	20
From 10 to 15 h.p.	25
Unit Heaters, Suspended Type:	
Duty up to 20,000 B.t.u./hr. ...	10
From 21,000 to 50,000 B.t.u./hr. ...	15
From 51,000 to 100,000 B.t.u./hr. ...	20
Radiators with 2 valves:	
Heating Surface up to 25 sq. ft.	3
26 to 50 sq. ft. ...	5
51 to 100 sq. ft. ...	7

BOILER HOUSE EQUIPMENT

ROOM HEATERS, RADIATORS ETC.

ROOM HEATERS, RADIATORS ETC

Description of Work	Time in hours
Radiators with 2 valves:—*Continued*	
Radiator Brackets	0·5
Radiator Top Stays	0·5
Removing and refixing one radiator ...	1·5
Towel Rail	8
Rayrad Panels on wall:	
Up to 3 sections at 12 in. width ...	4
From 4 to 6 sections at 12 in. width ...	6
From 7 to 10 sections at 12 in. width ...	8
Rayrad Panels on ceiling:	
Up to 3 sections at 12 in. width ...	6
From 4 to 6 sections at 12 in. width ...	8
From 7 to 10 sections at 12 in. width ...	10
Baseboard (Skirting) Heater per 2 ft. ...	0·5
Gravity Convector up to 2 ft. length ...	4
2 to 4 ft. length	6
Above 4 ft. length	8
Fan Convectors, freestanding cabinet type	5
Fan Convector, extended type, 2 grilles ...	10
Brackets and top stays to be marked by heating contractor and built in by builder	
Ventilation Plant Equipment, such as Fans, Heater Batteries, Air Filters, Ducting, etc., per 1 ton of equipment	90

VALVES ETC

Valves, size $\frac{1}{2}$ to $1\frac{1}{4}$ in.	0·5
size $1\frac{1}{2}$ to 2 in.	1·0
size $2\frac{1}{2}$ to 4 in.	2·0
size above 4 in.	3
Thermostatic and Motorised Valves:	
Up to $1\frac{1}{4}$ in.	2
$1\frac{1}{2}$ to 2 in.	4
$2\frac{1}{2}$ to 4 in.	6

	Description of Work	Time in hours
VALVES ETC	3-way Mixing Valves and Steam Reducing Valves:	
	Up to 2 in.	10
	$2\frac{1}{2}$ to 4 in.	$12\frac{1}{2}$
	5 to 6 in.	15
	Steam Traps: up to $\frac{3}{4}$ in.	2
	1 to $1\frac{1}{2}$ in.	3
	Thermometers	1·0
	Pressure Gauge with Cock...	2
	Altitude Gauge with Cock	2
	Dial Distance Thermometer with 6 ft. Capillary Tube	4
	Longer Capillary Tube, per 1 ft.	0·1

			Time in hours
TUBES	**Tubes:** including Brackets and Pipe Fittings such as Bends and Branch Tees		
	$\frac{1}{2}$ and $\frac{3}{4}$ in. n.b.		0·15
	1 and $1\frac{1}{4}$ in. n.b.		0·24
	$1\frac{1}{2}$ and 2 in. n.b.	Screwed connections per ft. lin.	0·33
	$2\frac{1}{2}$ and 3 in. n.b.		0·45
	4 in.		0·75
	5 in.		0·90
	$1\frac{1}{2}$ and 2 in. n.b.		0·20
	$2\frac{1}{2}$ and 3 in.		0·26
	4 in.		0·38
	5 in.		0·52
	6 in.	Welded connections per ft. lin.	0·60
	7 in.		0·68
	8 in.		0·75
	9 in.		0·82
	10 in.		0·90

OXYGEN WELDING

(Time in hours.   Gas in cu. ft.)

Pipe Size. Nom. Bore. in.	Time.	Gas.	Time.	Gas.	Time.	Gas.	Time.	Gas.	Time.	Gas.
3/8	0·10	2·2	0·12	2·6	0·3	4·2	0·5	5·0	0·2	3·0
1/2	0·10	2·5	0·13	3·0	0·3	4·2	0·5	5·0	0 2	3·0
3/4	0·15	2·6	0·15	3·1	0·4	4·5	0·6	6·5	0·3	3·5
1	0·15	2·8	0·20	3·3	0·5	4·6	0·6	7·5	0·3	3·5
1¼	0·20	3·3	0·25	3·9	0·5	4·6	0·7	8·5	0·4	4·0
1½	0·25	3·5	0·30	4·2	0·6	5·0	0·7	9·5	0·4	4·0
2	0·30	3·8	0·35	4·5	0·7	5·3	1·1	11·0	0·5	4·5
2½	0·35	4·5	0·4	5·3	1·0	6·0	1·3	13·0	0·6	4·5
3	0·4	5·5	0·5	6·5	1·2	7·0	1·6	16·0	0·7	6·0
4	0·5	7·5	0·6	8·5	1·6	9·5	2·3	21·0	1·0	8·0
5	0·6	9·0	0·7	11·0	1·9	12·0	2·9	26·0	1·2	10·0
6	0·7	11·0	0·8	13·0	2·2	14·0	3·2	26·0	1·3	12·0
7	0·8	13·0	0·9	15·0	2·7	17·0	3·6	36·0	1·6	13·0
8	1·0	15·0	1·1	17·0	3·3	19·0	4·0	42·0	1·8	15·0
9	1·7	17·0	1·3	20·0	3·8	22·0	4·6	48·0	2·1	17·0
10	1·2	19·0	1·4	22·0	4·2	25·0	5·2	55·0	2·2	19·0
11	1·3	21·0	1·6	24·0	4·8	27·0	5·7	60·0	2·5	21·0
12	1·5	24·0	1·8	28·0	5·2	31·0	6·2	65·0	2·8	24·0

LOW PRESSURE WELDING

| Thickness of Material ins. | Gas Consumption cu. ft. | | | | Filling Wire. | | Speed of Welding. ft. per hr |
| | Oxygen. | | Acetylene. | | Size. ins. | Consumption ins. per ft. | |
	per ft.	per hr.	per ft.	per hr.			
$\frac{1}{64}$	0·04	1·7	0·03	1·5		—	50
$\frac{1}{32}$	0·07	2·5	0·06	2·2	$\frac{1}{16}$	4	35
$\frac{3}{64}$	0·16	4·8	0·14	4·2		6	30
$\frac{1}{16}$	0·29	8·0	0·25	7·0		8	28
$\frac{3}{32}$	0·52	12·5	0·46	11·0	$\frac{1}{8}$	10	24
$\frac{1}{8}$	0·75	15·0	0·65	13·0		11	20
$\frac{3}{16}$	1·55	19	1·35	16		16	12
$\frac{1}{4}$	2·65	23	2·2	20	$\frac{3}{16}$	21	9
$\frac{5}{16}$	4·6	30	4·0	26		27	6·5
$\frac{3}{8}$	6·9	36	6	31		33	5·25
$\frac{1}{2}$	12·2	46	11	40	$\frac{1}{4}$	42	3·75
$\frac{5}{8}$	24	60	21	52		55	2·5
$\frac{3}{4}$	48	85	42	74		65	1·75
$\frac{7}{8}$	80	120	70	105	$\frac{1}{4}-\frac{3}{8}$	85	1·5
$1-1\frac{1}{2}$	84	125	74	110		100–150	1·5

CAST IRON WELDING

| Thickness of Material. ins. | Gas Consumption. cu. ft. | | | | Filling Rod. | | Speed of Welding. |
| | Oxygen. | | Acetylene. | | Size. ins. | ft. per ft. run. | |
	per ft.	per hr.	per ft.	per hr.			
$\frac{1}{4}$	0·48	3·6	0·45	3·4	$\frac{1}{4}$	1·8	7·5
$\frac{1}{2}$	4·0	11·0	3·6	10	$\frac{1}{4}$	4·5	2·75
$\frac{3}{4}$	14	28	13·0	26	$\frac{1}{4}$	9	2·0
1	36	45	34	42	$\frac{1}{4}$	13	1·25
$1\frac{1}{4}$	85	85	75	75	$\frac{1}{4}$	18	1·0
$1\frac{1}{2}$	193	145	183	137	$\frac{1}{4}$	23	0·75

NOZZLE SIZES, WORKING PRESSURES AND GAS CONSUMPTIONS FOR HIGH PRESSURE WELDING.

Blowpipe Nozzle (Litres)	Blowpipe B.O.C. Type	Mild Steel Plate, Thickness in inches	Regulator Pressure, lb./sq. in.		Gas Consumption Cu. ft./hr.
			Acetylene	Oxygen	
1–5	"O"	$\frac{1}{16}$	$1\frac{1}{2}$	$1\frac{1}{2}$	0·2
2–12	"O"	$\frac{1}{16}$	$2\frac{1}{2}$	$2\frac{1}{2}$	0·4
3–31	"O"	$\frac{1}{16}$	3	3	1·1
4–62	"O"	$\frac{1}{16}$	4	4	2·2
5–125	"O"	$\frac{1}{16}$	5	5	4·4
25	A	to $\frac{1}{32}$	2	4	0·9
50	A or B	$\frac{1}{32}$	2	4	1·8
75	A or B	$\frac{3}{64}$	2	4	2·7
100	A or B	$\frac{1}{16}$	2	4	3·3
150	A or B	$\frac{3}{32}$	2	4	5·3
225	A or B	$\frac{1}{8}$	3	5	8·0
350	B	$\frac{5}{32}$	3	5	12·4
500	B	$\frac{1}{4}$	4	8	17·7
750	B	$\frac{3}{8}$	5	10	26·5
1,000	B	$\frac{1}{2}$	6	15	35·3
1,500	B	$\frac{1}{2}-\frac{3}{4}$	9	18	53·0
2,000	B	1	12	25	70·7
2,500	B	1 and above	20	30	88·3

FORMS OF WELDED JOINTS

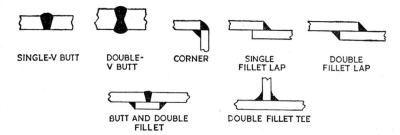

SINGLE-V BUTT   DOUBLE-V BUTT   CORNER   SINGLE FILLET LAP   DOUBLE FILLET LAP

BUTT AND DOUBLE FILLET   DOUBLE FILLET TEE

Section XIII

BOILER FEED WATER TREATMENT

HARDNESS OF WATER

A water is said to be hard when it is difficult to obtain lather with soap. Soap dissolves in soft water, but with a hard water it combines with the calcium and magnesium present, and forms an insoluble precipitate. It is necessary to add soap in order to obtain lather from hard water. About $\frac{1}{4}$ oz. of soap is required to remove 1 degree of hardness from 10 gallons of water.

Degrees of Hardness:

English (Clark's) degrees are grains of calcium carbonate per gallon, or parts per 70,000.

French (Continental) degrees are parts of calcium carbonate per 100,000 (by weight).

German degrees are parts of calcium oxide (lime) per 100,000.

1 English degree of hardness = 0·70 French degree of hardness.
1 English degree of hardness = 1·24 German degree of hardness.
1 French degree of hardness = 1·43 English degree of hardness.
1 German degree of hardness = 0·80 English degree of hardness.

In practice hardness varies from zero to 30 degrees, 5 English degrees is generally considered good.

Temporary Hardness is that which is removed by boiling the water. It is due to calcium bicarbonate and/or magnesium bicarbonate.

Permanent Hardness is that which remains after boiling. It is due to calcium and magnesium sulphate, especially $Ca\,SO_4$. Can be softened by chemical methods.

WATER SOFTENING

Removal of Temporary Hardness:

(a) Heating the water to a temperature of 150°F. to 212°F. When heated the soluble bicarbonates decompose into insoluble carbonates which settle to the bottom and can be removed:

$$Ca(HCO_3)_2 \longrightarrow CaCO_3 + H_2O + CO_2$$
Soluble Bicarbonate   Insoluble   Water   Carbon
         Carbonates   Dioxide

(b) Adding any alkali soluble in water (lime, caustic soda or baryta) in order to decompose the carbonates.

$$XCO_3 . H_2CO_3 + CaO \longrightarrow XCO_3 + CaCO_3 + H_2O$$
Soluble Bicarbonate + Lime   Insoluble + Water
                         Carbonates

Removing of Permanent Hardness:

(a) By distillation (evaporating and condensing).

(b) Soda-Lime Porter-Clerk Process:

Introducing lime (CaO) to remove temporary hardness. The soluble bicarbonates are converted into insoluble carbonates.

$$Ca(HCO_3)_2 + CaO \longrightarrow 2CaCO_3 + H_2O$$

Introducing soda Na_2Co_3 to remove the permanent hardness due to calcium sulphate $CaSo_4$. The calcium is precipitated as its carbonate

$$CaSO_4 + Na_2CO_3 \longrightarrow CaCO_3 + Na_2SO_4$$

The quantity of the addition depends upon the hardness and other properties of the water and has to be proportioned exactly.

Theoretical addition:

For 1° of Temporary Hardness:

4·4 grains slaked lime $Ca(OH)_2$ for 1 cu. ft. of water.

For 1° of Permanent Hardness:

8·3 grains sodium hydrate, caustic soda (NaOH) for 1 cu. ft. of water.

A careful surveying of the process is necessary. A final hardness of 3 to 4 degrees is attainable.

(c) Permutit Process (Dr. R. Gans):

Using Permutit, an artificial, porous, insoluble zeolite, as water filter. The zeolite is converted into its calcium or magnesium derivate and has to be reactivated by treatment with a solution of common salt (NaCl).

Softening:

$$Na_2Ze + Ca(HCO_3)_2 \longrightarrow 2NaHCO_3 + CaZe.$$
$$Na_2Ze + CaSO_4 \longrightarrow Na_2SO_4 + CaZe.$$

Re-activating:

$$CaZe + 2NaCl \longrightarrow CaCl_2 + Na_2Ze.$$
Ze = Symbol for a portion of molecule of artificial zeolite.

The process is automatic and no mistake due to adding too much or too little reagent can be made.

A zero hardness is attainable.

Consumption of salt for re-activation is 17·5 to 30·5 grains per cu. ft. of water per 1 degree of hardness.

Time for re-activation:

6 to 8 hours for Natriumpermutit.
1 hour for Neopermutit.

Corrosion:

Internal corrosion in boilers, pipes, etc., may be due to:

1. Acid in the feed water.
2. Acid formed by the decomposition of salts by heating the water.
3. Oxygen dissolved in the water.
4. Electrolysis.

Prevention of Corrosion:

1. Neutralizing the acid by an alkali, chalk milk of lime or sodium carbonate (soda).
2. De-aerating or de-gassing the feed water.
3. Inserting zinc plates connected metallically to the boiler plates, then zinc is corroded instead of iron.
4. Counter-electrolysis. by passing a direct electric current from anode in the boiler to the heating surface.
5. Coating the surface of the boiler or vessel.

Formation of Scale in Boilers:

(a) Soft, non-adherent sludge.
(b) Hard, adherent deposit (scale).

Prevention of Scale:

(a) By water softening.
(b) By adding some substance of a colloidal or gummy nature, causing the formation of sludge instead of scale.
(c) By passing a current of electricity through the water (seldom used).

Removal of Scale:

(a) Mechanically, by chipping with a hammer or chisel.
(b) Chemically, by adding caustic soda or other chemicals to the feed water.
(c) By electrolysis, small bubbles of hydrogen leave the surface of the boiler and loosen the scale.

Priming and Foaming:

Priming is a too violent boiling and projecting of droplets of water into the steam pipes.

Cause: Restricted steam-liberating area or sudden increase of load.

Foaming is the formation of a layer of bubbles on the water.

Cause: Oil, grease, or other organic impurities in water or high concentration of dissolved and suspended mineral salts.

Prevention—Provision of adequate steam place in boiler, no sudden opening of main steam valve, exclusion of oil or grease from boiler feed water.

pH Value

This is an arbitrary symbol adopted to express the degree of acidity or alkalinity of a solution.

The pH number is the common logarithm of the number of litres containing one gram-equivalent of hydrogen ion. A pH of 7 represents a neutral solution, lower values represent acidity, higher values alkalinity.

The alkalinity of boiler water is usually maintained between a pH value of 9·5 and 11·0.

Some Indicators for the Determination of the pH Value.

Thymol blue	1·2–2·8	Red–yellow	Litmus (Azolitmin)	5–8	Red–Blue.
Methyl Orange	2·9–4·6	Orange–red–orange–yellow	Phenolphthalein	8·3–10·0	Colourless–red.
Methyl red	4·4–6·2	Red–yellow	Thymolphthalein	9·3–10.5	Colourless–blue.

Blow-down

A steam boiler has to be blown-down in order to prevent the accumulation of dissolved solids (sludge and contamination of steam).

The theoretical amount of blow-down is $D = \dfrac{100F}{B}$ per cent,

where D=Blow down in per cent of the evaporation.
     F=Dissolved solids in feed water, in parts per 100,000.
     B=Permissible total of dissolved solids in boiler water in parts per 100,000.

Types of Blow-down

(a) *Intermittent Blow Down*, for less than 25 gallons per hour.
(b) *Continuous Blow Down*, by utilizing heat in a heat exchanger or flash vessel.

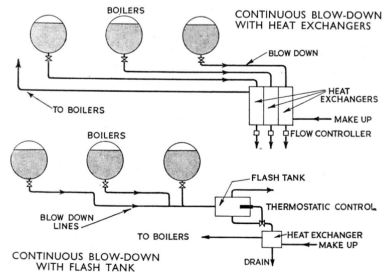

BOILERS

CONTINUOUS BLOW-DOWN WITH HEAT EXCHANGERS

BLOW DOWN

TO BOILERS

HEAT EXCHANGERS

MAKE UP

FLOW CONTROLLER

BOILERS

FLASH TANK

THERMOSTATIC CONTROL

BLOW DOWN LINES

TO BOILERS

HEAT EXCHANGER

MAKE UP

CONTINUOUS BLOW-DOWN WITH FLASH TANK

DRAIN

Section XIV

BIBLIOGRAPHY

HANDBOOKS

Computation of Heat Requirements for Buildings, 1950 Edition. Published by The Institution of Heating and Ventilating Engineers, 21, Tothill Street, London, S.W.1.

Drake's Heating, Cooking and Air Conditioning Handbook, by H. P. Manly. Fred. J. Drake & Co., Chicago.

Engineer's Year Book. Published by Morgan Bros. (Publishers), Ltd., 28, Essex Street, Strand, London, W.C.2.

Guide, American Society of Heating and Ventilating Engineers, 51, Madison Avenue, New York.

Maintenance Engineer's Pocket Book. George Newnes, Ltd., London.

Marks, Mechanical Engineer's Handbook. McGraw-Hill, New York and London.

Molesworth's Pocket Book of Engineering Formulae. E. & F. N. Spon, Ltd., London.

The Musgrave Pocket Book. Musgrave & Co., Ltd., Belfast.

Newnes Engineer's Pocket Book. George Newnes, Ltd., London.

Newnes Electrical Pocket Book. George Newnes, Ltd., London.

Pocket Book for Mechanical Engineers by David Allan Low. Longmans, Green & Co., London, New York, Toronto.

PERIODICALS

Air Treatment Engineer. (Mapon Press, 7, Princes Street, Westminster, London, S.W.1.)

Automatic Heat and Air Conditioning. (1900, Prairie Avenue, Chicago, Ill.).

Cheap Steam. (Published by Cheap Steam, Ltd., 28, Victoria Street, London, S.W.1.).

Combustion. (Published by Combustion Publishing Company, Inc., Combustion Engineering Co., Inc., 200, Madison Avenue, New York).

Fuel in Science and Practice. (Published by Fuel Publications, Ltd., 30 & 31, Furnival Street, Holborn, London, E.C.1).

Heating and Ventilating. (The Industrial Press, 148, Lafayette Street, New York).

Heating and Ventilating Engineer and Journal of Air Conditioning. (Technitrade Journals, Ltd., 8, Southampton Row, London, W.C.1).

Heating, Piping and Air Conditioning. (Published by Keeney Publishing Co., 6, North Michigan Avenue, Chicago, Ill.).

Industrial Heating Engineer, Air Conditioning and Ventilating. (Published by J. D. Troup, Ltd., 90/91, High Holborn, London, W.C.1.).

Industrial Power and Fuel Economist. (Fuel Journals, Ltd., Old Forge House, Hampton Loade, nr. Bridgnorth).

Plumber and Decorator and Journal of Heating, Ventilating, Gas and Sanitary Engineering. (Dale, Reynolds & Co., Ltd., Cannon Street, London, E.C.4.).

Power. (McGraw-Hill Publications, 330, Forty-second Street, New York).

Sanitary and Heating Engineering. (New York).

Steam Engineer. (90/91, High Holborn, London, W.C.1).

Water and Water Engineering. (30 & 31, Furnival Street, Holborn, London, E.C.4)

BOOKS

HEATING, VENTILATING AND AIR CONDITIONING

Adlam, T. Napier. *Radiant Heating.* (1947, The Industrial Press, New York).

Air Conditioning and Engineering. (1935, The American Blower Co. & Canadian Sirocco Co., Ltd., Detroit).

Allen, G. S., and Maxwell, R. S. *A Textbook of Heat.* (1943, Macmillan & Co., Ltd., London).

Barker, A. H. *The Theory and Practice of Heating and Ventilating.* (Carton Press, London).

Bedford, T. *Basic Principles of Ventilating and Heating.* (1948, H. K. Lewis & Co., Ltd., London).

Brown, S. P. *Air Conditioning and Elements of Refrigeration.* (1947, McGraw-Hill Publishing Co., Ltd., New York and London).

Carrier, W. H. *Modern Air Conditioning, Heating and Ventilating.* (1941, Pitman Publishers, New York).

Coleman, G. S. *Calculations in Heating and Ventilating.* (Longmans, Green & Co., Ltd., London).

Cornell, R. K. *Heating and Ventilating for Architects and Builders.* (1946, Paul Elek (Publishers) Ltd., London).

Dalzell, J. R. *Air Conditioning Furnaces and Unit Heaters.* (1938, American Technical Society, Chicago).

Davies, S. J. *Heat Pumps and Thermal Compression.* (1950, Constable & Co., Ltd., London).

Dye, F. W. *Steam Heating.* (E. & F. N. Spon, Ltd., London).

The Efficient Use of Fuel. Ministry of Fuel and Power. (1944, H.M. Stationery Office, London).

Faber, O., and Kell, J. R. *Heating and Air Conditioning of Buildings* (Second Edition). (1944, Architectural Press, Ltd., London).

Fuller, Ch. A. *Air Conditioning.* (1939, Sir Isaac Pitman & Sons, Ltd., London).

Gaskill, D. L. *Handbook of the National District Heating Assocation.* (1932, Greenville, Ohio, U.S.A.).

Goodman, W. *Air Conditioning Analysis.* (1943, Macmillan & Co., Ltd., New York).

Harding, L. A., and Willard, A. C. *Heating, Ventilating and Air Conditioning.* (1932, I. Willy & Sons, Ltd.).

Heating and Ventilating, Air Conditioning. 5 vols. A home study course. (1945, The American Technical Society, Chicago).

Henly, A. T. *Design Problems of Heating and Ventilating.* (1936, Crosby Lockwood & Son, Ltd., London).

Hermiker, Herbert, and Hermiker, Harold. *Air Conditioning.* (1947, Chemical Publishing Co., Inc., New York).

Holman, T. F., Cutler, C., Sandy, A. H., and Clark, L. M. *Textbook of Heating and Ventilating.* (1950, George Newnes, Ltd., London).

Holmes, R. E. *Air Conditioning in Summer and Winter.* (1938, McGraw-Hill Publishing Co., Ltd., New York and London).

Institution of Heating and Ventilating Engineers, 21 Tothill Street, London, S.W.1. *Recommendations for the Computation of Heat Requirements for Buildings.*

Jennings, B. H., and Lewis, S. R. *Air Conditioning and Refrigeration.* (1944, International Textbook Co., Scarnton, Pennsylvania).

Jones, A. A. *Modern Heating and Ventilating.* (Caxton Publishing Co., Ltd., London).

Joselin, E. L. *Ventilation.* (1934, Edward Arnold & Co., Ltd., London).

Kemble, E. N., and Ogleby, S., junr. *Heat Pump Applications.* (1947, McGraw-Hill Publishing Co., Ltd., New York and London).

Lyle, Oliver. *The Efficient Use of Steam*. (1947, H.M. Stationery Office, London).

March, M. C. *Controlled Humidity in Industry*. (1935, Ch. Griffin & Co., Ltd., London).

Mitchell, G. Eric. *Sanitation, Drainage and Water Supply*. (G. Newnes, Ltd., London).

Moyer, J., and Fittz, R. U. *Air Conditioning*. (1938, McGraw-Hill Publishing Co., Ltd., New York and London).

Northcroft, L. G. *Steam Trapping and Air Venting*. (Hutchinson's Scientific & Technical Publications, London, New York, Melbourne).

Overton, L. J. *Heating and Ventilating*. Fifth Edition. (1944, The Sutherland Publishing Co., Manchester).

Pallot, A. C. *Principles and Practice of Heating and Ventilating*. (G. Newnes, Ltd., London).

Raber, B. F. and Hutchinson, F. W. *Panel Heating and Cooling Analysis*. (1947, J. Wiley & Sons, Inc., New York, and Chapman & Hall, Ltd., London).

Reisbeck, E. W. *Air Conditioning*. (1939, The Goodheart Willcox Co., Inc., Chicago).

Rietschel-Brabee (translated from German). McGraw-Hill Publishing Co., Ltd., New York and London).

Rummel, A. J., and Vogelsang, L. D. *Practical Air Conditioning*. (1941, J. Wiley & Sons, Inc., New York).

Severns, W. H., and Fellows, J. R. *Heating, Ventilating and Air Conditioning Fundamentals*. (1949, J. Wiley & Sons, Inc., New York, and Chapman & Hall, Ltd., London).

Smith, F. C. *Warming Buildings by Electricity*. (E. & F. N. Spon, Ltd., London).

Sporn, P., Amorose, E. R., and Baumeister, Th. *Heat Pumps*. (1947, J. Wiley & Sons, Inc., New York, and Chapman & Hall, Ltd., London).

Stangel, W. H. *An Air Conditioning Primer*. (1940, McGraw-Hill Publishing Co., Ltd., New York and London).

Taylor, F. H. *Electric Heating and Lighting*. (1928, Chapman & Hall, Ltd., London).

Torok, Elmer. *Psychometric Notes and Tables*. (The American Rayon Corporation, New York).

Trane Air Conditioning Manual. (British Trane Co., Ltd., London).

Turpin, F. Burlace, and Roberts, A. Leonard. *Heating and Air Conditioning Equipment*. (1948, Sir Isaac Pitman & Sons, Ltd., London).

Vernon, H. M. *The Principles of Heating and Ventilation*. (Edward Arnold & Co., Ltd., London).

White, W. L. *Heating Engineer's Qualities*. (E. & F. N. Spon, Ltd., London).

Wignall, Norman. *Student's Textbook of Heating and Ventilation*. (Technitrade Journals, Ltd., London).

Wilcox, E. A. *Electric Heating*. (McGraw-Hill Publishing Co., Ltd., New York and London).

HEAT PUMPS

Davies, S. J. *Heat Pumps and Thermal Compression*. (1950, Constable & Co. Ltd., London).

Kemble, E. N., and Ogleby, S., junr. *Heat Pump Applications*. (1947, McGraw-Hill Publishing Co. Ltd., New York and London).

Sporn, P., Amorose, E. R., and Baumeister, Th. *Heat Pumps*. (1947, J. Wiley & Sons, Inc., New York, and Chapman and Hall, Ltd., London).

HEAT, HEAT TRANSFER, THERMODYNAMICS

Allen, H. S., and Maxwell, R. R. *Textbook of Heat*. (Macmillan, 1939).

Bailey, N. P. *Principles of Heat Engineering*. (Chapman & Hall).

Barton, A. W. *Textbook on Heat*. (Longmans, Green & Co., Ltd.).

Brown, A. I., and Marco, S. M. *Introduction to Heat Transfer*. (McGraw-Hill, 1942).

Cork, J. M. *Heat Transmission*. (Chapman & Hall).

Croft, Huber O. *Thermodynamics, Flow of Fluid and Heat Transmission*. (McGraw-Hill).

Duncan, J., and Starling, S. G. *Heat, Textbook of Physics*. 6th part. (Macmillan).

Everett, —. *Thermodynamics*. (D. van Nostrand Co., Inc., New York).

Fernald, E. M. *Elements of Thermodynamics*. (McGraw-Hill).

Inchley's *Theory of Heat Engines*. (Edited and revised by H. Wright Baker, Longmans, Green & Co., Ltd.).

Jakobs, M., and Hawkins, G. A. *Elements of Heat Transfer and Insulation*. (Chapman & Hall, 1942).

McAdams. *Heat Transmission*. (McGraw-Hill).

Moss, H. *Applied Heat*. (Blackie & Sons, 1927).

Robinson, W., and Dickson, S. M. *Applied Thermodynamics*. (Pitman, 1940).

Roberts, J. K. *Heat and Thermodynamics*. Third Edition. (Blackie & Sons, Ltd.)

Royds, Constable & Co., Ltd. *Heat Transmission by Radiation, Conduction and Convection*. (E. Benn, Ltd., London).

Schack, A. *Industrial Heat Transfer* (translation from German). (Chapman & Hall).

Stoever, H. J. *Applied Heat Transmission*. (McGraw-Hill, 1941).

Wrangham, D. A. *The Theory and Practice of Heat Engines*. (Cambridge University Press, 1942).

HYDRAULICS

Jameson, A. H. *An Introduction to Fluid Mechanics*. (Longmans, Green & Co.).

Lea, F. C. *Hydraulics*. (E. Arnold & Co., London).

Lewitt, E. H. *Hydraulics* (Engineering Degree Series). (Pitman, London).

FEED WATER TREATMENT

Batley, R. L., and Barber, E. G. *Boiler Plant Technology*. (Pitman, 1933).

Booth, W. H. *Water Softening and Treatment*.

James, S. V. *Water Treatment*. (The Technical Press).

Matthews, F. J. *Boiler Feed Water Treatment*. (Hutchinson's Scientific and Technical Publications, Paternoster House, London, E.C.4).

Ryan, W. J. *Water Treatment and Purification*. (McGraw-Hill, New York and London).

Suckan, Ch. A. *The Supervision and Maintenance of Steam Raising Plants*. (E. Benn, Ltd., London).

COMBUSTION

Batley, R. L., and Barber, E. G. *Boiler Plant Technology*. (Pitman, 1939).

Bone, W. A., and Himus, G. W. *Coal: Its Constitution and Uses*. (Longmans, Green & Co., Ltd., 1936).

Brame and King. *Fuel, Solid, Liquid and Gaseous*. (E. Arnold & Co., London, 1935).

Fischer, L. J. *Combustion Engineers' Pocket Book* (George Newnes, Ltd. 1959).

Himus, G. W. *Fuel Testing, Laboratory Methods of Fuel Technology*. (Leonard Hill, Ltd., 1942).

Kunitz, H. A. *Oil Heating Handbook*. (Lippincott, 1937).

McCulloch, A. *Gas Analysis*. (H. F. & S. Witherby, Ltd., 326, High Holborn, London, W.C.1).

Steiner, K., and Raunsbeck, F. *Oil Burner Service Manual*. (McGraw-Hill, New York and London, 1942).

FANS

Alden, J. L. *Design of Industrial Exhaust Systems*. (The Industrial Press, 148, Lafayette Street, New York, and London).

Baumeister, Th. *Fans*. (McGraw-Hill Book Co., New York and London).

Keller-Marks. *Axial Flow Fans*. (McGraw-Hill Book Co., New York and London, 1937).

Slade, F. H. *Design of Fans*. (Princes Press, Ltd., 7, Princes Street, London, S.W.1).

HOT WATER SYSTEMS

Molloy, E. *Hot Water Engineering*. (G. Newnes, Ltd.).

PUMPS

Deffeld, O., and Olliver, C. W. *A Practical Treatise on Single and Multi-Stage Centrifugal Pumps*. (Chapman & Hall, London).

De Laval, C. G. *Centrifugal Pumping Machinery (Centrifugal and Turbine Pumps)*. (McGraw-Hill Book Co., New York and London).

Higgins, G. *Centrifugal Pumps*. (Crosby, Lockwood & Son, London).

Sargeant, E. W. *Centrifugal Pumps and Suction Dredgers*. (Ch. Griffin & Co., Ltd., London).

Slade, F. H. *Design of Pumps*. (Princes Press, Ltd., 7, Princes Street, London, S.W.1).

MEASURING INSTRUMENTS

Eason, A. B. *Flow and Measurement of Air and Gases*. (Ch. Griffin & Co., 1930).

Griffiths, F. *Methods of Measuring Temperatures*.

Ower, E. *Measurement of Flow*. (Chapman & Hall, 1933).

Flow Measurement. (Published by Messrs. George Kent, Ltd., Luton and London).

The Mechanical Properties of Fluids. A Collective Work. (Blackie & Son, Ltd.).

WELDING

American Welding Society. *Welding Handbook*. (Published by American Welding Society, 33, W. Thirty-ninth Street, New York).

Atkins, E. A., and Walker. *Electric Arc and Oxy-Acetylene Welding*. (Pitman, 1942).

Bradtke, D. Kenney. *Technique of Modern Welding*. (Blackie & Son, Ltd.).

B.O.C. *Handbook for Welder*.

Davies, A. C. *The Science and Practice of Welding*. (The University Press, Cambridge, 1941).

Holslag, C. J. *Arc Welding Handbook*. (Electric Arc Corporation, 1941).

Lennings, R. F. *General Shop Gas and A.C. Arc Welding and Cutting*. (New York, 1942).

Kilburn, W. L. *Copper and Bronze Welding*. First Edition.

Lincoln, J. *Arc Welding Foundation, Arc Welding in Design, Manufacture and Construction*. (Cleveland, Ohio, 1929).

Lincoln Electric Co. *Procedure Handbook of Arc Welding Design and Practice*. 1942.

Lincoln Electric Co. *Lessons in Arc Welding*.

Newnes' *Complete Welder* (3 Volumes). (George Newnes, Ltd., Tower House, Southampton Street, Strand, London, W.C.2).

Philips' Practical Welding Course. (Published by Philips Industrial, Century House, Shaftesbury Avenue, London, W.C.2).

Sykes, F. W. *Drawing and Development for Practical Welding*. (Pitman, 1941).

Welding and Metal Cutting. (George Newnes, Ltd., Tower House, Southampton Street, Strand, London, W.C.2).

Welding Engineer's Pocket Book. (George Newnes, Ltd., Tower House, Southampton Street, Strand, London, W.C.2).

Section XV

BRITISH STANDARDS CODES OF PRACTICE APPLYING TO HEATING AND VENTILATING PLANTS

BRITISH STANDARDS

No.
4 : 1932 **Dimensions and properties of channels and beams for structural purposes.**
21pp. 4s. Amendment CD 3097, April 1934.

4A : 1934 **Dimensions and properties of equal angles, unequal angles and T bars for structural purposes.**
24pp. 4s. Partly superseding B.S. 6 : 1924.

10 : —— **Tables of pipe flanges (for land use).**
These tables are issued in five parts as follows:

10 : Part 1 : 1947 Pipe flanges for land use (for pressures up to 400 ft. head).
12pp. 3s. Amendment PD 1157, March 1951.
This British Standard deals with the dimensions of flanges for pipes, valves and fittings for maximum working water pressures up to 400 ft. head (173 lb./sq. in.) at a maximum temperature of 212° F., and it includes minimum mechanical requirements for cast iron, cast steel, bronze, wrought iron, wrought steel, and malleable cast iron pipe flanges.

10 : Part 2 : 1926 For working steam pressures up to 450 lb./sq. in. (tables D to P).
16pp. 3s. 6d. Amendment CC (ME) 6311, June 1927.

10 : Part 3 : 1929 For working steam pressures above 450 lb./sq. in. and up to 600 lb./sq. in. (table R).
16pp. 3s. 6d. Amendment CC 3901, April 1931.

10 : Part 4 : 1931 For working steam pressures above 600 lb./sq. in. and up to 900 lb./sq. in. and temperatures to 800° F. (427° C.) (table S).
16pp. 3s. 6d.

10 : Part 5 : 1932 For working steam pressures above 900 lb./sq. in. and up to 1400 lb./sq. in. and temperatures up to 800° F. (427° C.) (table T).
16pp. 4s.
In each case tables of dimensions for various nominal pipe sizes are given with metric equivalents and illustrative drawings, together with bolt circle and bolt sizes. Flanges may be of cast iron, bronze, cast steel, or forged iron or steel, where appropriate. For Parts 4 and 5, tensile and notched bar tests are required and the test specimens to be used are illustrated.

21 : 1957 **Pipe threads.**
32pp. 7s. 6d. Amendment PD 3453, July 1959.
Jointing threads and longscrew threads. The B.S.P. size range is from ½ in. to 6 in. nominal bore and details of thread forms, dimensions and tolerances are given.

40 : 1908 **Cast iron low pressure heating pipes, spigot and socket.**
16pp. 3s. 6d.
This specification covers quality, marking, and hydraulic testing of low pressure heating pipes and full particulars of necessary dimensions are listed in the tables for straight pipes up to 100 ft. head working pressure. Application to various fittings is illustrated in the last figure.

41 : 1946   **Cast iron spigot and socket flue or smoke pipes.**
20pp. 7s.
Provides for the dimensions and minimum weights of cast iron spigot and socket flue or smoke pipes, bends and offsets, of from four to twenty inches nominal bore.

57 : 1951   **B.A. bolts, screws, nuts, and plain washers.**
28pp. 4s. 6d. Amendment PD 4329, October 1961.
This specification gives the complete dimensions for B.A. screws and bolts with cheese, round, countersunk, raised-countersunk and hexagonal heads, and for hexagonal ordinary nuts and lock nuts, of sizes Nos. 0 to 16 inclusive. Two sizes of washers are standardized, namely, large washers for sizes 0 to 10 B.A. inclusive and small washers for sizes 0 to 8 B.A. inclusive.

61 Part 1 : 1947 Copper tubes (heavy gauge) for general purposes.
10pp. 3s.

61 Part 2 : 1946 Screw threads for copper tubes.
14pp. 3s. Amendment PD 766, April 1948.

78 : ——   **Cast iron spigot and socket pipes (vertically cast) and spigot and socket fittings.**
98pp. 15s. Amendments CE 9994, November 1938; PD 155, September 1943; PD 750, January 1948; PD 1591, March 1953.
This specification covers pipes from $1\frac{1}{2}$ in. diameter up to 48 in. in four classes according to test pressure. The quality of the material, mechanical tests, coating, tolerances on weight and dimensions are among the requirements laid down. Fully dimensioned drawings of the sockets are given, together with tables of dimensions for a wide range of fittings, including bends, tees, syphons and branches, plugs, flanges, caps, tapers, angle branches, crosses, collars, etc. The appendices contain details of flanges, bolts, etc., for various pressure heads.

78 Part 1 : 1961 Pipes.
20pp. 5s.

99 : 1922   **Copper-alloy pipe fittings screwed for low- and medium-pressure B.S. copper tubes.**
52pp. 7s. Amendment 3979, October 1927 cancelled.
The fittings dealt with in this specification are for domestic plumbings and similar work and for use with screwed copper pipe in accordance with B.S. 61. A table of nomenclature is given and form of ends of fittings, screw threads (Whitworth), material and testing procedure specified. Forms and dimensions of sockets, caps, plugs, bushes, elbows and tees for short- and long-sweep fittings, and of return bend, are specified and design methods described, for nominal sizes from $\frac{1}{8}$ in. to 4 in.

143 : 1952   **Malleable cast iron and cast copper alloy pipe fittings for steam, air, water, gas and oil. Screwed B.S.P. taper thread or A.P.I. line thread.**
56pp. 8s. 6d.
This specification gives standard dimensions for all of the customary types of equal and reducing fittings for nominal pipe sizes from $\frac{1}{8}$ in. to 6 in. inclusive. The fittings are, in general, suitable for working pressures up to 200 lb./sq. in. in the case of water, and up to 150 lb./sq. in. in the case of steam, gas or oil. Tests for porosity and ductility are prescribed.
The complementary standard for pipe fittings having B.S.P. taper male and parallel female threads is B.S. 1256.

308 : 1953   **Engineering drawing office practice.**
100pp. 10s. 6d. Amendment PD 2325, November 1955; PD 2688, February 1957.

Section One on 'General Practice' is based on the previous B.S. 308 : 1943, but its scope has been limited to principles and methods to be followed in the preparation of engineering drawings only.

Section Two on 'Dimensioning and Tolerancing' is entirely new, and lays down a number of principles of which the most important are that the drawing should define the finished product, and that dimensions affecting the function of the product should be expressed directly on the drawing. It also deals with ways of indicating dimensions, tolerances and notes on the drawings and with the dimensioning of common features.

An important part of this section is devoted to the principles and methods of geometrical tolerancing for straightness, flatness, parallelism, squareness, angularity, symmetry, concentricity, roundness and position. The use of such tolerances of form is essential in many cases to ensure interchangeability of components manufactured in quantity by different firms. The standard concludes with clauses on the dimensioning and tolerancing of profiles and the indication of machining and surface finish. It is profusely illustrated by diagrams and includes six typical drawings based on the recommended practice.

309 : 1958 **Whitehart malleable iron castings.**
12pp. 4s. Amendment PD 3003, March 1958.
This British Standard covers two grades (grade 1 and grade 2) of whitehart malleable iron castings.

The provision and heat treatment of test bars are specified and the test requirements are related to three different sizes of test bars selected according to the important sectional thickness of the castings. A tensile test and either a bend test or an analysis certificate of the phosphorus content are specified and provision is made for additional tests to be called for where appropriate.

Details are also included of workmanship and finish, machineability and testing facilities.

310 : 1958 **Blackheart malleable iron castings.**
12pp. 4s.
This British Standard covers three grades of blackheart malleable iron castings.

The provision, heat treatment and dimensions of test bars are specified. The various mechanical tests are also specified and a limit is placed on the phosphorus content. Details are included regarding micro-structure, hardness and hydraulic steam or air pressure tests.

350 : —— **Conversion factors and tables.**

350 : Part 1 : 1959 Basis of tables. Conversion factors.
116pp. 15s.
The scope of Part 1 of B.S. 350 has been considerably augmented by its revision and now covers a wide range of subjects of measurement falling under the general headings Metrology, Mechanics and Heat.

380 : 1958 **Performance of desk-type electric fans.**
24pp. 6s.
This applies to desk-type fans of blade sweeps up to 16 in. and speeds not greater than 1350 r.p.m. Clauses on rating requirements, speed regulation, starting capability, and limits of temperature rise are given. A method of determining air delivery is described and an example of tabulation of results of tests appears in an appendix.

416 : 1957 **Cast iron spigot and socket soil waste and ventilating pipes, fittings and accessories.**
48pp. 7s. 6d. Amendment PD 3064, May 1958.
Requirements for three grades of soil pipes, namely, 'extra heavy', 'heavy'

and 'medium', are specified for a range of sizes in each grade. Straight pipes have an *effective* length of 5 ft.

The clauses deal with quality of material, workmanship, length and weight, finish, marking and a hydraulic test. Tables of dimensions, illustrated by drawings, are included for straight pipes, sockets, bends, offsets, branches, holderbats, wire balloons, pipe inlets and sanitary connections.

417 : 1951 **Galvanized mild steel cisterns, tanks and cylinders.**
18pp. 3s. 6d. Amendments PD 1438, July 1952; PD 1889, June 1954; PD 2313, September 1955; PD 3414, June 1959. (Addendum No. 1; PD 2357, December 1955, sold separately, 2s.)

Provides for cisterns, tanks and cylinders mainly intended for domestic purposes in ranges of twenty-one sizes of cisterns up to 1,000 gallons nominal capacity, eight sizes of tanks from 17 to 53 gallons actual net capacity and eleven sizes of cylinders from 16 to 97 gallons actual net capacity.

Clauses cover sizes and gradings, material, manufacture, staying, screwed connections and holes, setting and marking and optional provision for fitting of an immersion heater.

Tables of sizes and dimensions are given together with three gradings, according to the test pressures and working heads, and appendices contain recommendations for the position of holes in cisterns and tanks, when these are required.

PD 2357 : 1955 Addendum No. 1 to B.S. 417 : 1951 Galvanized mild-steel covers for cisterns.
8pp. 2s.

437 : 1933 **Cast iron spigot and socket drain pipes.**
10pp. 4s. Amendment PD 148, August 1943.
The specification covers pipes from 2 in. to 9 in. diameter. The quality of material is stated and dimensions and weights are given for each size. Other requirements include a hammer test, finish and coating.

460 & 1205 : 1948 Cast iron rainwater goods.
53pp. 8s. 6d. Amendments PD1411, June 1952; PD 1727, October 1953.
Three grades of rainwater pipes are covered by the standard, light, medium and heavy, in sizes from 2 in. to 6 in., together with fittings and accessories; half-round gutters in sizes from 3 in. to 6 in. and ogee gutters in 4 in., 4½ in. and 5 in. sizes. The general clauses deal with quality of materials, freedom from defects, facilities for inspection, marking and rejection. Dimensions, weight, thickness, sockets, ears, hammer test and finishes relating to pipes and dimensions, thickness and finish relating to gutters are also specified.

486 : 1956 **Asbestos cement pressure pipes.**
20pp. 4s. 6d. Amendments PD 2877, August 1957; PD 3291, February 1959.
Covers a range of asbestos cement pressure pipes from 2 in. to 24 in. diameter and gives requirements for materials, manufacture, classification, dimensions, and tests for straightness, bore, hydraulic strength, water absorption, solubility in acid, bending, and crushing strength. Requirements for collars and jointing materials, coating, inspection and selection for testing, are also given. An appendix gives precautions for attaching ferrules and notes on jointing.

499 : 1952 **Glossary of terms (with symbols) relating to the welding and cutting of metals.**
126pp. 15s. Amendment PD 2220, June 1955; PD 2972 February, 1958; PD 3282, February 1959; PD 3496, September 1959.
In eight sections, the first size defining terms related to welding:
    Section 1. Terms relating both to welding with pressure and to fusion welding (welding without pressure).

Section 2. Terms relating to welding with pressure.
Section 3. Terms relating to fusion welding (welding without pressure).
Section 4. Terms relating to brazing and bronze welding.
Section 5. Terms relating to resting.
Section 6. Terms relating to weld imperfections.
Section 7. Sets out a scheme of symbols relating to welds. (Also published separately.)
Section 8. Deals with terms relating to cutting.

An appendix to Section 6 gives a number of terms relating to weld imperfections appropriate for radiographic examination.

499 : Section 7 : 1952 Scheme of symbols for welding.
48pp. 7s. (Also included in B.S. 499.)

The scheme is described under the essential features which are to be indicated, namely, the type, size, location and finish of weld. The scheme embraces arc, gas and resistance welding. The standard symbols are set out in a table and 63 figures illustrate the application of the scheme from the basic indications up to the complete indication of all necessary dimensions.

Appendices set out the information which should be given on welding procedure sheets, and two typical welding procedure sheets are included.

567 : 1954 Asbestos cement flue pipes and fittings—light quality.
32pp. 6s. Amendments PD 2161, April 1955; PD 2207, June 1955.

This British Standard covers the quality and dimensions of pipes and fittings up to 6 in. diameter intended primarily for use with gas appliances. The specification has been revised to include standard dimensions of the pipes and the fittings which are in general use. It also includes an appendix containing recommendations for the method of fixing, and for the testing of straight pipes and fittings.

569 : 1956 Asbestos cement rainwater pipes, gutters and fittings.
64pp. 11s.

Covers the quality and dimensions of a range of rainwater pipes and fittings up to 6 in. diameter, together with a range of gutters suitable for housing and industrial buildings. The gutters include the half-round, ogee, valley, northlight valley, boundary wall and box types. Test requirements for the material and tolerances on dimensions are laid down. Appendices show suggested methods of jointing and fixing.

570 : 1959 Plug-and-socket gas connectors for portable appliances.
8pp. 3s.

Specifies performance requirements, covering gas rate and gas soundness, operation of taps, and suitability of connections, washers, nuts and fixing screw-holes. General functional design, workmanship and materials are also specified.

573 : 1957 Dibutyl phthalate.
12pp. 4s.

The specification covers specific gravity and refractive index and includes limits for colour, colour stability, water, ash, volatile matter, acidity and ester content. Test methods are described.

574 : 1957 Diethyl phthalate.
8pp. 2s. 6d.

The specification covers colour, colour stability, specific gravity and refractive index and includes limits for water, ash, acidity and ester control. Test methods are described.

599 : 1939   **Pump tests.**
42pp. 7s. Amendment PD 368, June 1945.
This contains particulars of methods to be adopted for finding the performance and efficiency of water pumps, including centrifugal pumps. Attention
is given to general precautions, operating conditions and measurements of
discharge, including sections on types of weirs, venturi meters, pitot tubes,
etc. Terms used are defined, methods of measuring head and power input
are set out; the tables give figures for discharge over 90° and half 90° Vee
notches. A typical test sheet is included in the appendices.

602, 1085 : 1956 Lead pipes for other than chemical purposes.
30pp. 7s.
602 applies to lead pipes of three different compositions in standard sizes
¾ in. to 6 in. internal diameter.
1085 applies to lead pipes (silver-copper-lead) in standard sizes ⅜ in. to 2 in.
internal diameter.

659 : 1955   **Light gauge copper tubes for water, gas and sanitation.**
12pp. 3s.
This specification relates to copper tubes for connection by compression
fittings or capillary fittings or by bronze or autogenous welding. The standard
dimensions are given for water and gas tubes from ⅛ in. to 6 in. nominal size,
these being suitable for working water pressures up to 200 lb./sq. in. in the
case of tubes up to 2 in. nominal size, 150 lb./sq. in. for tubes 2½ in. to 4 in.
nominal size, and 100 lb./sq. in. for tubes of 5 and 6 in. Tubes for sanitation
are standardized in nominal sizes from 1 in. to 6 in.
The quality of the tubes is standardized by reference to B.S. 1172 and 1174.
Hydraulic pressure tests and mechanical tests are included.

669 : 1960   **Flexible tubing and connector ends for appliance burning town gas.**
20pp. 5s. Amendment PD 4183, June 1961.
Specific dimensions, materials, marking, performance requirements and tests
for the following types of tubing.
      (*a*) Flexible non-metallic tubing and connector ends.
      (*b*) General purpose flexible metallic tubing.
      (*c*) Heavy duty armoured flexible tubing and connector ends.

699 : 1951   **Copper cylinders for domestic purposes.**
19pp. 3s. Amendments PD 1888, June 1954; PD 2212, June 1955 (superseding
PD 1888); PD 2319, October 1955; PD 2535, July 1956; PD 2901, October
1957; PD 3208, November 1958.
Specifies a range of copper cylinders having actual capacities of 17¼ to
91 gallons, and covers the external dimensions, gauges of metal, sizes and
position of connections and methods of manufacture. A table gives details
of sizes with corresponding actual capacities and gauges of metal for working
heads of 30 ft., 60 ft. and 100 ft. of water with their appropriate test pressures.
Appendices suggest positions for immersion heaters and circulators, together
with details of handholes. A schedule gives details to be supplied to the
manufacturer when ordering.

749 : 1952   **Underfeed stokers (ram- or screw-type).** (Confirmed 1960.)
20pp. 3s. 6d. Amendment PD 2132, March 1955.
Specifies requirements for stokers rated up to 1,200 lb. of coal per hour for
all applications except metallurgical or other high-temperature furnaces.
Recommendations for installation and maintenance, rating by heat output,
and suitable fuels are given in appendices. (See also **CP 3000.**)

758 : ——   **Small domestic hot-water supply boilers using solid fuel.**

        758 : Part 1 : 1955 Manually controlled boilers.
32pp. 6s. Amendments PD 2418, April 1956; PD 2698, May 1957; PD 4317,
October 1961.

758 : Part 2 : 1960 Thermostat-controlled boilers.
24pp. 7s. 6d. Amendment PD 4139, April 1961.
Applies to small thermostat-controlled boilers which are designed to burn solid smokeless fuel.

759 : 1955 Valves, gauges and other safety fittings for application to land boilers and piping installations for and in connection with land boilers.
28pp. 4s. 6d. Amendment PD 2660, December 1956.
Deals with safety valves, high and low water alarms, stop valves, feed valves, blow-down fittings, water gauges, pressure gauges, test connection and fusible plugs. It does not provide for fittings for calorifiers or for certain low pressure and hot water boilers.

761 : 1951 Vertical multitubular boilers of riveted construction. (Confirmed 1960.)
50pp. 10s. Amendments PD 3692, February 1960; PD 4157, April 1961.
Applies solely to vertical multitubular boilers of the smoke tube and water tube types exclusive of brickwork setting and insulation, and mountings and furnace fittings.

766 : 1938 Bafflers or draught diverters on gas appliances, including recommendations for flue terminals.
11pp. 3s. Amendment CE 7619, May 1938.
Deals principally with the performance of bafflers under various draught conditions and includes clauses dealing with strength and resistance to corrosion.

778 : 1951 Steel pipes and flanged joints for hydraulic purposes.
36pp. 5s. Amendment PD 1242, August 1951.

779 : 1961 Cast iron boilers for central heating and hot water supply.
52pp. 15s.

780 : 1938 Riveted steel boilers for hot water central heating and hot water supply.
33pp. 7s. 6d. Amendment CF 2733, November 1939.

788 : 1938 Wrought iron tubes and tubulars, gas (light), water (medium), and steam (heavy) qualities.
23pp. 4s. 6d. Amendments CE 7087, March 1938; CF 577, January 1939.
Applies to welded, screwed and socketed, and plain end tubes from $\frac{1}{8}$ in. to 6 in. nominal bore, with corresponding tubulars (i.e. pieces, long-screws, bends, springs, return bends, and barrel nipples). It prescribes the quality of material, workmanship, hydraulic, bend, and flattening tests, marking and packing. The dimensions, tolerances and weights are given for three thicknesses of tubes. For similar tubes in steel, see **B.S. 1387.**

799 : 1953 Oil-burning equipment.
60pp. 11s. Amendments PD 1892, June 1954; PD 2294, September 1955; PD 2804, June 1957; PD 3593, December 1959.
Covers items of equipment (without sizes) for oil-burning equipment of the fully automatic, semi-automatic and hand-controlled types, including particulars of storage tanks, fittings, oil pipe lines, etc.

835 : 1959 Asbestos cement flue pipes and fittings, heavy quality.
36pp. 7s. 6d.
Covers quality and dimensions of flue pipes and fittings up to 24 in. diameter for use with appliances burning solid smokeless fuels and also the larger gas appliances.

843 : 1954   Thermal-storage electric water-heaters.
28pp. 4s. 6d.
Applies to thermostatically controlled thermal-storage electric water-heaters having copper or nickel-copper alloy containers from $1\frac{1}{2}$ to 100 gallons rated water capacity.

845 : 1961   Code for acceptance tests for industrial type boilers and steam generators.
28pp. 7s. 6d.
Indicates the methods which should be adopted and the data which it is desirable to obtain when carrying out a simple efficiency test at minimum cost on hot water and steam raising plants, using solid or liquid fuel, to obtain a satisfactory measure of performance under reasonably steady load conditions.

848 : 1939   Testing of fans for general purposes (excluding mine fans).
47pp. 7s.
Methods of measuring pressure and air velocity and of calculating air volume are described and general instructions for testing are given.

853 : ——   Calorifiers for central heating and hot water supply.

853 : Part 1 : 1960 Mild Steel and cast iron.
64pp. 17s. 6d.
Applies to riveted and welded steel calorifiers and cast iron calorifiers for central heating and hot water supply.

853 : Part 2 : 1960 Copper.
84pp. 20s.
Applies to copper calorifiers for hot water supply and central heating.

855 : 1961   Welded steel boilers for central heating and hot water supply.
108pp. 30s.
This specification applies to welded steel boilers (other than boilers with cylindrical shells over 6 ft. in diameter) for central heating and hot water supply.

864 : 1953   Capillary and compression fittings of copper and copper alloy for use with copper tube complying with B.S. 659 and B.S. 1386.
28pp. 4s. Amendments PD 2915, December 1957; PD 3925, September 1960.
The fittings dealt with are for use with light gauge copper tube in accordance with B.S. 659 and B.S. 1386. The standard lays down such dimensions and requirements as are essential to ensure satisfactory installation and performance. It applies to the most commonly used types of fittings of nominal sizes, ranging from $\frac{1}{8}$ in. to $2\frac{1}{2}$ in. inclusive. The standard includes a number of general requirements relating to design, construction, and indicates the working pressures and temperatures for various installations.

874 : 1956   Definitions of heat insulating terms and methods of determining thermal conductivity.
24pp. 6s.
Part 1 contains definitions of heat insulating terms and a summarized list of relevant symbols and dimensions of units. The measurement of thermal conductivity and emissivity is described in Part 2, including methods used for different types of materials for various temperature ranges. Conversion tables for units in common use are included in the appendices.

1010 : 1959   Draw-off taps and stop-valves for water services (screw-down pattern).
50pp. 10s. Amendments PD 3493, September 1959; PD 3739, April 1960; PD 4367, November 1961.

Gives the requirements for screw-down pattern draw-off taps and stop-valves from ¼ in. to 2 in. size, and details the materials and workmanship for casting and hot pressing.

1016 : —— Methods for the analysis and testing of coal and coke.

1016 : Part 1 : 1957 Total moisture of coal.
16pp. 3s. 6d.

1077 : 1942 Welded joints in copper vessels.
4pp. 2s.
Refers to the welding of deoxidized copper by the oxy-acetylene process. Requirements are laid down in respect of the parent metal for welded copper pressure vessels, and of the filler rod. A tensile test is specified for testing the welding technique. Appendices give notes on copper for welding and the suggested chemical composition of a suitable copper.

1192 : 1951 Drawing office practice for architects and builders.
40pp. 7s. 6d. Amendment PD 2046, December 1954.

1211 : 1958 Centrifugally cast (spun) iron pressure pipes for water, gas and sewage.
24pp. 6s. See ISO/R 13.
Covers cast iron straight pipes with spigot and socket joints manufactured by the centrifugal process in either metal or sand moulds. It corresponds generally to B.S. 78 : 1938, which covers vertically cast pipes.

1212 : 1953 Ball-valves (Portsmouth type), excluding floats.
32pp. 7s. Amendments PD 1932, August 1954; PD 2262, August 1955; PD 2333, November 1955; PD 2460, April 1956; PD 3237, January 1959; PD 3545, November 1959.

1250 : —— Domestic appliances burning town gas.

1250 : Part 1 : 1955 General requirements.
24pp. 6s.
Gives requirements for the construction and performance of appliances and includes methods of test common to all appliances. An appendix gives information on general conditions of test and details of the quality of test gases.

1252 : 1957 Domestic solid fuel cookers with integral boilers.
32pp. 7s. 6d. Amendments PD 3383, May 1959; PD 4212, July 1961.
General requirements and performance requirements are given for various types of solid-fuel cookers fitted with boilers for domestic hot water supply.

1256 : 1952 Malleable cast iron (whiteheart process) and cast copper alloy pipe fittings for steam, air, water, gas and oil. Screwed B.S.P. taper male thread and parallel female thread.
56pp. 8s. 6d. See ISO/R 49.
Specifies dimensions of reinforced malleable cast iron (whiteheart process) and cast copper alloy pipe fittings suitable for working pressures up to 200 lb./sq. in. in the case of water and up to 150 lb./sq. in. in the case of steam, air, gas and oil.

1289 : 1945 Pre-cast concrete flue blocks for gas fires (of the domestic type) and ventilation.
18pp. 3s. 6d.
Provides for two types of flue way, type 1 for use with gas fires of not more than 15,000 B.t.u. and type 2 suitable for use with gas fires over 15,000 B.t.u. Specifies the material, the surface texture and the dimensions of the flue

together with the terminals and joints. It also specifies the compressive strength and drying shrinkage, together with methods of test for determining these properties.

1294 : 1946   Soot doors for domestic buildings. (Confirmed 1954.)
6pp. 2s. 6d. Amendment PD 489, March 1946.
A range of five sizes of soot doors for use in concrete and brickwork flues of domestic buildings, such as flats, houses and schools, is provided.

1306 : ——   Non-ferrous pipes and tubes for steam services.

1306 : Part 1 : 1955   Non-ferrous pipes and piping installations for and in connection with land boilers.
16pp. 3s. 6d.
Applies to the design and construction of non-ferrous pipework connecting a land steam boiler to engine, turbine or industrial plant and all auxiliary pipework.

1306 : Part 2 : 1948   Seamless copper tubes for steam services.
16pp. 3s. 6d.
Deals with seamless copper tubes with plain or screwed ends, suitable for steam, feed, blow-down and similar boiler services.

1307 : 1946   Gas-fired boilers and waste-heat boilers (with or without auxiliary firing). (Confirmed 1960.)
90pp. 8s. 6d.
An industrial acceptance test for each type of boiler is given, followed by separate comprehensive test codes for both types. A simplified method for estimating the thermal efficiency of the boilers is described and an appendix gives directions as to the sampling and analysis of fuel and flue gases.

1334 : 1959   Pre-formed thermal insulating materials for central heating and hot and cold water supply installations.
28pp. 6s.
Relates to pre-formed materials suitable for central heating and hot and cold water supply installations inside a building. The basis of the standard is the required minimum thickness of insulating material, according to the manufacturer's declared value of conductivity.

1339 : 1946   Humidity of the air. Definitions, formulae and constants.
8pp. 3s.
The terms recommended for use in hygrometric measurement are defined, and simple formulae are given for determining the vapour pressure, and indirectly the moisture content, absolute humidity, density, humid volume and total heat of moist air, from wet- and dry-bulb temperature readings. Each formula is accompanied by a table of constants for various systems of units.

1365 : 1951   Short-range short-term thermometers.
13pp. 2s. 6d. Amendment PD 2931, December 1957.

1386 : 1957   Copper tubes to be buried underground.
12pp. 3s.

1387 : 1957   Steel tubes and tubulars suitable for screwing to B.S. 21 pipe threads.
32pp. 6s. See ISO/R 50, 65.
Applies to welded and seamless screwed and socketed and plain end tubes, from $\frac{1}{8}$ in. to 6 in. nominal bore with corresponding tubulars (i.e. pieces, long-screws, bends, springs, return bends and barrel nipples). It prescribes the quality of material and workmanship, together with hydraulic, bend and

flattening tests on the tubes and the mechanical expansion tests on the sockets.

Requirements are also included in regard to quality of galvanizing, identification marking and packing. The dimensions, tolerances and weights are given for three thicknesses of tubes designated 'light', 'medium' and 'heavy'.

1394 : 1947 Power-driven circulators for heating plants.
10pp. 2s. 6d.
Deals with direct coupled, motor-driven and belt-driven centrifugal, axial flow or mixed flow pumps used to create a flow in water mains for heating purposes at temperatures not exceeding 200°F., and static heads not exceeding 100 ft.

1427 : —— Tests for water used in steam generation.
Group A : 1949 Control tests.
80pp. 12s. 6d. Amendment PD 2536, August 1956.
Provides simple control tests and more difficult control tests covering raw water, softened water, condensates, and boiler water, as well as appendices covering the preparation of indicators and standard volumetric solutions, as well as abbreviations, definitions, equivalents and conversion factors.
Detailed tests are given for the following:
Appearance, density, electrical conductivity, pH value, free carbon dioxide, alkalinities, total and ghost point hardness (Wanklyn method), alkaline hardness, non-alkaline hardness, calcium, magnesium, chloride, dissolved solids, phosphate, silica, copper, free chlorine, oil sulphate, sulphite, dissolved oxygen, free and saline ammonia, aluminium, iron (dissolved, suspended and total).

1549 : Part 1 : 1949 Methods of sheet metal pattern development.
30pp. 3s. 6d. Amendment PD 971, November 1949; PD 3965, November 1960.
After reference to the neutral line and its effect on bend allowance, Part 1 deals with sheet metal assemblies in which, by reason of size simplicity of outline or thinness of material, the neutral line may be mainly disregarded. The methods of development included are (S) Radial line, (B) Parallel line, and (C) Triangulation.
Twenty illustrative geometrical and calculation examples are included.

1563 : 1949 Cast iron sectional tanks (rectangular).
35pp. 6s.
Deals with bolted sectional cast iron tanks up to 40 ft. square and 12 ft. deep, excluding supporting structures not subject to pressure other than static head. The tanks specified are with either internal or external flanges and open or closed tops, made from unit plates 2, 3 or 4 ft. square. Details are included of mild steel tie rod ends and turnbuckles, and sizes and thicknesses of unit plates. Four half-tone illustrations of typical tanks, four tables of scantlings and seven tables of approximate weights and nominal capacities are provided.

1564 : 1949 Pressed steel sectional tanks (rectangular).
20pp. 3s. 6d.
Deals with bolted sectional pressed steel tanks up to 52 ft. square and 16 ft. deep, excluding supporting structures not subject to pressure other than static head. The tanks specified are with internal or external flanges, with open or closed tops made from unit plates 4 ft. square. Details are included of the thicknesses of unit plates, and staying and welded connections. Ten drawings, and four tables of approximate weights and nominal capacities for tanks with external flanges are provided.

1565 : 1949 Galvanized mild steel indirect cylinders.
16pp. 3s. 6d.
One of a series of standards relating to domestic hot water storage vessels, the others being B.S. 417, B.S. 699 and B.S. 1566. It provides for a range of seven sizes of indirect cylinder in two classes, suitable for maximum permissible working heads of 60 ft. and 30 ft. respectively.
The standard deals with minimum thickness of material, minimum heating surfaces, methods of manufacture, radius of curvature, bolted ends and handholes, method of galvanizing, screwed connections for pipes and screwed connections for auxiliary electric heating. The latter provision gives a variety of methods so that purchasers may choose that most suitable for the operating conditions. The test requirements deal with primary heaters and complete cylinders. A marking clause gives the various marks to be added in all cases, and recommends the incorporation of further information likely to assist in installation. All the main dimensions are set out in a table and drawings illustrate the methods of measuring them.

1566 : 1949 Copper indirect cylinders.
18pp. 4s. 6d. Amendments PD 1945, August 1954; PD 222, July 1955 (superseding PD 1945); PD 2279, September 1955.
One of a series of standards relating to domestic hot water storage vessels, the others being B.S. 417, B.S. 699 and B.S. 1565. It provides for a range of seven sizes of indirect cylinders in two classes, suitable for maximum permissible working heads of 60 ft. and 30 ft. respectively.
The standard deals with minimum thicknesses of material, minimum heating surfaces, methods of manufacture, radius of curvature, handholes, screwed connections for pipes and screwed connections for auxiliary electric heating. The latter provision gives a variety of methods so that purchasers may choose that most suitable for the operating conditions. The test requirements deal with primary heaters and complete cylinders. A marking clause gives the various marks to be added in all cases, and recommends the incorporation of further information likely to assist in installation.
All the main dimensions are set out in a table and drawings illustrate the methods of measuring them.

1588 : 1949 Thermal insulating materials suitable for use within the temperature range 200° F. to 450° F.
36pp. 7s.
Relates to thermal insulating materials for use on hot surfaces within specified temperature range, particularly to their use on steam-raising plant, process plant, and transmission lines for hot fluid, but excluding transmission lines embedded underground. Standard minimum thicknesses, derived from the declared value of conductivity repayment time and value of heat are given. Tests for thermal conductivity, thickness, and weight per cubic foot are specified and recommendations regarding practice, application and finish are included as an appendix.

1589 : 1950 Thermal insulating materials (plastic composition, flexible and loose-fill).
14pp. 3s 6d.
Deals with plastic thermal insulating materials for central heating, and hot and cold water supply installations, inside buildings, which may be extended to short outdoor runs of piping.

1710 : 1960 Identification of pipe lines.
6pp. 6s.
Recommends an identification colour code for the contents of pipe lines in buildings, industrial installations and also for water and land transport.

1737 : 1951 Jointing materials and compounds for water, town gas and low-pressure steam installations.
45pp. 6s. Amendment PD 1683, August 1953.
Relates to the materials, composition, strength and sizes of compressed asbestos fibre, plain rubber, rubber insertion and corrugated metal joint rings. The properties of jointing compounds are covered in a special section while methods of testing are given in a range of appendices.

1740 : 1951 Wrought pipe fittings, iron and steel, screwed B.S.P. thread.
38pp. 7s. Amendments PD 1248 (restricted issue), August 1951; PD 2634 October 1956; PD 2995, March 1958. See ISO/R 50.

1747 : 1961 Methods for the measurement of air pollution.

1747 : Part 1 : 1961 Deposit gauges.
16pp. 5s.

1756 : 1952 Code for the sampling and analysis of flue gases.
78pp. 12s. 6d.
Describes methods for sampling and analysing flue gases from steam-raising appliances, heating boilers and from processes for the manufacture of iron, steel, non-ferrous metals, pottery, refractories, heavy clay ware, food, cement, glass, certain chemicals and coal gas.

1780 : 1960 Bourdon tube pressure and vacuum gauges.
60pp. 15s. Amendment PD 4288, August 1961.

1846 : 1952 Glossary of terms used for solid-fuel burning and allied appliances
(Confirmed 1959.)
26pp. 3s. 6d.
Provides a considerable range of terms covering cooking, space heating and. water heating appliances, steam boilers, pulverized fuel and gasification plant.

1894 : 1952 Electrode boilers of riveted, seamless, welded and cast iron construction for water heating and steam generating.
100pp. 15s.

1965 : 1953 Seamless steel butt-welding pipe fittings.
16pp. 3s. 6d. Amendments PD 1746, November 1953; PD 2524, July 1956; PD 2996, March 1958.

1966 : 1953 Domed ends for tanks and pressure vessels.
12pp. 3s.

2017 : 1953 Copper tubes for general purposes.
20pp. 3s. 6d.
Applies to solid drawn copper tubes for general purposes. It specifies quality of material and mechanical properties and includes details of mechanical tests. Tolerances on outside diameter, thickness and length are tabulated. Section Two gives specific requirements for copper tubes for use in refrigeration plant.

2035 : 1953 Cast iron flanged pipes and flanged fittings.
40pp. 7s. Amendment PD 2011, October 1954; PD 2202, June 1955.
Deals with a range of pipes and fittings from 2 in. to 48 in. diameter, specifying quality, tolerances, hydraulic testing and inspection among other requirements necessary to ensure a satisfactory product. An extensive series of tables gives dimensions and weights.

2060 : 1953   Copper alloy globe valves for general purposes.
24pp. 4s. 6d. Amendments PD 2106, February 1955; PD 2473, May 1956; PD 3264, January 1959.

2074 : 1954   Size analysis of coke.
38pp. 7s.

2079 : 1954   Steam receivers and separators.
84pp. 15s.

2455 : 1954   Methods of sampling and testing boiler water deposits.
48pp. 7s. Amendment PD 1967, September 1954.

2456 : 1954   Floats for ball-valves (plastics) for cold water.
12pp. 3s. 6d. Amendment PD 2953, January 1958; PD 3917, September 1960.

2619 : 1955   Method of test and rating for steam-heated air-heater batteries.
(Confirmed 1960.)
20pp. 3s. 6d.
Specifies a method of test for steam-heated air-heater batteries. It describes the equipment required, gives instructions for calculation and interpretation of results, and has a section on *type testing*.

2740 : 1956   Simple smoke alarms and alarm metering devices.
16pp. 3s. 6d.
Describes instruments designed to give an alarm when the emission of black or grey smoke from a chimney exceeds a chosen Ringlemann shade.

2741 : 1957   Recommendations for the construction of simple smoke viewers.
12pp. 3s.

2742 : 1958   Notes on the use of the Ringlemann Chart.
8pp. 2s. 6d. Amendment PD 3901, September 1960.
Gives notes on the preparation and use of the chart for the visual assessment of the darkness of smoke emitted by chimneys.

2767 : 1956   Valves and unions for radiators (low-pressure hot water).
12pp. 3s. 6d. Amendments PD 3065, May 1958; PD 4118, March 1961.
Covers screw-operated gate and angle valves, tail pieces and nuts, together with straight and elbow unions, for use with low-pressure hot water radiators. Specifies materials and dimensions and hydraulic tests for valves and components of $\frac{1}{2}$ in., $\frac{3}{4}$ in., 1 in. and $1\frac{1}{4}$ in. nominal size.

2773 : ——   Domestic space heaters for use with butane/propane gases.

2773 : Part 1 : 1956 Space heaters for use with butane gas.
24pp. 4to. 6s. Amendments PD 2776, April 1957; PD 3573, November 1959; PD 3790, May 1960.

2790 : 1956   Cylindrical land steam boilers of welded construction (other than water-tube boilers).
128pp. 12s. 6d. Amendments PD 3694, March 1960; PD 4159, April 1961.
Applies to direct-fired and waste-heat cylindrical and loco-type boilers of fusion-welded construction for land purposes. It deals with materials, construction and workmanship, rules for scantlings, inspection and testing.

2811 : 1957   Smoke density indicators and recorders.
16pp. 3s. 6d.
Describes instruments for measuring the emission of black or grey smoke from a chimney in terms of optical density or percentage obscuration.

Requirements are given for the indicating meter used and for the recorders and alarms when these are fitted, with guidance on the installation of the instrument and on setting the alarm point.

2831 : 1957 Methods of test for air filters used in air-conditioning and general ventilation.
44pp. 7s. 6d.
Relates solely to methods of testing air filters, and does not specify performance standards.

2852 : 1957 Rating and testing refrigerated air-conditioning units.
52pp. 12s. 6d. Amendment PD 3816, May 1960.
Prescribes two sets of standard conditions upon which ratings of refrigerated air-conditioning units are based. Covers units operating without frosting and having a net total cooling effect up to 10 standard tons of refrigeration. Appendices give a recommended method of measuring air flow, the requirements for the measurement of other quantities and lists of approved psychrometric charts and tables.

2869 : 1957 Oil fuels.
40pp. 7s. 6d.
Covers seven classes of fuel for internal combustion engine, domestic, industrial and marine use, together with limits for impurities and methods of test.

2879 : 1957 Draining taps (screw-down pattern).
8pp. 2s. 6d. Amendments PD 3841, July 1960; PD 4076, February 1961.

3048 : 1958 Code for the continuous sampling and automatic analysis of flue gases. Indicators and recorders.
80pp. 15s.

3063 : 1959 Dimensions of gaskets for pipe flanges.
24pp. 6s. Amendment PD 3526, October 1959.
Specifies the *plan* dimension for full-face and *inside bolt circle* gaskets for flanges in accordance with B.S. 10 and 2035 and full-face gaskets for flanges to B.S. 1770. The tables giving dimensions bear the same designation as the flange tables in the appropriate pipe flange standard. Marking of gaskets for purchasing and identification are specified.

3128 : 1959 Constructional and performance requirements for inset open fires with boiler and without convection.
28pp. 6s. Amendments PD 3667, February 1960; PD 3980, November 1960; PD 4100, March 1961.

3142 : —— Manufactured solid smokeless fuels for household use.

Part 1 : 1959 Cokes for domestic open fires.
32pp. 7s. 6d.

3156 : 1959 Methods for the sampling and analysis of fuel gases.
142pp. 25s. Amendment PD 4136, April 1961.

3198 : 1960 Combination hot water storage units (copper) for domestic purposes.
16pp. 4s. 6d.
Gives general requirements and tests for both direct and indirect types of hot water storage units of 25 gallons capacity, made in copper.

3208 : 1960   **Methods of test and rating for hot-water air-heater batteries.**
32pp. 7s. 6d. Amendment PD 3737, April 1960.
Specifies a method of test for hot-water air-heater batteries. It describes the equipment required, gives instruction for the calculation and interpretation of results.

3274 : 1960   **Tubular heat exchangers for general purposes.**
48pp. 4to. 20s. Amendments PD 3998, December 1960; PD 4147, April 1961.
Specifies design, construction, inspection and testing of cylindrical shell and plain tube heat exchangers for general applications, within the range of nominal shell diameters from 6 in. to 42 in. with the tube lengths from 6 ft. to 16 ft., and tube diameter from $\frac{1}{2}$ in. to $1\frac{1}{2}$ in. The following types of heat exchanger are included:
    Type 1. Fixed tube-plate (non-removable tube bundle).
    Type 2. U-tube (removable tube bundle).
    Type 3. Floating head (removable tube bundle).

3376 : 1961   **Open fires with convection, with or without boiler.**
16pp. 4s. 6d.
Specifies the essential design requirements and the performance of overnight or intermittent fires supplying convection heating as well as radiation.

3377 : 1961   **Back boilers for use with domestic solid fuel appliances.**
8pp. 3s.
Specifies materials and methods of construction suitable for boilers other than those for independent domestic hot water supply or central heating.

3378 : 1961   **Domestic heating stoves using coke and other solid fuels.**
20pp. 5s.
Specifies performance standards of openable and closed solid fuel stoves for domestic use. Part One deals with openable stoves, with or without bolier, and Part Two with closed stoves. In each case the method of rating the stove is specified.

3429 : 1961   **Sizes of drawing sheets.**
8pp. 3s.
Specifies sizes of sheets for drawings and tracings and gives tolerances on the dimensions.
Section One specifies sheet sizes in inch dimensions for use in engineering drawings and gives minimum frame sizes.
Section Two specifies sheet sizes in millimetres for use in building and architectural drawings.

CODES OF PRACTICE

CP 3 : ——   **Code of Functional Requirements of Buildings.**

    CP 3 : Chapter I (C) : 1950 Ventilation.
22pp. 5s.
This deals with the ventilation of buildings for human habitation. The recommended rates of fresh air supply for different types of occupation are tabulated. The Appendix advises on the choice between natural and mechanical ventilation to meet individual circumstances. For natural ventilation, formulae are given for calculating the rate of air flow due to wind through openings and to temperature differences. Mechanical ventilation is advised when a satisfactory standard cannot be obtained by natural means. The different types are referred to.

CP 3: Chapter VIII: 1949 Heating and thermal insulation.
13pp. 3s. 6d.

This chapter points out that heating and insulation should be considered together in the early stages of design. It examines the conditions affecting the temperature in dwellings, and recommends standards of warmth for rooms and for indoor places of public assembly. It indicates a method of calculating the degree of insulation appropriate to a building in terms of costs of structure, of heating and of expenditure on fuel, and sets out maximum permissible thermal transmittances for external parts of structure.

CP 131.101 : 1951 Flues for domestic appliances burning solid fuel.
68pp. 12s. 6d. Amendment PD 1445, July 1952.

This deals with flues depending for their operation upon natural draughts. It is restricted to appliances having a maximum heat output of 100,000 B.t.u. per hour where the temperature of the flue gases leaving the appliance does not exceed 850° F. Recommendations are made regarding sizes and heights of flues for various appliances, the general constructions of chimneys of different materials and the height and position of chimneys and outlets above roofs in relation to fire hazard and wind effects. An appendix sets out the causes and cures of condensation in flues.

CP 331.103 : 1947 Gas installation pipes.
20pp. 3s. 6d.

This deals with the internal pipe systems, and is applicable to all classes of buildings. Recommendations are given as to suitable materials for pipes and fittings; and for the method of testing installation pipe systems in new property. A table is provided showing sizes of pipes with their capacities in cubic feet per hour for various lengths. The effect of inserting elbows, tees, etc., in a run of pipe is expressed in terms of additional length of pipe.

CP 331.104 : 1947 Flues for gas appliances.
29pp. 7s. 6d.

This code relates to the choice and installation of any flue to which a gas-fired appliance (other than industrial appliances) may be fitted. Recommendations are made as to the components and suitable materials to be used in flue construction. A table sets out the minimum areas for flues for gas fires and water-heaters to give ventilation and to remove diluted products of combustion. Other sections of the code give advice on the terminal position of flues; avoidance of condensation; connection of flue pipes to gas appliances; fire precautions; precautions to be taken when appliances are to be connected to existing flues, and canopy or hood ventilation for large-scale cooking equipment.

CP 332.201 : 1947 Domestic hot water supply by gas (single family dwellings).
41pp. 6s.

This code deals with both instantaneous and storage water heating. It sets out the conditions under which the various types of installations are best used and lists the ancillary equipment required to complete the installation.

CP 332.202 : 1948 Domestic hot water supply by gas (schools).
50pp. 6s.

This code deals with systems of heating water for domestic use in schools by means of gas appliances, including auxiliary heating for clothes-drying when central heating is not in use. Consideration is given in the code to the selection of systems and of types of appliances suitable to meet the varying purposes and demand rates required in schools. Necessary requirements are also set out for provision of alternative heating by gas in central heating systems using solid fuel.

CP 332.301 : 1961 Domestic space heating by means of independent gas appliances.
40pp. 10s.
This code gives comprehensive guidance on the selection and installation of radiant or convector fires to provide degrees of thermal comfort according to calculated standards, by full heating, background, or supplementary heating. Tables are provided for calculation purposes. In an appendix the methods of calculating heat requirements are explained, and a method of fitting gas fires to existing brick chimneys is discussed as well as use of precast flue blocks for hearth and panel fires and converted flue systems for tall buildings.

CP 332.303 : 1951 Installation of gas-fired boiler for central heating by hot water.
29pp. 6s.
This code affords guidance on the selection of the type and number of boilers most suitable for the heating installation to be served. Details of clearances are given and recommendations made on fire precautions, on gas supply and connections, including the master control cock and safety devices. Various automatic controls are described, and advice given on points of design.

CP 341.300-307 : 1956 Central heating by low pressure hot water.
110pp. 15s.
The code comprises a head-code and seven sub-codes covering in detail: boilers and calorifiers; storage vessels; pipework, fittings, valves, taps and cocks; appliances (column radiators, surface panels, convectors); unit heaters; power-driven circulating pumps for low pressure hot water heating installations; and thermal insulation. The head-code deals with the general aspects of central heating by low pressure hot water.

CP 342 : 1950 Centralized domestic hot water supply.
90pp. 12s. 6d. Amendments PD 1171, April 1951; PD 1444, July 1952; PD 1588, April 1953; PD 1677, July 1953.
This code deals with the installation of boilers, calorifiers, storage vessels, pipework and electrically driven circulators in central systems of domestic hot water supply for buildings ranging from small dwelling-houses to hotels and schools, and also with the application of thermal insulating materials to the appliances as needed.

CP 352 : 1958 Mechanical ventilation and air conditioning in buildings.
112pp. 20s.
This code deals with the work involved in the general design, planning, installation, testing and maintenance of mechanical ventilating and air-conditioning installations whereby air is forced into or extracted from buildings. It consists of a head-code and eight sub-codes covering in detail: fans, motors and starting gear; air heaters; air distribution system; air cleaning devices; thermal insulation; sound-proofing and anti-vibration devices; temperature and humidity controls; cooling and dehumidification. The head-code deals with the general aspects of the subject.

CP 403 : 1952 Open fires, heating stoves and cookers burning solid fuel.
74pp. 10s.
This code deals with the installation of domestic heating appliances in houses. The section on design considerations includes recommendations on fire precautions relating to the construction of hearths and of walls above the hearth. Convector fires and non-convector fires, both with and without back boilers, are treated separately. An appendix gives guidance on the selection of the correct type and size of solid fuel appliance for a particular duty.

CP 403.101 : 1952 Small boiler systems using solid fuel.
32pp. 6s.
This code describes and deals with the installation of hot water supply systems and combined heating and hot water supply systems using solid fuel. It applies to independent boilers having from 2 to 5 sq. ft. of heating surface or back boilers having 1 to 5 sq. ft. of heating surface fitted in open fires, cooking ranges or stoves, and gives the basic design requirements for installations in small dwelling-houses of a floor area of up to about 1,500 sq. ft., including full treatment of the piping installations.

CP 413 : 1951 Design and construction of ducts for services.
30pp. 5s. Amendment PD 1392, April 1952.
This code deals with the design and construction of all forms of ducts for the accommodation of pipes, cables, etc., within and adjacent to buildings. Types of ducts, chases, trenches and subways to suit the various requirements of the services they carry are described in detail and guidance is given on the methods of, and materials for, construction. Such matters as access, suppression of noise, avoidance of heat transmission and precautions against increasing fire risk are dealt with.

CP 3000 : 1955 Installation and maintenance of underfed stokers.
16pp. 3s.
In addition to the installation, care and maintenance of underfed stokers used with domestic, sectional, shell and small-tube boilers, this code makes recommendations on the design of boiler room, fuel storage, flues and chimneys, and on the provision of automatic safety controls. This code replaces Appendix A of B.S. 749 : 1952 'Underfeed stokers (ram or screw type)'.

CP 3002 :—— Oil firing.

CP 3002 Part 1 : 1961 Installations burning class D fuel oil and C.T.F. 50.
44pp. 10s.
This part of the code deals with the installation of oil-burning equipment designed to burn C.T.F. 50 or class D fuel oils in heating boilers, air heaters and cooking equipment connected to flues. It sets out specification data for class D petroleum oil fuel and for coal tar fuel 50 extracted from current British Standards and other relevant data, and also gives in tabulated form approximate design data for all fuels available in the U.K.
Information is given on oil-burning and auxiliary equipment for small and medium-sized installations, including the influence of boiler design, selection of burners, fuel feed to burners, new burner installations, conversion of existing installations, etc. Recommendations are given on the selection and installation of oil-storage tanks and ancillary equipment as well as the installation of service tanks.

INDEX

CHART 1.—PIPE SIZES FOR HOT WATER HEATING—1°F DROP

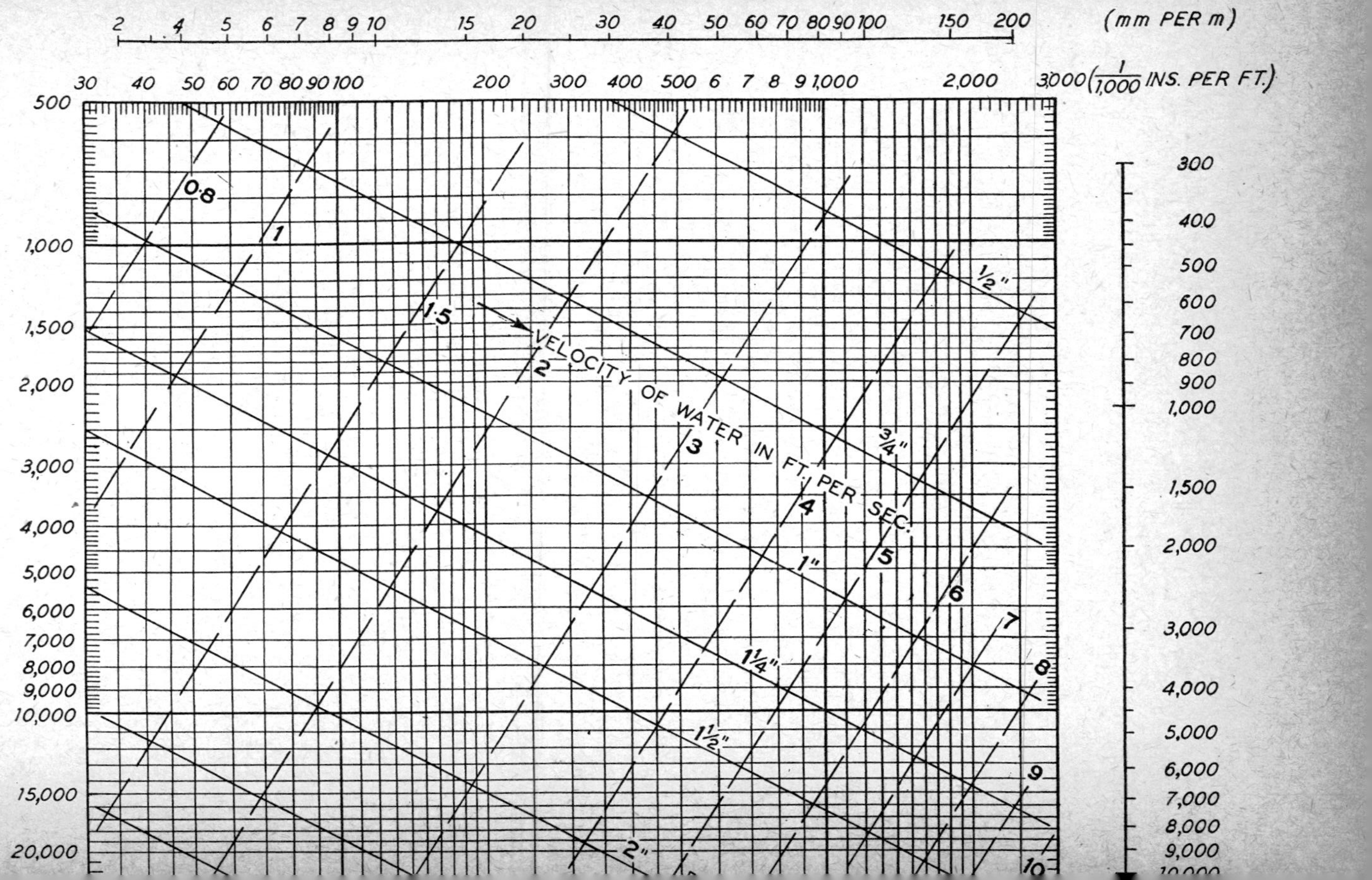

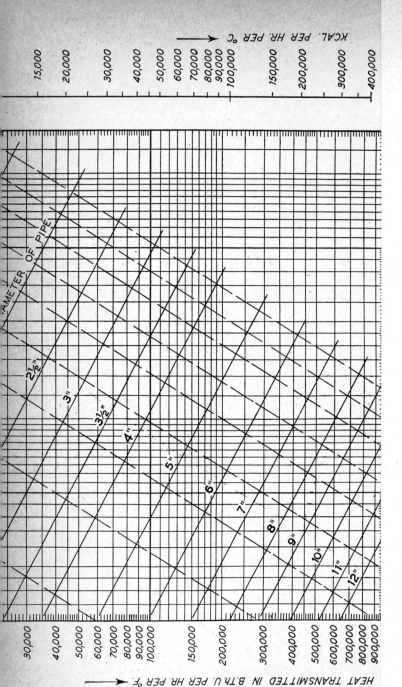

CHART 1a.—PIPE SIZES FOR HOT WATER HEATING—1°F DROP

→ FRICTIONAL RESISTANCE IN $\frac{1}{1000}$ INS WC PER RUN FT OF PIPE.

KCAL. PER HR. PER °C.

HEAT TRANSMITTED IN B.T.U. PER HR. PER °F.

DIAMETER OF PIPE

SO COSY...
SO SAFE

with made to measure comfort by

HULL RAD

Where it is essential to maintain even room temperature under all weather conditions, HULL RAD radiators provide the safest and most efficient way of ensuring constant, balanced warmth which can be regulated with finger-tip ease.

HULL RAD column and panel radiators are manufactured in a standard range of 5 heights, 'tailor-made' in any desired length, and curved or angled to suit specification requirements. Send for comprehensive catalogue and price information to Department No. HUA/1

HULL STEEL RADIATORS LTD.

1515 HEDON ROAD   HULL

Telephones: HULL 75251/2   'Grams: HULLRAD

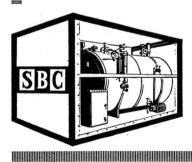

THIS CATALOGUE C14 IS INDISPENSABLE TO THOSE WHO WISH TO INSTALL THE BEST CALORIFIERS

RYCROFT

Appreciation of our Calorifier Catalogues comes in from many sources at home and overseas. We are sure that the new edition will be of even greater service. It will, as usual be backed up by the personal interest and co-operation from our staff which has gained us many friends together with a constantly expanding business.

RYCROFTS (CALORIFIERS) LTD.
129 SUNBRIDGE ROAD, BRADFORD 1

Telegrams: RYCO BRADFORD
Telephone: 31563 BRADFORD

POST THIS COUPON TODAY

Please send a copy of the
Rycroft Calorifier Catalogue C. 14

Name ....

Company ....

Address ....

....

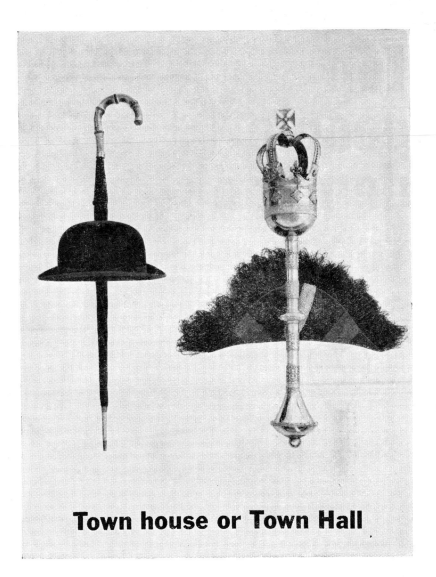

Town house or Town Hall.

For heating on any scale
pick a Potterton

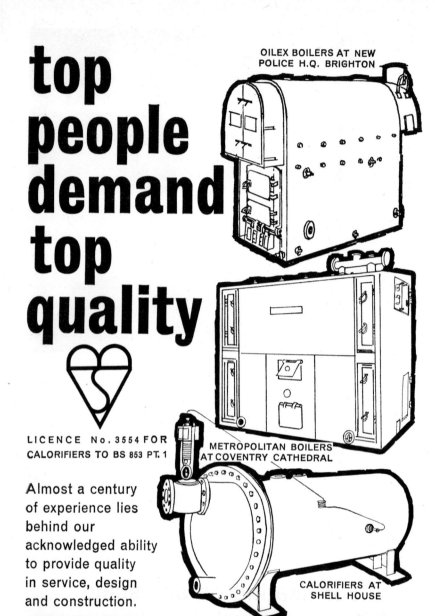

POWELL DUFFRYN

HAVE THE
RIGHT
APPROACH TO
HEATING

Right for you. Right for any installation you undertake. Gulf radiators tailored to measure. Janitor boilers for all fuels. Only Powell Duffryn can supply all the equipment you need and deliver it direct to the building site.

JANITOR boilers for all fuels

The Powell Duffryn range of Janitor boilers includes new gas-fired models with ratings from 30,000 to 85,000 Btu/h, oil-fired models (for inside or outside installation) and solid fuel models both with ratings from 40,000 to 140,000 Btu/h. All are welded steel with stoved enamel finish for inside installation.
Janitor boilers think for themselves—are fitted with all necessary safety and comfort controls.

GULF radiators tailored to any length

Decor-designed to harmonise with any room setting, Gulf panel radiators can be supplied in four heights—11″, 18″, 24″ and 30″ in any length and can be curved or angled to fit full window width to eliminate down-draught. Gulf radiators are made of steel, strong but light and frost and fracture-proof. They have high heat emission and quick response to thermostatic control. Gulf column radiators can also be supplied to any length and curved if required.

TAYCO solid fuel boilers

—solid fuel models for the smaller house. Easy to run, simple to clean. New Tayco Quartic waterway gives 5.8% more heating surface and is a dramatic advance in boiler design. Available in several sizes and in six colours.

POWELL DUFFRYN HEATING LTD.,

Vale Road, Camberley, Surrey. Telephone: Camberley 3491
London Showrooms: 229 Regent Street, London, W.1

NEW GAS-FIRED MODELS

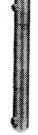

TEMPERATURE CONTROL OF BLOCK STORAGE SPACE HEATER

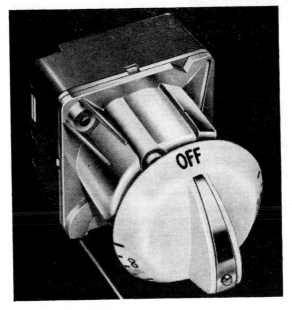

Ideal control of these heaters
can be obtained by using this
specially developed hydraulically
operated 20TH Series Thermostats, rated
at 16 amps, 250 volts AC. *Details on application.*

DIAMOND H CONTROLS LIMITED
GUNNERSBURY AVENUE, CHISWICK, LONDON, W.4

Telephone: CHiswick 6444. *Cables:* Diamonhart London, W.4

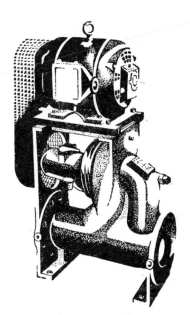

THE GROSVENOR ENGINEERING SERVICES LTD.